IF YOU ARE SERIOUS ABOUT STUDY
IF YOU WANT TO IMPROVE YOUR GRADES
IF YOU WANT TO APPROACH EXAMS WITH CONFIDENCE

Use of this **Study Guide** by Robert C. Koch provides you with the additional help you need to reinforce your grasp of PHYSICAL GEOLOGY, Seventh Edition, by Judson, Kauffman, and Leet.

The author guides you toward an in-depth understanding of the basic principles of geology and sharpens your problem-solving skills. He suggests that you read the text chapters thoroughly before moving on to the summaries in the **Study Guide.**

His approach to the subject, using illustrative and supplementary material, helps you pinpoint the areas where you need further study.

This clear, step-by-step approach makes self-study easy. The **Study Guide** is an enriching means toward a more complete understanding of the course and the achievement of higher grades in class work and on exams.

ROBERT C. KOCH

STUDY GUIDE

SEVENTH EDITION

PHYSICAL GEOLOGY

SHELDON JUDSON
MARVIN E. KAUFFMAN
L. DON LEET

Prentice-Hall, Inc.

Englewood Cliffs, New Jersey 07632

Cover design: Christine Gehring-Wolf
Manufacturing buyer: Barbara Kelly Kittle
Cover photograph: Massive sandstone cliffs
 in Zion Canyon, Utah. (Charlie Blecker)

Printed in the United States of America

10 9 8 7 6 5 4 3 2 1

ISBN 0-13-669953-7

Prentice-Hall International (UK) Limited, *London*
Prentice-Hall of Australia Pty. Limited, *Sydney*
Prentice-Hall Canada Inc., *Toronto*
Prentice-Hall Hispanoamericana, S.A., *Mexico*
Prentice-Hall of India Private Limited, *New Delhi*
Prentice-Hall of Japan, Inc., *Tokyo*
Prentice-Hall of Southeast Asia Pte. Ltd., *Singapore*
Editora Prentice-Hall do Brasil, Ltda., *Rio de Janeiro*

CONTENTS

DESCRIPTION OF THIS STUDY GUIDE

This study guide is designed to be used with the text <u>Physical Geology</u> by Judson, Kauffman, and Leet.

Each chapter in the guide, which is correlated with the equivalent chapter in the text, contains the following eight sections:

    OVERVIEW
    LEARNING OBJECTIVES
    KEY TERMS AND CONCEPTS
    NOTES
    PROGRAMMED REVIEW
    SELF-TESTS
    SUGGESTED ESSAY QUESTIONS
    ANSWERS TO SELF-TESTS

These sections are described below.

OVERVIEW

This will describe briefly what the chapter is about, how the contents are related to the field of geology, and how the authors have presented the material. The Overview might be regarded as a "road map" of the chapter. This section should be read before studying the text chapter.

LEARNING OBJECTIVES

The minimum knowledge that you should plan on acquiring from this chapter is listed in this section. After studying each chapter, you should be able to describe certain geological phenomena and events, to discuss specific geological concepts and theories, to relate the various components of any given geological problem, to define certain geological terms, and to explain certain geological phenomena and events, whether they are theoretical or directly observable.

This section should be read before studying the text and consulted frequently during your study of the text.

KEY TERMS AND CONCEPTS

The Key Terms and Concepts contains the basic vocabulary of each chapter. The number of terms will vary with each chapter, but will usually be fairly extensive. It is not necessary to memorize these terms, but, after reading the text chapter and working through the guide, you should be able to go through the list as a final review and recall most, if not all, of the listed items.

NOTES

Certain concepts and terms will present difficulties, which may be alleviated by referring to specific notes which are correlated with each section in the text chapter. These notes will call attention to major points about a concept and emphasize any important relationship. This section should be referred to as the text chapter is studied.

PROGRAMMED REVIEW

The Programmed Review consists of a series of sentences with key words or phrases left out. The sentences cover the main points or concepts of the chapter. The correct responses are supplied on the right margin of the page, and a page reference for the statement is given at the end of each item. Cover the answers as you read each statement, and check your process as you proceed. If you studied the text chapter carefully and efficiently, you most likely will finish this section in a half hour or less.

SELF-TESTS

This is a comprehensive self-test, which consists of a "true-false" portion (Part A) and a "multiple choice" section (Part B). Check your answers after taking the complete test by referring to the answers section. For your own record, indicate the number of correct responses in each section. This test should be taken only after you have studied the text and, although it may not be absolutely necessary, after you have gone through the Programmed Review.

SUGGESTED ESSAY DISCUSSION QUESTIONS

Each text chapter contains elements which especially lend themselves to an essay response or discussion. Some of the more probable essays and discussions are noted in this section, along with discussion-type questions which normally may arise in a study of the concepts of the chapter. These questions may, in fact, generate considerable discussion within the actual classroom.

ANSWERS TO SELF-TESTS

Answers and acceptable responses to the Self-Test items are presented in this section. Any incorrect answers or unacceptable responses should be noted and appropriate review and restudy be undertaken.

USING THE
STUDY GUIDE

To obtain the maximum benefit from this handbook, you must use it properly.

First, before studying each text chapter, read the Overview in the handbook. This will give you some idea of what to expect.

Next, look over the Learning Objectives and Key Terms and Concepts so that you will have an idea of what is expected of you and the new vocabulary you will have to master. As you study the text, use the Learning Objectives as a check on your progress. Refer to it frequently to make sure you are fulfilling the objectives.

Return to the Notes section as you study the text chapter. This will assist you in understanding the more difficult concepts.

When you are finished studying the text chapter, you should then use the Programmed Review section of the handbook.

Finally, taking the Self-Tests will give you some idea of your accomplishment.

To enhance your knowledge about a specific chapter, you may want to refer to the section entitled Suggested Essay Discussion Questions. Try replying to a few of these items, or try to involve other students and teachers in a discussion of them. This can benefit you tremendously and will help prepare you for a major test.

STUDY GUIDE

PHYSICAL GEOLOGY

CHAPTER 1

TIME AND A CHANGING EARTH

OVERVIEW

The introductory paragraphs of this chapter will give you an excellent idea of what geologists are interested in. Read it carefully and think about it as you do. The entire chapter is a brief summary of some of the major ideas of geology, ideas with which you will become familiar as you go through the course. These basic concepts include: (1) uniformitarianism-- the idea that the geological processes occurring today also occurred in the past; (2) geologic time--the necessity of extremely long time intervals; (3) the rock cycle--the concept of rocks constantly being changed and recycled to form new rocks; (4) plate tectonics--the concept of huge and distinct portions of the earth's surface moving around, bumping and shoving one another to create some of the earth's major features. Although none of these concepts are presented in great depth but only as an introduction, it is important that you acquire a good, approximate idea of the meaning and implications of these introductory ideas.

LEARNING OBJECTIVES

After studying this chapter, you should be able to:

1. State reasonable values for the ages of the earth and universe.

2. Define the concepts of absolute and relative time and to describe the difference between them.

3. State an elementary definition of radioactivity.

4. Define and contrast the terms geologic column and geologic time.

5. Define the concept of uniformitarianism.

6. List the types of rocks.

7. Describe briefly the origin of the types of rocks.

8. Describe in detail the concept of rock cycle.

9. Define each of these terms and sketch their spatial relationships:
   lithosphere, asthenosphere, crust, mantle.

10. Define the terms basalt and granite.

11. Describe the concept of isostasy.

12. Describe the major ideas involved in plate tectonics.

13. Describe the relationship between the rock cycle concept and the
    mechanism of plate tectonics.

KEY TERMS AND CONCEPTS

geology
geologic-time scale
geologic column
relative time
absolute time
radioactive element
parent element
daughter element
James Hutton
principle of uniformitarianism
the present is the key to the past
rock families
igneous
metamorphic
sedimentary
magma
lava
ash
cinder

plate tectonics
sea-floor spreading
continental drift
Alfred Wegener
lithosphere
asthenosphere
crust
mantle
basalt
granite
oceanic crust
continental crust
vertical movement
horizontal movement
isostasy
plates
rift valley
subduction zone
rock cycle

NOTES

Sec. 1.1: Some Introductory Observations

The role of geology and what geologists do is presented in this section.
Most significant is the extension of geologic principles and methods of
study to other bodies in our solar system.

Sec. 1.2: Time

The distinction between absolute and relative time is basic, so be familiar
with it. Before absolute time measurements were available to geologists,
they had to devise relative time scales. This resulted in the geologic
column. Eventually, absolute time measurement techniques helped refine the
geologic column. Radioactivity is only one of the methods used to
determine absolute times.

The "doctrine of uniformitarianism" is an extremely useful concept and you
should think about it while studying the examples. Try to think of
something occurring today, geologically speaking, that did not or could not
have occurred in the distant past. Also, be aware that, while we generally
think of geologic processes acting very slowly over extremely long periods
of time, "catastrophic" events have occurred in the past and will happen in
the future. The rate and intensity of an event may vary greatly, but the
basic principles of change apply to all geologic events.

Sec. 1.3: Earth Materials and the Rock Cycle

Rocks are made of minerals, and you will be introduced to the important
rock-forming minerals in the next chapter. This section notes the three
kinds of rocks and emphasizes the rock cycle. Keep in mind that the rock
cycle is a model which is an excellent approximation of one aspect of
nature. It is strongly suggested that you are able to reproduce the rock
cycle diagram from memory. As a model, it will prove to be very useful in
your study of geology.

Sec. 1.4: Plate Tectonics, Sea-Floor Spreading, and Continental Drift

The upper zones of the earth are described very briefly, but enough
information is given so that you should be able to describe some
characteristics of each. Note that the upper mantle includes the
asthenosphere and all except the upper part of the lithosphere. Basalt and
granite are mentioned in terms of oceanic and continental materials.
Later, you will learn considerably more about these two very important
rocks. The idea of isostasy is barely explored here, and a much more
detailed treatment will be given in Chapter 9. For now, you should know
that the crust can be depressed or rise (rebound) in response to the load
in that section of the crust. The sinking involves a depressing of the
asthenosphere; and, since the asthenosphere can flow (it's hot!), a
depression in one zone will result in another nearby zone being pushed up.
Again, as far as plate tectonics is concerned, you will explore it in much
more detail in Chapter 11. Just be aware of the large scale aspects of the
theory, such as the fact that the continents ride on these plates and that
ocean basins can be enlarged or closed due to plate motion. What happens
at plate boundaries is significant and, as a start, you should know what
geologic features are formed and what processes are occurring at these
boundaries. Note the relationship to the rock cycle and how molten
material is generated.

Sec. 1.5: Some Practical Considerations

Two major problems which involve the subject of geology are resource
depletion and environmental degradation. Any real solutions to these

problems will involve knowledge from many fields, but especially from geology. As you progress through this course, keep in mind that what you learn could contribute to the kind of future that you think should be created.

PROGRAMMED REVIEW

1. The idea of placing geologic events in sequence without regard to a specific number of years defines the concept of _____. (3) — relative time

2. The concept of _____ enables one to refer to a geological event at a reasonably specific date in earth history. (3) — absolute time

3. _____ elements are the most effective means of measuring absolute time. (4) — radioactive

4. The original radioactive material is known as the _____ element, while the new element that results from the radioactive decay is called the _____ element. (4) — parent / daughter

5. A hypothetical pile of rocks arranged in a chronological sequence using the relative ages of rock units and geological events is called the _____. (4) — geologic column

6. The _____ was formulated on the principle that the laws of nature are unchanging. (4) — doctrine of uniformitarianism

7. The statement _____ may be considered to be a logical summary of uniformitarianism. (5) — the present is the key to the past

8. The _____ and _____ of any natural process can never be uniform all over the world at any particular time or through any extended period of geologic time. (5) — rate / intensity

9. Even though the uniformitarian doctrine allows for slow, imperceptible changes over long periods of time, some events, rarely experienced by humans, may be termed _____ and have taken place in a geologic instant of time. (5) — catastrophic

10. Based on their mode of origin, all rocks can be divided into three major groups, namely, _____, _____, and _____. (6) — igneous / metamorphic / sedimentary

11. Any molten rock material beneath the Earth's surface is called _____. (6) — magma

4

12. If molten rock should breach the surface and flow as a stream of hot rock, it is known as _____. (6)

lava

13. Explosive volcanic eruptions of molten rock material commonly form layers of _____ and _____. (6)

ash
cinder

14. Most _____ rocks are formed from the breakdown of preexisting rock and are characteristically _____ in appearance. (6)

sedimentary
layered

15. Any rock that has been altered by heat, pressure and chemically active fluids beneath the surface is called _____. (6)

metamorphic

16. The concept that under changing environmental conditions and time a rock may be changed from one type to another defines the _____. (7)

rock cycle

17. Based on the rock cycle, an igneous rock that is remelted to form a new magma should eventually crystallize to an _____ rock. (7)

igneous

18. _____ and _____ are processes explaining the origins of the continents and ocean basins and the location of volcanoes and earthquakes. (8)

plate tectonics
sea-floor
    spreading

19. The outermost 50 to 100 km rigid shell of rock making up the earth is called the _____. This shell is underlain by a weak or soft zone where a temperature of around 1000 degrees centigrade and enough pressure exists to make rock flow. This region is called _____. (8)

lithosphere
asthenosphere

20. The uppermost portion of the lithosphere is known as the _____. This part of the lithosphere may be subdivided on the basis of composition into a continental portion underlain by _____ and an oceanic region underlain by _____. (9)

crust
granite
basalt

21. The rocks underlying the continents are _____ (less, more) dense than oceanic crustal rocks. (9)

less

22. Rocks beneath the crust constitute the _____. The lower part of the _____ and the _____ are part of the _____ mantle. (9)

mantle
lithosphere
asthenosphere
upper

23. Precise surveys and the geologic record itself have shown the earth undergoes both _____ and _____ movements. (9)

horizontal
vertical

24. The delicate balance whereby portions of the earth's crust rise or sink slightly into the asthenosphere is called _____. (9)

isostasy

25. If glaciers were to greatly expand over the   sinking
    northern hemisphere, one would expect the crust
    in the northern continental regions to adjust
    by _____ in those areas. (9)

26. The _____ of the earth's lithosphere are rigid,   plates
    large, relatively inactive and are bounded by
    well-defined belts of volcanic and earthquake
    activity. (10)

27. If the motion along plate boundaries results in   rift
    a divergence or pulling apart, one might expect
    a _____ valley to develop. (10)

28. Any new crustal material being added at the   sea-floor
    Mid-Atlantic Ridge is slowly transported laterally   spreading
    away from the ridge by the process of _____. (11)

29. If new crustal material is being created in one   subduction
    region of the earth, older crustal material must
    be destroyed in another region to allow space for
    the new material. This destruction takes place
    along a _____ zone where the edge of one plate
    may be forced beneath the edge of another. (11)

30. During the subducting process a large amount of   friction
    thermal energy is produced. The thermal energy   radioactivity
    is largely the result of the _____ generated
    between plates and the heat of _____ in the
    thickened rock pile. (11)

31. The hypothesis of _____ has been modified from   continental
    its original meaning since we now know from   drift
    plate tectonics and sea-floor spreading that   oceanic
    continents do not move as isolated units, but
    move as portions of plates which may include
    _____ as well as continental crust. (11)

32. The _____ model provides a mechanism to drive the   plate tectonics
    processes in the concept of the rock cycle. (11)

SELF-TESTS

Part A: True-False Statements

Each of the following statements is either true or false. Encircle either
T or F for each item.

  1. Geologic time never involves accurate dates so the   T   F
     concept of absolute time is not useful in geology.

  2. Radioactive substances which are useful in absolute   T   F
     time determinations are uranium and hydrogen.

6

3. The geologic column is the arrangement of rock layers in order of age, with the oldest on the bottom.　　　T　　F

4. The concept of uniformitarianism maintains that the same earth processes at work today were also operating millions of years ago.　　　T　　F

5. Today, because of the work of geologists, we can actually see a river valley being cut or a mountain chain built.　　　T　　F

6. The major factor which is vital in explaining the processes at work on the earth is the concept of a very long period of time.　　　T　　F

7. There are more than 2000 minerals but only about a dozen make up most of the minerals which occur in the earth's rocks.　　　T　　F

8. There are only three major types of rocks on the earth.　　　T　　F

9. Igneous rocks originate from magma, which is molten or melted rock materials.　　　T　　F

10. Igneous rocks which we see today could never have been formed below the earth's surface.　　　T　　F

11. Metamorphic rocks are formed by the application of heat and pressure to other rock units.　　　T　　F

12. The rock cycle is a concept which maintains that a particular rock is only a temporary condition of the material in the rock and that it is destined to undergo further change.　　　T　　F

13. The complete melting of a metamorphic rock will result in an igneous rock.　　　T　　F

14. Surface processes, such as weathering and erosion, acting on an igneous rock could transform it into a metamorphic rock.　　　T　　F

15. The lithosphere is the region above the mantle and below the crust.　　　T　　F

16. The continental crust consists mostly of granite.　　　T　　F

17. The concept of isostasy is used to explain the formation of valleys and ocean basins.　　　T　　F

18. The earth's continents and ocean basins can be divided into large sections called plates.　　　T　　F

19. If two plates move away from one another, the result is that material from the mantle will flow upward.　　　T　　F

20. In this chapter, you were given strong evidence for the   T   F
     existence of plates.

Part B: Multiple Choice Items

Each of the following can be completed correctly by choosing only one word
or phrase. Encircle the letter a, b, c, or d, designating your choice.

1. When expressing events in terms of a relative time scale, the order of
    events

    a. must be expressed in terms of years.
    b. can never be arranged accurately.
    c. does not require a measurement in minutes or other similar units.
    d. is determined only by knowing the exact ages of the events.

2. Radioactivity is a process

    a. which is used to determine relative time values.
    b. in which one element changes into one or more different elements.
    c. which varies according to the temperature of the environment.
    d. which only can be used to date events that occur on the earth.

3. The age of the earth is probably closest to

    a. 10 million years.   c. 5 billion years.
    b. 500 million years.   d. 15 billion years.

4. James Hutton was the

    a. discoverer of radioactivity.
    b. formulator of the doctrine of uniformitarianism.
    c. discoverer of the age of the earth.
    d. inventor of the concept of the rock cycle.

5. The doctrine of uniformitarianism can best be summarized by which of
    the following phrases?

    a. All rocks are made of four chemicals.
    b. The future lies in the past.
    c. The present is the key to the past.
    d. Here today, gone tomorrow.

6. In the formation of the earth's features, what factor is most
    essential to our understanding of the processes which formed these
    features?

    a. geologic time   c. the rock cycle
    b. continental drift   d. isostasy

7. Igneous rocks are formed by

    a. the solidification of magma.   c. isostasy.
    b. volcanoes.   d. metamorphism.

8. In the rock cycle, the material forming igneous rocks

   a. must be remelted before it can be formed into another rock.
   b. could never form a sedimentary rock.
   c. had to originate in metamorphic rocks.
   d. could eventually become part of either sedimentary or metamorphic rock.

9. The chronological order of the processes in the formation of sedimentary rocks is

   a. erosion, transportation, weathering, sediments.
   b. crystallization, erosion, weathering, sediments.
   c. weathering, transportation, erosion, sediments.
   d. lithification, erosion, weathering, sediments.

10. Which one of the following groups would best describe the temporary fate of a metamorphic rock unit?

    a. weathering, transportation, erosion, sediments
    b. melting, lithification, crystallization
    c. metamorphism, erosion, sediments
    d. crystallization, lithification, metamorphism

11. What factor is most important in distinguishing the lithosphere and asthenosphere?

    a. depth   c. composition
    b. temperature   d. age

12. What zone of the earth is composed mostly of separate sections of granite and basalt?

    a. mantle   c. lithosphere
    b. crust   d. asthenosphere

13. What features would you expect to find along the boundary of diverging plates?

    a. high continental mountains and deep-sea trenches
    b. two or more continental mountain ranges
    c. continental volcanic action and earthquakes
    d. deep submarine valleys and molten basalt

14. Along the boundary of the Nazca and South American plates, the Nazca is moving

    a. up and over the South American plate.
    b. into the South American plate to form the Andes.
    c. alongside the South American plate.
    d. downward beneath the South American plate.

SUGGESTED ESSAY QUESTIONS

The items below represent the type of discussion question to which you might be expected to respond. Try writing a response to these and then discuss your work with another student.

1. Discuss the difference between absolute and relative time.

2. Discuss the statement that "time makes possible what seems impossible".

3. Sketch and label a diagram which illustrates the concept of the rock cycle.

4. What is meant by the doctrine of uniformitarianism?

5. Describe the ways in which plates move relative to one another and what geological features might be formed due to this motion.

ANSWERS TO SELF-TESTS

Part A:	1. F	6. T	11. T	16. T	Part B:	1. c	6. a	11. b
	2. F	7. T	12. T	17. F		2. b	7. a	12. b
	3. T	8. T	13. T	18. T		3. c	8. d	13. d
	4. T	9. T	14. F	19. T		4. b	9. c	14. d
	5. F	10. F	15. F	20. F		5. c	10. a	15. b

CHAPTER 2

MINERALS AND MATTER

OVERVIEW

Substances called minerals make up the rocks of the earth. Since much of
geology is concerned with a study of rock formations, changes experienced
by rocks and the various relationships among types of rocks, it is vital
that the student acquire a basic knowledge about minerals. Consequently,
the authors begin by discussing how matter is composed of minute particles
called atoms and how they are structured and subsequently held together and
arranged to form the elements and compounds we call minerals. The minerals
are then described and discussed thoroughly and their particular and unique
structures examined in detail. Emphasis is placed on the most common rock-
forming minerals--silicates. Native elements, halides, oxides, sulfides,
carbonates, and sulfate minerals are described in lesser detail. The major
physical properties of minerals, such as crystal habit, hardness, luster,
cleavage, etc., are then explained. The authors conclude with a cosmic
view of the distribution of elements in nature, which minerals are found
associated in specific geological settings, and the locations where new
minerals are being formed from old ones.

LEARNING OBJECTIVES

After studying this chapter, you should be able to:

1. Describe the atom in terms of its fundamental particles: the
    electrons, protons, and neutrons.

2. Define the terms mass number and atomic number.

3. State what each of these are and how they are related: atom, ion, element, isotope, molecule, compound.

4. Distinguish between an anion and a cation.

5. Distinguish between metals, nonmetals, and metalloids.

6. Describe the mechanism of ionic, covalent, metallic, and van der Waal's bonding.

7. Explain the concepts of polymorphism and isomorphism.

8. Explain the concept of a solid-solution mineral series.

9. List the typical minerals comprising each of the following groups: native elements, oxides, sulfides, carbonates, sulfates, halides, ferromagnesians, nonferromagnesians.

10. Describe in detail the silicon-oxygen tetrahedron.

11. Describe the chemical structure, composition, and physical properties of each of the various silicate minerals.

12. Describe the chemical composition of each of these groups: oxides, sulfides, carbonates, sulfates, halides.

13. Distinguish between chemical and physical properties of minerals.

14. Define and describe each of the following physical properties: luster, hardness, cleavage, specific gravity, density, striations, twinning, streak, color.

15. Contrast the relative abundance of elements found in the universe and on earth.

16. State why minerals are commonly found associated in specific geological settings.

17. State why and under what conditions mineral combinations and compositions are constantly undergoing change.

KEY TERMS AND CONCEPTS

matter
atoms
fundamental particles
protons
neutrons
electrons
elements
molecules
rock-forming minerals
solid solution
isomorphism

polymorphism
silicon-oxygen tetrahedron
ferromagnesian minerals
mafic
nonferromagnesian minerals
compounds
electron cloud
electrical charge
mass number
atomic number
nucleus

metals
nonmetals
metalloids
isotopes
ions
cation
anion
angstrom
ionic radii
electron shell
bonding
ionic bond
ionic compound
covalent bond
positive pole
negative pole
dipole
dipolar compound
metallic bond
van der Waals' bond
van der Waals' forces
native elements
oxides

halides
sulfides
carbonates
sulfates
chemical properties
physical properties
internal atomic arrangement
unit cell
constancy of interfacial angles
crystal habit
luster
cleavage
hardness
specific gravity
density
twinning
striations
color
streak
Big Bang theory
Jovian planets
terrestrial planets
mineral associations

NOTES

Sec. 2.1: Particles of Matter

The idea that matter is composed of atoms is established, along with the
fundamental atomic particles--electrons, protons, and neutrons. Notice
that all atoms are composed of the same fundamental particles, but they may
be differentiated by the number and arrangement of the particles in an
atom. The atomic number and mass number will enable you to identify the
different atoms. Know how to read these numbers and what they mean. Be
sure to have some idea about the relative sizes of nuclei and atoms, how
ions can form, and how isotopes of an element differ from one another.

Sec. 2.2: Bonding

An extremely important section is presented to establish how atoms of
different elements are combined to form compounds through the process of
bonding. The mechanisms for bonding are four: ionic, covalent, metallic,
and van der Waals'. Notice that all types of bonding depend on the same
type of force, but in the case of ionic, covalent, and metallic bonding the
difference depends on the role of the outer shell electrons. Be aware that
the van der Waals' bonding is not confined to the outer electron but rather
the total electron orbital distribution setting up a temporary imbalance of
charge. It should also be pointed out that, since ionic bonds involve the
formation of ions, there will be a change in the radii of the ions. Notice
that in the covalent bond and to some extent with the van der Waals'
bonding, a concentration of negative and positive zones in a molecule can
result. Finally, be aware that the basic properties of metals (high
electrical conductivity, malleability and ductility) are the results of the
free movement of outermost electrons that occur with metallic bonding.

Sec. 2.3: Distribution of the Elements in Nature

The origin of the elements is a question of how the universe evolved. Most astronomers accept the Big-Bang Theory. Notice that the fundamental particles (electrons, protons, and neutrons) seem to have been derived from the decay of photons at extremely high temperatures (billions of degrees) and that the first two elements of the universe, hydrogen, and helium, were formed within the first three minutes of the beginning of the universe. Notice also that elements from atomic number 3 (lithium) and all other heavier or so-called planetary elements were not formed during the Big-Bang, but rather evolved as a result of the birth and death of stars. Be careful when you look at the percentages by weight for the relative abundance of the terrestrial elements. You must differentiate between relative elemental abundance for the whole earth (core, mantle, and crust) and that portion of the planet we inhabit, the crust. Don't try to memorize the percentages, but rather note that only four elements comprise 95% of the whole earth (iron, oxygen, silicon, and magnesium), while in crustal rocks oxygen and silicon comprise 75% of the total while iron drops considerably. Finally, note that within our solar system the large, outer planets differ markedly in elemental composition from the inner or terrestrial planets.

Sec. 2.4: Characteristics of Minerals

From your study of the previous section, the authors are now able to present to you a more complete definition of a mineral. Up to this point a mineral was described as being formed by natural processes and having a diagnostic chemical composition. The key component of this section states that every mineral has a unique orderly internal arrangement of its elements. It is this factor that allows us to identify minerals on the basis of their physical properties. An important physical property is crystal habit. The precise identification of a crystal will often permit the mineral to be identified. Notice that a crystal shape is defined by flat, plane surfaces which are arranged at very specific angles relative to one another (constancy of interfacial angles). Be aware that a mineral may exhibit more than one crystal habit (polymorphism) and that more often than not, a mineral will not show its crystal form which is the outward reflection of its orderly internal arrangement of elements. If the proper physical environment is not present, the crystal form cannot develop. The idea of the unit cell and how this results in a crystal is discussed thoroughly, using copper, halite, and quartz as examples. The idea of cleavage should be studied thoroughly, especially how it is related to crystal shapes and, therefore, the internal structure. Notice that all minerals do not possess cleavage. The other physical properties which reflect the atomic structure are twinning, striations, and hardness. Know the hardness scale and be able to locate certain common minerals on the scale. Luster is another very useful property, especially for separating minerals into metallic and nonmetallic groups. Color and streak are also useful in identifying minerals. Notice that the color of the mineral powder (the streak) is not usually the color of the mineral itself. Mineral color may vary considerably, whereas the streak is constant. The density of an object is defined as its mass divided by its volume. The density of water is one gram per cubic centimeter. Specific gravity, which is another physical property, is a concept defined as the density of a material divided by the density of water. Be aware, therefore, that the

numerical value of the density is the same as the numerical value of the
specific gravity, but the latter is a dimensionless number since the units
(grams per cubic centimeter) are eliminated during the division operation.
These two concepts are frequently confused.

Sec. 2.5: The Most Common Minerals

The common rock-forming minerals are described, with emphasis on the
silicates, which have as their structural unit the silicon-oxygen
tetrahedron. Be able to describe this structural unit thoroughly as it is
very important in the structure of all silicate minerals. The silicate
minerals will have certain properties which can be explained by the
orientation of the silicon-oxygen tetrahedra and how they may, at times, be
changed in composition. Pay particular attention to the various
arrangements of the tetrahedra, which involve the sharing of oxygen ions.
Notice that the phenomenon of solid solution, while a common event, does
not always result in a solid solution series or isomorphism. Know the
structure of each of the major silicate minerals and their composition as
well. A classic example of isomorphism is the plagioclase minerals.
Although different minerals result, the same crystal form is maintained
(isomorphism). This occurs also in the mineral olivine. You will run
across this phenomenon in more detail when you study the crystallization of
magmas and the formation of igneous rocks in the next chapter. Note also
the uniqueness of quartz due to its structure. Finally, the other common
rock-forming minerals, although not as basic or common as the silicates,
also should become familiar to you, especially in their chemical
composition.

Sec. 2.6: Organization and Association of Minerals

Except for the definition of a mineral, the ideas mentioned here will be
developed further in later chapters. Be particularly aware of the basic
factors involved in the definition of a mineral and the associations of
mineral groups with a particular geologic setting or environment.

Sec. 2.7: Reshuffling the Elements and Minerals

The major idea here is that minerals are not eternal but are changed and
recycled into other minerals. This occurs predominately in specific
locations on the earth, such as along plate boundaries. An awareness of
the existence of this perpetual process of change is helpful in a study of
the earth.

PROGRAMMED REVIEW

1. The most common states of matter are _____,
    _____, and _____. (16)

    solid
    liquid
    gas

2. All matter is composed of _____ which are
    combinations of the fundamental particles
    _____, _____, and _____. (16)

    atoms
    protons
    electrons
    neutrons

3. An atom is considered to be the smallest unit of   element
    an _____. (16)

4. Most atoms form compounds by _____ and _____   exchanging
    electrons. (17)   sharing

5. The only substance to occur naturally on earth as   water
    a solid, liquid, and gas is _____. (17)

6. Bombarding atoms with highly accelerated particles   open or empty
    has shown them to be largely _____ space. (17)

7. In basic structure, an atom has a central core   nucleus
    called the _____ composed of _____ and _____   protons
    that is surrounded by a cloud of orbiting   neutrons
    _____. (17)   electrons

8. Since all atoms are _____ neutral, the number   electrically
    of _____ must equal the number of _____.   protons
    (17)   electrons

9. The mass of an atom is almost exclusively due   protons
    to its _____ and _____. (17)   neutrons

10. The _____ of an atom is determined by the number   mass number
    of protons and neutrons in its nucleus. (17)

11. The atomic number of an element corresponds to   protons
    the number of _____ in its _____. (17)   nucleus

12. The addition of a new proton and matching   element
    electron to an atom produces a new _____. (17)

13. The number of _____ does not have to equal   neutrons
    the number of protons or _____. (17)   electrons

14. All elements are classified into the major   metals
    categories of _____, _____, and _____. (17)   nonmetals
                                                              metalloids

15. All metals are good _____ of electricity or   conductors
    heat. (17)

16. A _____ shares the characteristics of metals   metalloid
    and nonmetals. (17)

17. Elements that have the same atomic number but   isotopes
    different mass numbers are called _____. (17)

18. The differing masses of isotopes are the result   neutrons
    of differences in the number of _____ in their
    nuclei. (18)

16

19. All atoms are electrically _____, but may attain a charge by the _____ or _____ of an _____ from its outermost shell. (18)

neutral
loss
gain
electron

20. An electrically charged atom is called an _____. (18)

ion

21. _____ possess a positive charge and _____ possess a negative charge. (18)

cations
anions

22. The dimensions of ions and atoms are commonly measured in units called _____. (18)

angstroms

23. The various ways in which atoms are "held" together are called _____. (18)

bonding

24. The _____ or _____ of electrons from the outermost shell of atoms results in _____ bonding. (18)

gain
loss
ionic

25. An atom with seven electrons in its outermost shell will most likely _____ an electron to complete its outermost shell, while one with a single electron in the outermost shell will _____ this electron. (18)

gain
lose

26. If an atom loses a single electron from its outermost shell, it will have a _____ charge and become a _____. (18)

positive
cation

27. If an atom gains an electron in its outermost shell, it will acquire a _____ charge and become an _____. (18)

negative
anion

28. The smallest recognizable unit of a compound is known as a _____. (18)

molecule

29. In the _____ bond, atoms complete their outermost shell by _____ electrons. (18)

covalent
sharing

30. Covalent bonding in the water molecule produces a molecular geometry similar to a magnet. As a result, one end acts as a _____ pole and the other a _____ pole. (19)

positive
negative

31. The positive end of the water molecule will attract negative ions or _____ and the negative end will attract _____ ions or _____. (19)

anions
positive
cations

32. Any molecule that has a polar geometry is called a _____ and results in _____ compounds. (19)

dipole
dipolar

33. A very weak force called _____ force results   van der Waals'
    when orbiting _____ temporarily cluster on one   electrons
    side of an atom or molecule. Because of this   positive
    phenomenon, the opposite of the atom or molecule
    momentarily acquires a _____ charge. (19)

34. Most rock-forming minerals are homogeneous   pure
    crystalline materials but are usually not   ionic
    _____ substances because the composition may
    vary as a result of _____ substitution. (26)

35. The replacement of one ion by a different ion of   solid
    similar size is called _____ solution. (26)

36. The general tendency of two or more ions to   isomorphism
    substitute for one another is called _____.   solid-solution
    This free substitution results in a _____
    mineral series. (26)

37. Copper, gold, silver, and graphite may be found   native
    uncombined in nature and are often referred to
    as _____ elements. (26)

38. _____ occur as precipitates from evaporating   halides
    ponds, salt flats, and natural brines. _____   rock
    salt or its crystal form _____ are the most   halite
    common minerals of this group. (26)

39. The direct union of a cation with oxygen results   oxides
    in a mineral group known as _____. Many   metallic
    minerals of this group are valuable _____
    ores. (26)

40. In rock-forming silicates such as olivine,   iron
    pyroxene, amphibole and biotite, the silicon-oxygen   magnesium
    tetrahedra are joined by ions of _____ and   mafics
    _____. Because of the predominance of the   ferromagnesium
    latter two ions in the mineral's structure, these
    minerals are commonly referred to as _____ or
    _____ minerals. (27)

41. If one were to visually inspect the mafic   dark
    minerals, they would tend to be _____ in color.   density or
    Furthermore, they all have a higher _____   specific
    than other silicate minerals because of their   gravity
    iron and magnesium content. (27)

42. Because iron and magnesium may freely substitute   isomorphism
    for each other in olivine without changing its
    structure, olivine represents a classic example
    of _____. (27)

43. Olivine also forms a _____ series since one end   solid-solution
    member is entirely a magnesium silicate and the
    other end member is entirely an iron silicate. (27)

44. The crystalline structure of pyroxenes is based
    on _____ chains of tetrahedra while the
    crystalline structure of the chemically similar
    amphiboles is based on a _____ chain of
    tetrahedra. (28)

    single
    double

45. _____ and _____ are the two most common minerals
    of the pyroxene and amphibole groups. (28)

    augite
    hornblende

46. In biotite the tetrahedra are constructed in
    _____. Because of this structure, biotite
    and the other mica minerals may be easily
    _____ into flexible sheets. (28)

    sheets
    cleaved or
      peeled

47. Silicate minerals that do not contain iron and
    magnesium are known collectively as _____.
    Unlike the ferromagnesium minerals, they are
    _____ in color and have a lower _____.
    (29)

    nonferromag-
      nesium
    light
    density or
      specific
      gravity

48. _____ mica is structurally similar to biotite
    mica but contains no iron or magnesium and
    considerably more potassium and aluminum. (29)

    muscovite

49. _____ are the most abundant rock-forming
    silicates. They may be subdivided into two
    groups known as _____ and _____. (29)

    feldspars
    potassium or
      K-spar
    plagioclase
      feldspars

50. K-spar is _____ since any replacement will
    alter its crystalline structure. On the other
    hand, plagioclase is _____ since replacement
    of sodium by calcium in the structure is another
    example of a _____ series. (30)

    polymorphous
    isomorphous
    solid-solution

51. _____ is the only rock-forming silicate
    containing no metallic cations in its structure
    which is composed exclusively of tetrahedra.
    Because its crystalline structure has no planes
    of weakness, you would not expect any _____.
    However, fracturing along smooth curving surfaces
    known as a _____ fracture is often very
    distinctive. (30)

    quartz
    cleavage
    conchoidal

52. Even though minerals may vary from one sample
    to another, the _____ atomic arrangement of its
    component atoms is identical in all specimens of
    a given mineral species. (20)

    internal

53. Crystal habit, cleavage, and hardness are examples
    of _____ properties of a mineral. (21)

    physical

54. If a mineral has room to grow during its formation, it will develop a unique _____. (21)

crystal habit

55. In every crystal the atoms are arranged in a three-dimensional pattern or lattice that repeats itself regularly. The smallest repeat unit of this pattern is known as the _____. (21)

unit cell

56. While the size of a crystal of a given mineral species may vary in size, the corresponding crystal faces will always meet at the same angle. This defines the law of _____. (21)

constancy of interfacial angles

57. Every mineral has a unique crystal habit and, based on crystal geometry, may be classified into one of six different _____. However, a mineral may develop in more than one system. This is an example of _____. (22)

crystal systems
polymorphism

58. _____ is the tendency of a mineral to break along certain preferred directions in smooth plane surfaces. (23)

cleavage

59. The intergrowths of two or more single crystals of the same mineral with different geometric orientations defines the property called _____. (23)

twinning

60. Parallel, threadlike lines or narrow bands found on the crystal or cleavage surfaces of some minerals are known as _____. (23)

striations

61. The degree or ease with which one mineral may "scratch" another or be scratched by some object like a piece of steel defines the property of _____. (23)

hardness

62. If a mineral scratches a glass plate, you may conclude that the mineral is _____ than the glass. (23)

harder

63. The comparison of the mass of a mineral with the mass of an equal volume of water defines the _____ of a mineral. The ratio of the mass of any mineral to its volume defines the _____ of the mineral. (25)

specific gravity
density

64. The physical property of _____ is not very reliable for most minerals, but may be diagnostic for a few. As a general rule, those minerals containing iron are usually _____ while those containing aluminum are usually _____ in color. (25)

color
dark
light

65. The _____ of a mineral is the color it displays in finely powdered form. (25)

streak

66. The quality and intensity of light reflected from a mineral surface is characteristic of the mineral's _____. Although mineral luster may vary considerably, most specimens can usually be grouped into two broad categories called _____ and _____. (26)

luster
metallic
nonmetallic

67. Most astronomers believe the universe began 10 to 20 billion years ago as an expanding sea of high energy _____. This theory is commonly referred to as the _____. (20)

photons
big-bang

68. Subsequent cooling of the expanding universe soon after its birth enabled photons to decay into _____, _____, and _____. (20)

protons
electrons
neutrons

69. Even though the universe was cooling, the temperature early in its history was so high that nuclear reactions could fuse particles into _____ and _____. These two elemental gases make up approximately 99% of the weight of the known _____. (20)

hydrogen
helium
universe

70. If we consider the relative abundance of elements found on earth, 90% by weight of the total mass of the earth consists of only four elements. These are in decreasing abundance, _____, _____, _____, and _____. (20)

iron
oxygen
silicon
magnesium

71. However, if we confine our elemental analysis to crustal rocks, we find that 75% by weight is composed of only two elements, namely, _____ and _____. By contrast with the total earth, there is a significant drop in _____ and _____ in crustal rocks. (20)

oxygen
silicon
iron
magnesium

72. From an analysis of the elemental composition of the crustal rocks, it should be readily apparent why _____ are the most common rock-forming minerals. (20)

silicates

73. Certain mineral groups or assemblages are often indicative of the environmental conditions at the time of their formation. That is, some minerals may have formed under conditions of high or low _____ and _____. (31)

temperature
pressure

74. Since rocks continuously undergo changes with the passage of time, their component minerals must also be altered. Much of this change occurs along _____ boundaries within the earth's _____. These changes are almost entirely the result of the extremely high _____ and _____ encountered in these regions. (31)

plate
lithosphere
temperatures
pressures

75. Minerals found in rocks at or near the earth's   weathering
    surface are commonly altered by the process of   erosion
    _____ and _____. (31)

A final note on minerals. You will learn more about mineral associations
and alterations when you study the next few chapters on the origin of the
major rock groups. As you go through those chapters, keep in mind that it
is often said that all rocks are formed from other rocks.

SELF-TESTS

Part A: True-False Statements

Each of the following statements is either true or false. Encircle either
T or F for each item.

1. A proton is a positive charge with a mass equal to the   T   F
    mass of an electron.

2. The size of an atomic diameter could be about 100 angstroms.   T   F

3. An ion is an atom or group of atoms with a charge.   T   F

4. The atomic number of an atom is the number of protons.   T   F

5. The Big-Bang Theory holds that the universe began in an   T   F
    explosion of a core of protons.

6. The relative abundance of the elements on the earth is   T   F
    comparable to the abundance of elements throughout the
    universe.

7. About 90% of the earth's crust consists of iron, oxygen,   T   F
    silicon, and magnesium.

8. The unit cell is a combination of atoms which repeats   T   F
    itself to form a crystal.

9. A specific substance with a definite chemical composition   T   F
    can grow only one crystal form.

10. Cleavage occurs because of the existence of impurities   T   F
    within the substance, thus weakening the bonds.

11. A physical property which is described by how easy it is   T   F
    to scratch a mineral with a known material is called
    streak.

12. The mass per volume of a mineral defines the specific   T   F
    gravity of that mineral.

13. The specific gravity of most minerals is about 5.5.   T   F

14. An ionic compound forms when one atom loses one or more   T   F
    electrons and another atom gains one or more electrons.

15. The oxide minerals, which are compounds of oxygen and   T   F
    another element, are the most abundant rock-forming
    minerals.

16. The net charge of the silicon-oxygen tetrahedron is a   T   F
    negative four.

17. In the silicate minerals, the silicon-oxygen tetrahedra   T   F
    are combined with elements such as iron, magnesium,
    sodium, and aluminum.

18. Augite is a ferromagnesian with a structure described as   T   F
    a chain of silicon-oxygen tetrahedra, with each chain
    bonded to another chain.

19. Sulfide minerals are minerals formed by the union of   T   F
    sulfur, iron, and a variety of other elements.

20. Olivine and plagioclase feldspars are good examples of   T   F
    polymorphous minerals.

Part B: Multiple Choice Items

Each of the following can be completed correctly by choosing only one word
or phrase. Encircle the letter a, b, c, or d designating your choice.

1. The types of electric charge are

    a. positive, negative, neutral.   c. electrons, protons, neutrons.
    b. positive, negative.   d. atomic, nuclear.

2. The mass number of an atom is the

    a. number of protons plus the number of neutrons.
    b. number of neutrons minus the number of electrons.
    c. number of electrons plus the number of protons.
    d. number of electrons in its outer shell.

3. Atoms of the common elements have diameters which are about equal to

    a. 2 angstroms.   c. one-ten thousandth angstrom.
    b. 10 angstroms.   d. 100 angstroms.

4. An ionic bond is due to

    a. electric forces.   c. constant movement of electrons.
    b. sharing of electrons.   d. a decrease in atomic size.

5. Which characteristic does not pertain to the silicon-oxygen tetrahedron?

   a. four oxygen ions and a silicon ion
   b. charge of negative four
   c. silicon ion surrounded by three ions
   d. chemical structure with four faces

6. Which group of minerals below lists only silicate minerals?

   a. graphite, augite, quartz, magnesite
   b. orthoclase, muscovite, olivine, anhydrite
   c. sphalerite, corundum, halite, gypsum
   d. muscovite, plagioclase, olivine, augite

7. Which set of characteristics describes the silicate mineral augite?

   a. sheets of silicon-oxygen tetrahedra joined by potassium, magnesium, iron, and aluminum
   b. double chains of silicon-oxygen tetrahedra joined by iron, magnesium, calcium, sodium, and aluminum
   c. sheet and chain structure of silicon-oxygen tetrahedra joined by iron, magnesium, and aluminum
   d. single chains of silicon-oxygen tetrahedra, joined by iron, magnesium, calcium, sodium, and aluminum

8. Which mineral group contains no oxygen atoms?

   a. carbonates   c. sulfates
   b. sulfides   d. silicates

9. What mineral has a structure in which silicon ions share three oxygen ions to form sheets which are held together by magnesium and iron to form double sheets?

   a. hornblende   c. biotite
   b. muscovite   d. orthoclase

10. Which group below lists only members of the nonferromagnesians?

    a. muscovite, gypsum, anhydrite, calcite
    b. plagioclase, dolomite, magnetite, pyrite
    c. hematite, magnetite, corundum, sphalerite
    d. muscovite, orthoclase, plagioclase, quartz

11. Which of these groups list feldspars only?

    a. orthoclase, albite, anorthite
    b. muscovite, biotite, hornblende
    c. dolomite, calcite, magnetite
    d. halite and sylvite

12. Which two minerals are the end members in a solid solution series?

    a. biotite and muscovite   c. albite and anorthite
    b. orthoclase and feldspar   d. halite and sylvite

13. Hornblende should be classed with which one of the following?

    a. double-chain tetrahedra, olivine, biotite, amphiboles
    b. muscovite, tetrahedral sheets, biotite
    c. single-chain, olivine, quartz, aluminum
    d. double-chain tetrahedra, potassium aluminum silicates

14. Which mineral is composed entirely of silicon-oxygen tetrahedra?

    a. olivine   c. halite
    b. quartz   d. orthoclase

15. Which two minerals are formed by the union of iron with another oxygen?

    a. anhydrite, gypsum   c. halite, sylvite
    b. chalcocite, pyrite   d. magnetite, hematite

SUGGESTED ESSAY QUESTIONS

The items below represent the type of discussion questions to which you might be expected to respond. Try writing a response to these and then discuss your work with another student.

1. Explain why ions will have smaller dimensions than their corresponding atoms.

2. Describe how the structure of biotite and muscovite are similar and how they differ.

3. Explain why the minerals orthoclase, albite, and anorthite are related and classed together.

4. Define and discuss the concept of a mineral, being sure to explain thoroughly the major characteristics of the definition.

5. Explain why the tetrahedral structure of orthoclase is not an example of a solid solution series even though aluminum substitutes for silicon.

ANSWERS TO SELF-TESTS

Part A:					Part B:			
	1. F	6. F	11. F	16. T		1. b	6. d	11. a
	2. F	7. T	12. F	17. T		2. a	7. d	12. c
	3. T	8. T	13. F	18. T		3. a	8. b	13. a
	4. T	9. F	14. T	19. F		4. a	9. c	14. b
	5. T	10. F	15. F	20. F		5. d	10. d	15. d

CHAPTER 3

ORIGIN AND OCCURRENCE OF INTRUSIVE IGNEOUS ROCKS

OVERVIEW

Practically all igneous rocks result from the progressive crystallization of minerals from a hot molten liquid called magma. This magma, while ultimately derived from deep within the earth, may in places breach the surface through vents to form volcanoes or along extensive fissures where it may develop vast plateau landscapes (Ch. 4). In many, if not most cases, the magma does not reach the surface, but rather remains trapped within the Earth's crust where it crystallizes over millions of years. Whether the igneous rocks result from volcanic activity or are the products of deep-seated processes now exposed by erosion, they are of prime importance to an understanding of the evolution of the earth since they constitute about 95 percent of the outermost 10 km of the Earth.

This textbook chapter approaches igneous activity and igneous rocks by first considering the source of the Earth's heat and its role in the formation of melted rock called magma and lava. The formation of the igneous rocks are then extensively discussed from the viewpoint of the unique chemistry of crystallizing magmas as proposed in the pioneer studies of N.L. Bowen. The authors then present the parameters for the classification of the igneous rocks and then describe the major igneous rock types.

The chapter closes with a brief section on the relationship of magmas to tectonic settings and a major section describing and classifying the intrusive rock bodies called plutons.

LEARNING OBJECTIVES

After studying this chapter, you should be able to:

1. Describe the major sources of the Earth's heat and its relationship to igneous activity.

2. State how all igneous rocks form.

3. Understand the unique processes involved in magmatic crystallization as presented by the Bowen's Reaction Principle.

4. Discuss the role magmatic crystallization plays in the types of igneous rocks produced.

5. List the principle objections or limitations of the Bowen's Reaction Principle in the origin of igneous rocks.

6. Describe the igneous rock texture.

7. State the conditions that determine which type of texture will develop.

8. State how magmas form and how they are classified.

9. Discuss the significance of the viscosity and composition of magmas on the type of rock produced.

10. Describe and classify plutonic bodies.

11. Classify and name the common igneous rocks.

KEY TERMS AND CONCEPTS

geothermal gradient
heat flow
pyroclastic debris
crystallization
melt
magma
lava
Bowen's Reaction Principle
reaction series
continuous reaction series
discontinuous reaction series
fractionation or fractional
crystallization
mafic
ultramafic
sialic
gabbro
basalt
diorite

andesite
granite
rhyolite
dunite
peridotite
granodiorite
rate of crystallization
texture
phaneritic
aphanitic
glassy
porphyritic
groundmass
phenocrysts
porphyry
pegmatitic structure
pegmatite
graphic structure
simple or granite pegmatite

27

complex pegmatite
"dark-colored minerals"
"light-colored minerals"
tholeiitic gabbro
alkali olivine gabbro
trap rock
primary magma
secondary magma
pluton
massive pluton
tabular pluton
concordant pluton

discordant pluton
sill
dike
ring dikes
cone sheets
dike swarms
lopoliths
laccoliths
stocks
batholiths
stoping
granitization

NOTES

Sec. 3.1: The Earth's Heat

The thermal gradient is noted as being variable from place to place with an average value of about 30°C/km. However, while it is axiomatic that temperature increases with depth, you cannot extrapolate the thermal gradient blindly. If this value were a strict linear increase, temperatures high enough to melt any rock would be reached within 40-50 km below the surface. Since we know this is not the case, there must be another factor involved. Here you must consider the thermal conductivity of a rock which considered with the thermal gradient expresses heat flow. Heat travels very slowly through rock, and studies show that heat flow is fairly constant over wide areas of the globe even though the thermal gradient may vary considerably.

Also be aware that all the heat needed to generate magmas can be derived from radioactive decay (largely a phenomenon of continental rocks) and the frictional energy of plate movement.

Sec. 3.2: Formation of Igneous Rocks

The crucial element in this section is understanding magmatic crystallization as explained by the Bowen's Reaction Series. To comprehend the discussion, let's consider three factors, namely, the discontinuous and continuous reaction series, fractionation, and the rate of crystallization.

A homely analogy may explain the distinction between the continuous and discontinuous series. Suppose you construct a wall of a specific shape with red bricks. Upon completion you like the shape of the wall but not the color of the bricks. How could you keep the same shape, but have some of the red bricks replaced by yellow ones? No, you cannot paint the bricks! The only thing you can do is replace the red bricks with yellow bricks of the same size and shape. You start out with a wall of 100% red bricks and may progress to a wall of 100% yellow ones with any combination in between. The only stipulation is the size and shape of the bricks. With reference to the continuous series, calcium is a red brick and sodium is a yellow one. The shape of the wall is the silicate structure of plagioclase. The radii of the calcium and sodium ion are close enough in size that one can freely substitute for the other in the plagioclase structure. Therefore, you wind up with the same structural framework but a different mineral composition. This is not the case with the discontinuous series. When olivine reacts with the liquid fraction of the magma, it is converted to a pyroxene. In this case, not only is the composition different, but so is the silicate framework. You may want to refer back to Table 2.2 in Chapter 2 of your text to note the different silicate structures.

As crystallization proceeds, those elements going into the makeup of the ferromagnesian rich minerals (olivine, pyroxene, amphibole) leave the liquid fraction deficient in these constituents but richer in silica, sodium, potassium, and aluminum (the so-called sialic components). Since the earlier formed minerals also have a higher specific gravity, they may also settle through the relatively fluid liquid fraction to the lower reaches of the magma chamber. This allows for the reaction process to continue and also increases the sialic content of the main body of the magma. This process is fractionation, also known as gravity separation.

The rate of crystallization plays a critical role in the degree to which the process moves towards completion and, therefore, the final composition of a rock resulting from magmatic crystallization. If the process begins with a basic (basaltic) magma and the rate of crystallization is fairly rapid, the reaction process will be short-circuited and the resulting rock will be of basaltic composition. On the other hand, if the process proceeds at a slow enough pace, the fractionation processes will continue to operate and rocks of a more intermediate and maybe even acidic composition will form.

A note on terms like silica rich, siliceous, and silica content when used in the context of igneous rocks and magmas. When referring to the composition of igneous rocks, it is convenient to express values in percentage of oxides. That is, silica content is expressed as percent silicon dioxide (SiO_2) while the iron content would be expressed as percent silicon dioxide (Fe_2O_3 and FeO). If you digest some of the information in the chart, you will have a much better understanding of the terms acidic, basic, ultrabasic, highly siliceous, etc. These terms are used throughout this chapter.

Acidic		Intermediate		Basic		Ultrabasic	
Rock	% SiO_2	Rock	% SiO_2	Rock	% SiO_2	Rock	% SiO_2
Granite	70	Diorite	57	Gabbro	48	Dunite	40
Rhyolite	71	Andesite	59	Basalt	49	Peridotite	35
% Iron Oxides[*]		% Iron Oxides		% Iron Oxides		% Iron Oxides	
Granite	3.5	Diorite	7.7	Gabbro	9.1	Dunite	8.6
Rhyolite	2.5	Andesite	6.6	Basalt	12.1	Peridotite	9.2

[*] Note the trend of increasing iron oxide content with decreasing silica.

Be aware that there are some objections to Bowen's hypothesis that a basaltic magma can yield on acidic rock like granite. This will be covered more fully in Chapter 7 on the origin of granite.

Sec. 3.3: Texture of Igneous Rocks

A key point is that texture refers to the size, shape, and geometrical arrangement of the grains in a rock. Do not confuse texture with a smooth or rough feel of a rock.

Keep in mind that texture in igneous rocks is primarily a function of the rate of cooling, gas content, amount of water vapor, and the viscosity of the magma.

Memorize the texture terms given.

Sec. 3.4: Classification of Igneous Rocks

The igneous rocks are classified on the basis of texture and composition. Study the chart given in Fig. 3.8 and try to get a feel for various mineral assemblages that make up the different igneous rocks. You will probably have ample time to use and digest this chart or a similar one in your laboratory activity on igneous rock identification.

Sec. 3.5: Origin of Magmas

Note the difference between the production of the primary magma (remelting) and secondary magma (fractionation or other alteration of the primary magma). Also be aware that there are only two or possibly three types of primary magmas, yet there are many different types of igneous rock. Know the factors that can change the primary magmas to produce the large variety found in the igneous rocks. Finally, be able to place the primary magmas in a given tectonic setting.

Sec. 3.6: Masses of Igneous Rocks

This section is concerned more with the shapes and methods of emplacement of intrusive igneous rock bodies rather than specific igneous rock types. The composition of some intrusives, like dikes and sills, can range considerably, but certain types have a rather restrictive composition. Note that batholiths are acidic (granite-like), while lopoliths are more basic in composition.

Since the batholiths are the largest and make up by volume the greatest abundance of the intrusive igneous rocks, you should know the basic factors described in their occurrence and formation.

PROGRAMMED REVIEW

1. Igneous activity is dependent upon the accumulation of _____ in the Earth's interior. (36)

   heat

2. The _____ describes the _____ (increase, decrease) in temperature with depth in the Earth. (36)

   geothermal gradient increase

3. The melting point of rock _____ (increases, decreases) with higher pressure. (36)

   increases

4. Rocks at great depth within the Earth are probably
   _____ (solid, melted), although very hot,
   because of the high _____ encountered deep
   in the Earth's interior. (36)

   solid
   pressure

5. _____ is a way of expressing the rate at which
   heat travels through rock and soil. (36)

   heat flow

6. The rate at which heat travels through rock is
   a function of the geothermal gradient and the
   _____ of Earth materials. (36)

   thermal conduc-
    tivity

7. Studies have shown that the overall heat flow
   within the Earth is relatively _____, although
   it may be considerably higher along the margins
   of _____ depending upon local volcanic and
   tectonic activity (36)

   constant
   plate boundaries

8. Molten rock under the Earth's surface is known
   as _____ but is called _____ when extruded
   onto the surface and _____ if blasted into the
   atmosphere by a violent volcanic eruption. (36)

   magma
   lava
   pyroclastic
    debris

9. Magma may form from the partial remelting of the
   _____ or by the _____ of the lithosphere
   along plate margins. (36)

   mantle
   subduction

10. _____ defines the process of magma solidification.

    crystallization

11. In its early stages a magma is a liquid solution
    at high temperature known as a _____, but
    as the temperature decreases and crystallization
    begins, the magma becomes a mixture of liquid,
    _____ and released _____. (37)

    melt
    solids
    gases

12. A magma differs from ordinary solutions because
    the end product of the crystallization may be
    very _____ (different, similar) to the composition
    of the original melt. (37)

    different

13. The idea that a magma of a given composition may
    crystallize into a number of different types of
    rock was developed by _____. (37)

    N. L. Bowen

14. The process by which a newly crystallized mineral
    reacts with the remaining melt or liquid is known
    as _____. (37)

    reaction

15. Bowen's laboratory experiments were done on melts
    of _____ composition. (37)

    silicate

16. Bowen's experimental results enabled him to arrange igneous rock forming silicate minerals into a _____ series. If a newly formed mineral reacts with the melt and is converted to a new mineral with the _____ (same, different) crystalline structure, it forms part of the _____ reaction series. If the newly crystallized minerals react with the melt to form a new mineral with a _____ (same, different) crystalline structure, it is placed in the _____ reaction series. (37)

reaction
same
continuous
different
discontinuous

17. _____ minerals make up the _____ reaction series, while _____ minerals constitute the composition of the _____ reaction series. (37)

ferromagnesian
discontinuous
feldspar
continuous

18. During the process of _____, a newly formed mineral settles out or is removed from the main body of the melt. (38)

fractionation

19. If olivine does not fractionate but reacts with the melt, it should be converted to _____ which has a _____ (similar, different) crystal structure and would be placed in the _____ reaction series. (38)

augite
different
discontinuous

20. As the crystallization and fractionation processes continue, the composition of the magma _____ (increases, decreases) in silica content and _____ (increases, decreases) in ferromagnesian composition. (38)

increases
decreases

21. According to the reaction principle, it should be possible to begin with a magma of _____ (high, low) mafic or ferromagnesian content and eventually develop a magma with a _____ (high, low) silicious composition. (38)

high
high

22. A _____ or _____ would be representative of a rock formed in the early stages of the reaction process, while a rock of _____ composition would be representative of the latter stages of the process. (39)

gabbro
basalt
granitic

23. A rock of intermediate composition should contain a mixture of _____ minerals and alumina-rich or _____ minerals. The rocks _____ and _____ would be representative of this composition. (39)

mafic or ferro-
  magnesian
sialic
diorite
andesite

24. For the fractionation process to develop, a _____ (large, small) magma body would have to crystallize _____ (rapidly, slowly) at _____ (great, shallow) depth. (39)

large
slowly
great

25. The major objection to the Bowen hypothesis lies in the _____ (large, small) volume of silicious rocks that could possibly be produced by the reaction process from a magma of basaltic composition. Since the continents are composed predominantly of _____ rocks, it seems another process may be required to account for the overall composition of the continental sialic rocks. (39)

small
granite or
  granitic

26. The general term _____ is used to describe the physical characteristics or appearance of all rocks. When referring to the igneous rocks, the term specifically describes the _____, _____, and geometric arrangement of the rock's mineral grains. (39)

texture
shape
size

27. The term _____ describes the texture of an igneous rock whose mineral grains are visible to the naked eye. If the mineral grains can only be seen under a microscope, the rock would be described as having an _____ texture. (39)

phanertitic
aphanitic

28. Under certain conditions a magma may crystallize very rapidly so that the mineral grains do not get the chance to develop a crystalline structure. The resulting rock would be described as having a _____ texture. The rock _____ is typical of this type. (40)

glassy
obsidian

29. Two factors that determine the texture of an igneous rock are the rate of _____ and the _____ of the parent magma. (40)

cooling
viscosity

30. It is very rare to find a glassy textured rock of mafic or basaltic composition. Most glassy rocks are _____ or _____ in composition because of the _____ (high, low) viscosity and _____ (high, low) gas content of their magmas. (40)

sialic
granitic
high
high

31. _____ solutions or end stage fluids develop in the late phases of magma crystallization. (40)

hydrothermal

32. The rock _____ is a product of end stage fluids and is characterized by an extremely coarse texture called _____ and a composition consisting of the highly silicious minerals _____ and _____. In some of these rocks, the quartz and feldspar are intergrown to form a wedge-shaped pattern known as _____ structure. (40)

pegmatite
pegmatitic
potassium
  feldspar
quartz
graphic

33

33. Almost 90 percent of all pegmatite bodies have a
    granitic composition and are referred to as
    _____ pegmatites, while about 10 percent
    maintain the overall composition of granite, but
    contain a variety of rare minerals and are
    classified as _____ pegmatites. (41)

    simple
    complex

34. Although microscopic examination is often required
    for a detailed identification and classification
    of rocks, most rocks can be readily identified in
    the field on the basis of their _____ and
    _____. (41)

    texture
    mineral
      composition

35. On the basis of color, most igneous rocks show a
    progression from _____ (light, dark) color where
    _____ minerals predominate to _____ (light, dark)
    where _____ minerals predominate. (41)

    dark
    mafic
    light
    sialic

36. Olivine, augite, and hornblende are examples of
    _____ minerals that are _____ (light, dark)
    in the color. (41)

    ferromagnesian
      or mafic
    dark

37. Feldspars are usually _____ (light, dark) in
    color, but those plagioclase feldspars with a
    _____ content are usually _____ (light, dark)
    in color.

    light
    calcium
    dark

38. When describing color in a rock, shades of green,
    _____ and _____ are considered to be dark
    while shades of _____, _____, and _____ are
    referred to as light in color. (42)

    black
    dark gray
    white
    pink
    light gray

39. Though igneous rocks vary considerably in
    composition, there are great similarities within
    a given geologic setting or environment. Thus,
    oceanic crustal rocks tend to be _____ in
    composition and _____ (light, dark) in color,
    while continental crustal rocks tend to be _____
    in composition and _____ (light, dark) in color. (42)

    mafic (basaltic)
    dark
    sialic
      (granitic)
    light

40. A gabbro or basalt containing two pyroxenes,
    plagioclase feldspars, and maybe some olivine
    is classified as being _____ in composition,
    while those composed of a single pyroxene,
    plagioclase feldspar and a higher percentage of
    olivine are known as _____. (42)

    tholeiitic
      (tholeiite
      basalts or
      gabbros)
    alkalic (alkali
      olivine
      basalts or
      gabbros)

41. _____ gabbros or basalts are usually associated
    with the deep ocean or oceanic ridges, while
    _____ gabbros or basalts commonly occur on
    oceanic islands. (42)

    tholeiitic
    alkalic

42. _____ is a term referring to basalts that tend to form column-like structures that result from the development of joints during the cooling of the magma or lava. (42)

trap rock

43. Rocks with a very large percentage of olivine are known as _____, while those containing olivine and a high percentage of other mafic minerals are called _____. (42)

dunite
peridotite

44. _____ are phaneritic rocks of intermediate composition and _____ are their aphanitic equivalents. (42)

diorite
andesite

45. Rocks of _____ composition are the most common of the continental crustal rocks. The most abundant of the phaneritic crustal rocks of the continents is _____, while _____ is its aphanitic equivalent. (42)

granitic
granite
rhyolite

46. Magmas may be classified by their mode of origin and composition. Magmas derived from the partial melting of portions of the lower crust are termed _____ magmas, while those produced by fractionation or alteration of other magmas are classified as _____ magmas. (43)

primary
secondary

47. While the composition of secondary magmas may be somewhat variable, most primary ones are usually _____, _____, and probably _____ in composition. (44)

basaltic
granitic
andesitic

48. When magmatic bodies have been emplaced, crystallized and subsequently exposed by erosion, they may be described on the basis of their _____, _____, and in some cases their _____. (44)

size
shape
composition

49. All intrusive igneous bodies are referred to as _____. If this body cuts across the prevailing rock structure, it is known as being _____, while a body that tends to follow the structural trend of the invaded rocks and their layering is called _____. (44)

plutons
discordant
concordant

50. Sills and dikes are representative of _____ shaped plutons. They differ from each other because sills are _____ and dikes are _____. (44)

tabular
concordant
discordant

51. Any intrusive igneous body must be _____ (older, younger) than the rock it invades. (44)

younger

52. A concordant tabular pluton with a sagging roof and floor is known as a _____. (45)

lopolith

53. Any plutonic body that does not have a tabular shape is classified as _____. A relatively small (a few square kilometers), non-tabular and dome-shaped concordant pluton is called a _____. (45)

massive
laccolith

54. Extremely large (over 100 sq. km), discordant plutons located in the cores and axial regions of mountain ranges are called _____. (46)

batholiths

55. Most batholithic bodies are primarily composed of _____ or _____, although they sometimes contain blocks of rock broken off the invaded or country rock. These blocks are known as _____. (46)

granite
granodiorite
xenoliths

56. The mechanism by which the magma of batholithic proportions moves upward into the crust by engulfing the invaded country rock is called _____. However, most batholiths do not show clear and distinct boundaries, but rather appear to have replaced the invaded rocks. The process called _____ describes the chemical replacement of invaded rock by magmatic solutions which converts them to granite or granite-like rocks. (46)

stoping
granitization

SELF-TESTS

Part A: True-False Statements

Each of the following statements is either true or false. Encircle either a T or F for each item.

1. Heat generated by radioactive decay and friction of moving plates can account for the total heat needed to generate magmas. T   F

2. Dikes are concordant, tabular plutons. T   F

3. Batholiths are always found associated with mountain ranges. T   F

4. N. L. Bowen believed it was possible for an acidic rock to develop from a basic magma by a process he called reaction. T   F

5. During the crystallization of a basic magma, amphiboles may react with the magma and be converted to pyroxene. T   F

6. A rapid cooling of a magma will produce a rock whose texture may be described as aphanitic. T   F

7. A variable cooling rate in a magma may produce a rock with a porphyritic texture. T   F

8. The increase of temperature with depth is called heat flow. T   F

9. The greatest variation in heat flow seems to occur at the margins of lithospheric plates.   T   F

10. All igneous rocks have been formed from the solidification of magma.   T   F

11. In the continuous reaction series, early formed minerals are converted into new minerals by continuously changing their composition and crystal structure.   T   F

12. The process called reaction refers to removal from the magma of early formed minerals by gravity.   T   F

13. The later formed minerals in magma crystallization are more silicious and alumina-rich than the earlier ones.   T   F

14. The texture of an igneous rock is usually a good indicator of the viscosity of its parent magma.   T   F

15. Phenocrysts should be very common in glassy textured rocks.   T   F

16. Hydrothermal solutions develop early in the crystallization of a magma.   T   F

17. Quartz and potassium feldspar are typical light colored igneous minerals.   T   F

18. A piece of sandstone found "floating" in a basalt intrusion would be called a xenolith.   T   F

19. Stoping refers to the process by which rock is slowly changed to a granitic composition.   T   F

20. Most lopoliths are dome-shaped and composed of rock that has been differentiated into alternating layers of light and dark minerals.   T   F

Part B: Multiple Choice Items

Each of the following can be completed or answered correctly by choosing only one of the selections. Encircle the letter a, b, c or d designating your choice.

1. The process where some of the early-formed minerals settle out of the magma is known as

   a. discontinuous reaction.   c. continuous reaction.
   b. fractionation.   d. reaction.

2. If a basic magma crystallizes at a rapid rate and no minerals settle out of the magma, the resulting rock may be a(n)

   a. andesite.   c. rhyolite.
   b. basalt.   d. syenite.

3. As the earlier formed minerals of a crystallizing magma react with the melt and settle out, the remaining fraction of the magma is enriched in

   a. ferromagnesians.
   b. calcium.
   c. silica.
   d. carbonates.

4. Which of the following rocks does not belong in association with the others?

   a. gabbro
   b. granite
   c. diorite
   d. rhyolite

5. A rock is described as having a granular texture and a mineral composition of predominantly calcium plagioclase and ferromagnesian minerals. The rock is probably

   a. granite.
   b. gabbro.
   c. rhyolite.
   d. basalt.

6. Which mineral pair would not be found in the same igneous pool?

   a. quartz and olivine
   b. calcium and sodium plagioclase
   c. orthoclase and muscovite
   d. biotite and orthoclase

7. Which of the following rocks has the lowest percentage of ferromagnesian minerals?

   a. periodotite
   b. rhyolite
   c. dunite
   d. andesite

8. A large plutonic body would most probably possess a texture described as

   a. aphanitic.
   b. glassy.
   c. porphyritic.
   d. granular.

9. A principle objection to Bowen's hypothesis is

   a. the amount of granite found on the continents is much greater than the amount that could be produced from a basic magma.
   b. the amount of basic rocks on the continents far exceeds the amount of granitic material.
   c. it does not account for the development of pegmatites.
   d. it does not explain why olivine and quartz are so commonly found together in the same igneous rock.

10. A massive concordant pluton that was created when magma pushed up overlying rock structures into a dome is called a

   a. laccolith.
   b. lopolith.
   c. batholith.
   d. cactolith.

11. A type of tabular, spoon-shaped intrusion that has been differentiated into alternating layers of light and dark minerals is a

    a. sill.
    b. dike.
    c. laccolith.
    d. lopolith.

12. Calculations of heat flow values in different regions of the world show that

    a. the rate is greatest in continental areas.
    b. the rate is greatest in oceanic areas.
    c. the rate is quite uniform in continental and oceanic areas.
    d. the evidence is still too inconclusive to determine the variability of heat flow on a global basis.

13. The geothermal gradient indicates that temperature increases would melt any rock at about a depth of 50 km. However, we know that most rock at this depth is solid. The most probable reason for this is because

    a. heat travels slowly through earth materials.
    b. the melting point of rock increases with increasing pressure.
    c. at this depth most of the volatiles escape and cause a drop in temperature.
    d. at this depth the average geothermal gradient is not as great as it is at shallower depths.

14. In the continuous reaction series a calcium-rich feldspar would be converted to

    a. olivine.
    b. sodium-rich feldspar.
    c. potassium-rich feldspar.
    d. quartz.

15. Based on the density of a mineral, which of the following would be the most likely to fractionate from a melt?

    a. muscovite
    b. quartz
    c. pyroxene
    d. orthoclase

SUGGESTED ESSAY QUESTIONS

The items below represent the type of discussion questions to which you might be expected to respond. Try writing a response to these and then discuss your work with another student.

1. Distinguish between the following:

    a. basaltic magma and andesitic magma
    b. tholeiitic basalt and alkalic basalt
    c. continuous reaction series and discontinuous reaction series
    d. geothermal gradient and heat flow

2. What factors control the magmatic stoping?

3. Describe the process of magmatic stoping.

4. Show how it is possible to derive a granite from a basaltic magma.

5. Describe the major igneous rock textures and what they reveal about the cooling history of the rock's parent magma.

6. On the basis of texture and mineral composition, distinguish between the following:

   a. gabbro and rhyolite
   b. granite and basalt
   c. andesite and diorite

   d. dunite and peridotite
   e. rhyolite and obsidian
   f. granite and syenite

ANSWERS TO SELF-TESTS

Part A: 1. T   6. F   11. F   16. F   Part B: 1. b   6. a   11. d
        2. F   7. T   12. F   17. T   2. b   7. b   12. c
        3. T   8. F   13. T   18. T   3. c   8. d   13. b
        4. T   9. T   14. F   19. F   4. d   9. a   14. b
        5. F   10. T   15. F   20. F   5. b   10. a   15. c

CHAPTER 4

ORIGIN
AND OCCURRENCE
OF EXTRUSIVE
IGNEOUS ROCKS

OVERVIEW

There are many factors that govern the production of igneous rocks. Since igneous rocks are the products of magmatic crystallization, the parameters dealing with the generation of magmas, their composition and chemistry of crystallization, and the environment of the crystallizing magma are important factors in igneous activity and origin of the igneous rocks.

In this chapter, the extrusive or volcanic rocks are considered from the perspective of the volcanic development, the mechanics of volcanic eruptions, the nature of lavas, and the classification of volcanic types. The case history of a few classic volcanoes are also described, as well as the unique nature and distribution of fissure eruptions.

LEARNING OBJECTIVES

After studying this chapter, you should be able to:

1. Distinguish between a magma and lava.

2. Distinguish between a fissure eruption and a volcanic eruption.

3. Describe the general cycle of a volcanic eruption.

4. Recognize the difference between continental and oceanic volcanic rocks.

5. Recognize the importance of the role played by temperature and gases in volcanic eruptions.

6. Describe the different types of volcanic materials.

7. Describe the local and worldwide effects of volcanic activity.

8. Classify volcanoes.

9. Differentiate between active, dormant, and extinct volcanoes.

10. Describe the history of some classic volcanoes.

11. Describe the origin of plateau or flood basalts.

12. Describe the origin of craters and calderas.

13. Discuss the relationship between volcanic activity and earthquakes.

KEY TERMS AND CONCEPTS

volcanoes
crater
caldera
volcanic eruptions
shield volcano
cinder cone volcano
composite volcano
basic lava
intermediate lava
silicic lava
carbonatites
pahoehoe
aa
volatiles
pyroclastic debris
tephra
ash
cinder
lapilli

blocks
bombs
pumice
fiery clouds (pyroclastic flows)
nuées ardentes
fumaroles
lahars
active volcanoes
dormant volcanoes
extinct volcanoes
lava lake
midocean ridge basalts (MORB)
pillows (pillow lavas)
fissure eruptions
lava flood
flood basalts
plateau basalts
volcanic tremor

NOTES

Sec. 4.1: Volcanoes

It is important to note that volcanoes are surface expressions of deep-seated igneous processes. Therefore, for any volcano to develop, it must have a conduit to the surface (vents, fractures, fissures). The types of eruption that develop will largely be determined by gas pressure, temperature, and viscosity of the rising magma. Note that these factors are a function of the composition of the magma. Notice that volcanoes may be classified by shapes and composition of rock and debris (physical) and their degree of activity through time (historical). Try to familiarize yourself with both classification schemes, and be able to give specific examples as they are extensively described in this chapter. Finally, note that many volcanic eruptions have profound worldwide effects on climate.

Sec. 4.2: Basalt Plateaus

Basaltic plateaus develop to great thicknesses and cover a vast areal extent. Be aware that acidic lavas do not build extensive plateaus. The low viscosity required for lavas to flow over large areas is the primary reason why only basaltic lavas form plateaus. A secondary reason lies in the great abundance of basalts (it is by far the most common volcanic rock). Acidic lavas constitute a very small percentage of the volume of volcanic material when considered on a global basis.

Sec. 4.3: Igneous Activity and Earthquakes

An important point is the association of volcanic activity and earthquakes. By studying seismic activity in volcanic areas, geologists hope to be able to monitor more precisely impending volcanic activity.

PROGRAMMED REVIEW

1. Evidence of igneous activity is marked at the surface by the presence of _____. (50)

   volcanoes

2. A steep-walled depression out of which volcanic material is ejected is known as a _____. A much larger basin-shaped depression called a _____ is formed when the volcanic vent or crater is enlarged by further explosive eruptions and associated collapse. (50, 57)

   crater
   caldera

3. An explosive volcanic eruption results when _____ components of a rising magma are trapped causing very high _____ to develop. (51)

   volatile
   (gaseous)
   pressure

4. Magmas rich in mafic components but with low silica and volatile contents would most likely produce a _____ (passive, explosive) eruption. However, rhyolitic magma with its high viscosity, silica, and large vapor content usually results in _____ (passive, explosive) eruptions. (51)

   passive
   explosive

5. Depending upon the types of materials that have accumulated around their vents, volcanoes are classified as _____, _____, and _____ types. (51, 52)

   shield
   cinder cone
   composite

6. The steepest volcanic slopes are developed by _____ volcanoes, while the most gentle slopes are associated with the passive eruptions and lava flows of the _____ type volcanoes. (52)

   cinder cone
   shield

7. _____ content is the primary factor in classifying   silica
    lavas on the basis of their composition. (52)

8. As a general rule, as the proportions of silica   increases
    increase and the mafic components decrease,   increasesrole
    the viscosity _____ (increases, decreases) and
    the gas content _____ (increases, decreases). (53)

9. _____, _____, and _____ are representative of   basaltic
    lava types listed in order of increasing silica   andesitic
    content. (53)   rhyolitic

10. As a general rule, _____ lavas are associated   rhyolitic
    with continental regions far from plate margins;   basaltic
    _____ lavas occur in ocean basins and in rift   andesitic
    zones on the continents; and _____ lavas are
    associated with the subduction zones that ring
    the Pacific. (53)

11. Magmas that ingest highly reactive limestone rock   carbonatite
    during their ascent will produce a unique type
    of lava known as _____. (53)

12. It should be apparent that magmas generated in   uniform
    and ascending through rock of similar composition   variable
    will produce lavas of _____ (uniform, variable)
    composition, while magmas ascending through rock
    of different composition will produce lavas of
    _____ (uniform, variable) content. (53)

13. _____ describes the surface of a basaltic lava   pahoehoe
    having a rope-like appearance, while _____ is   aa
    the name given to a basaltic lava whose surface
    is a jumble of sharp, angular blocks. (53)

14. Almost 70 percent by volume of volcanic gases   steam
    are _____. (54)

15. The term _____ describes all _____ debris that   tephra
    accumulates through vertical airfall. (54)   pyroclastic

16. The finest pyroclastic debris is _____, while   dust
    the largest fragments are classified as _____   blocks
    or _____ if they are rounded or streamlined in   bombs
    shape as a result of molten material congealing
    as it travels through the air. (55)

17. Pyroclastic debris that is a dense mixture of   fiery
    incandescent ash, steam, and other gases will   nuées ardentes
    tend to roll or flow down slopes as a _____
    cloud or commonly referred to by the French
    equivalent _____. (55)

18. Vents called _____ may develop in pyroclastic flow deposits, allowing steam and other gases to escape into the atmosphere long after a volcanic eruption. (55)

    fumaroles

19. Mudflows composed of volcanic debris called _____ may form when saturated by water from melting snow and other sources. (55)

    lahars

20. Volcanic eruptions have been responsible for altering worldwide weather patterns when large quantities of _____ are ejected into the _____. (56)

    dust
    upper atmosphere
      or
    stratosphere

21. From an historical perspective, volcanoes are classified by their degree of activity and erosional alteration. In order of decreasing activity and alteration, these are _____, _____, and _____. (57)

    active
    dormant
    extinct

22. The classic example of the reawakening of a dormant volcano that destroyed the Roman cities of Herculanium and Pompeii is _____. (58)

    Vesuvius

23. The world's greatest explosive eruption took place in 1883 at _____ between the islands of Java and Sumatra in the Indonesian archipelago. (58)

    Krakatoa

24. With the exception of Mt. St. Helens, the Mexican volcano _____ has been the most closely studied active volcano in history. (59)

    Paricutin

25. The Hawaiian Islands are classified as _____ type volcanoes and have developed where the Pacific plate has moved over a zone of melting in the Earth's mantle called a _____. When this happens, _____ spots develop and lavas of _____ composition emerge and eventually form islands. (61)

    shield
    plume
    hot
    basaltic

26. Since the Pacific plate is in constant motion, the age of the islands should be _____ (younger, older) at the hot spots and should be progressively _____ (younger, older) with distance from the spots. (62)

    younger
    older

27. Lava that rises into and covers the floor of a caldera forms a _____ which may stabilize or fall when the lava reservoir is drained. (62)

    lava lake

28. Submarine lava flows develop a characteristic _____ shape and are sometimes referred to as _____ or MORB. (63)

    pillow
    midocean ridge
    basalt

29. Volcanic eruptions that spread lava over vast areas without the development of volcanic cones are known as _____. (64)

fissure eruptions or lava floods

30. The rocks produced by these extensive eruptions are called _____. (64)

flood basalts or plateau basalts

31. The _____ Plateau in Washington, Oregon, Idaho, and northeastern California has been built up by fissure eruptions. (64)

Columbia

32. _____ is a good predictor of an impending volcanic eruption. (65)

earthquakes or seismic activity

33. The phenomenon called _____ results in the continual shaking of the ground as earthquake activity is on the decline. This type of activity is commonly associated with magma moving _____ (upward, downward) through the crust. (65)

volcanic tremor upward

34. The _____ of an earthquake and volcanic tremor may give some clues to where a magma enters a volcano's "plumbing system." (65)

depth

SELF-TEST

Part A: True-False Statements

Each of the following statements is either true or false. Encircle either T or F for each item.

1. Molten rock that is extruded to the surface of the earth will always build up land forms known as volcanoes.   T   F

2. Volcanic eruptive cycles generally begin with the production of acidic lavas.   T   F

3. Highly viscous lava flows are associated with oceanic eruptions.   T   F

4. Samples of lava dredged from the deep ocean floor are high in alkalies like sodium and potassium.   T   F

5. The volatile components of a magma are the primary agents in producing a volcanic eruption.   T   F

6. Highly siliceous lavas are viscous and explosive.   T   F

7. Lavas containing 70 percent or more silica are called basic.   T   F

8. A ropy surface to a lava, known as pahoehoe, develops   T   F
   from low-viscosity, basaltic type lavas.

9. Measurements made on lava flows show a generally higher   T   F
   temperature in acidic flows.

10. Calderas may be formed by an explosion of a volcano,   T   F
    crater collapse, or a combination of both.

11. A volcano built of pyroclastic debris and lava flows is T   F
    called a composite volcano.

12. Since radiometric dates of Hawaiian Island basalts show T   F
    the southeastern portion of the chain to be younger than
    the northwestern ones, we can infer a relative southeastern
    motion of the Pacific Plate.

13. The Hawaiian volcanoes are good examples of composite   T   F
    type volcanoes.

14. Magmas working their way through limestone rock would   T   F
    most likely produce carbonatite lavas.

15. Carbon dioxide and nitrogen are the most abundant   T   F
    volcanic gases.

16. Pumice is a general term used to describe all pyroclastic T   F
    debris that accumulates through vertical airfall.

17. Ash, cinder lapilli, and blocks are examples of   T   F
    pyroclastic debris listed in order of increasing size.

18. Lahars are produced when hot ash is mixed with steam   T   F
    and other volcanic gases.

19. Mt. St. Helens was a good example of an extinct volcano. T   F

20. Iceland is an excellent example of a region producing   T   F
    plateau basalts.

Part B: Multiple Choice Items

Each of the following can be completed or answered correctly by choosing
only one of the selections. Encircle the letter a, b, c, or d, designating
your choice.

1. Assume you are in a region where rivers have cut deep canyons through
   several hundred meters of almost horizontal layers of basalt. You may
   conclude that

   a. shield volcanoes must have been the source of the lava.
   b. they are the result of fissure eruptions.
   c. they are tholeiitic in composition.
   d. they must overlie a batholitic intrusion that supplied the basic
      magma for the eruptions.

2. Which of the following pyroclastic debris would you be able to trace furthest from its source?

   a. cinders
   b. ash

   c. lapilli
   d. bombs

3. A lava flow is described as having a smooth, ropy surface. You may conclude that

   a. the flow was of high-viscosity and acidic.
   b. the flow was of low-viscosity and acidic.
   c. the flow was of high viscosity and basic.
   d. the flow was of low-viscosity and basic.

4. The primary agents in volcanic eruptions are

   a. hot spots.
   b. plumes.

   c. lahars.
   d. volatiles.

5. Volcanoes whose slopes are very gentle and are the product of relatively quiet eruptions are called

   a. composite volcanoes.
   b. dormant volcanoes.

   c. shield volcanoes.
   d. cinder cone volcanoes.

6. Which sequence lists the composition of lavas in order of decreasing silica content?

   a. basaltic, andesitic, rhyolitic
   b. rhyolitic, basaltic, andesitic
   c. rhyolitic, andesitic, basaltic
   d. basaltic, rhyolitic, andesitic

7. Which of the following rocks would most likely produce a carbonatite lava when reacting with a rising magma?

   a. limestone
   b. granite

   c. sandstone
   d. gabbro

8. Which sequence lists lava types in order of increasing viscosity?

   a. basaltic, andesitic, rhyolitic
   b. rhyolitic, andesitic, basaltic
   c. andesitic, rhyolitic, basaltic
   d. andesitic, basaltic, rhyolitic

9. The most abundant volcanic gas is

   a. water vapor.
   b. carbon dioxide.

   c. nitrogen.
   d. sulfur gases.

10. The greatest long-lasting worldwide effects of volcanic activity are the result of

    a. associated earthquakes.
    b. associated sonic booms.
    c. dust blown into the upper atmosphere.
    d. the fiery clouds produced in some eruptions.

11. Volcanoes producing rhyolitic lavas are most common in

    a. ocean basins.
    b. the middle of continental regions.
    c. along the rift zones of midocean ridges.
    d. the subduction zones around the rim of the Pacific.

12. Which of the following lava types are listed in order of increasing temperature?

    a. rhyolitic, andesitic, basaltic
    b. basaltic, andesitic, rhyolitic
    c. andesitic, basaltic, rhyolitic
    d. andesitic, rhyolitic, basaltic

13. As pyroclastic debris accumulates on volcanic slopes, it may, under proper conditions, develop into a

    a. tephra flow.   c. nuees ardente.
    b. lahar.   d. fumarole.

14. Evidence of volcanic eruptions may be found

    a. in rocks of all ages.
    b. only in relatively recent rocks.
    c. only in very ancient rocks.
    d. only in regions where the bedrock is igneous.

15. The depth of a magma source may be estimated by monitoring

    a. temperature changes in lavas.
    b. seismic activity.
    c. gas content in lavas.
    d. the changes in the composition of lavas.

SUGGESTED ESSAY QUESTIONS

The items below represent the type of discussion question to which you might be expected to respond. Try writing a response to these, and then discuss your work with another student.

1. Distinguish between the following:

    a. crater and caldera   c. lahar and fiery cloud
    b. pahoehoe and aa   d. lava flow and lava lake

2. What factors control the composition and behavior of lavas?

3. Discuss the development of the Hawaiian volcanic chain.

4. Discuss the role of volatiles in volcanic eruptions.

5. Contrast the physical and historical classifications of volcanoes.

6. Discuss the development of basalt plateaus.

7. Discuss the relationship between volcanic eruptions and seismic activity.

ANSWERS TO SELF-TESTS

Part A:
				Part B:			
1. F	6. F	11. T	16. F		1. b	6. c	11. b
2. F	7. F	12. F	17. T		2. b	7. a	12. a
3. F	8. F	13. F	18. F		3. d	8. a	13. b
4. F	9. F	14. T	19. F		4. d	9. a	14. a
5. T	10. T	15. F	20. T		5. c	10. c	15. b

CHAPTER 5

WEATHERING AND SOILS

OVERVIEW

Forces operating at and near the surface of the earth act to define its surface geometry. However, the authors point out that these forces (gravity, running water, wind, and ice) are not confined to the planet earth, but seem to operate, or have at least operated in the past, on other planets in the Solar System. This chapter deals specifically with the destructive process, called weathering, which operates on all materials (and presumably on other planets) at or near the surface of the earth that are in contact with air, water, and living matter.

The chapter will discuss the energy sources needed for weathering to proceed, the types of weathering (mechanical and chemical), and the products that result from each type. A fairly detailed section considers the chemical weathering of the more common igneous rocks, as well as the rate and depth of the process. The chapter concludes with a discussion of the role of weathering in the production of soils and how the development of a soil is controlled by such factors as type of bedrock, topography, climate, and time.

This chapter serves as a very important introduction to the next chapter (Chapter 6), where you will be concerned with how the weathering products are incorporated as sediment and eventually become the raw materials of the sedimentary rocks.

LEARNING OBJECTIVES

After studying this chapter, you should be able to:

1. Describe the role of weathering in the rock cycle.

2. Discuss the relationship between energy and weathering.

3. Distinguish between mechanical and chemical weathering.

4. Describe the various types of mechanical weathering.

5. Explain the role of particle size and water in chemical weathering.

6. Describe and contrast the chemical weathering of the common igneous rocks.

7. Know which rocks are most and least susceptible to chemical weathering.

8. Discuss the role of most and least susceptible to chemical weathering.

9. Relate the rate of mineral weathering to a mineral's original environment of formation.

10. Contrast the processes of weathering and erosion.

11. Describe what factors permit weathering to operate at depths well below the surface.

12. Discuss or briefly describe methods used to estimate average rates of erosion.

13. Describe the development of soils.

14. Classify the major soil types.

KEY TERMS AND CONCEPTS

weathering
solar constant
mechanical weathering
disintegration
chemical weathering
decomposition
frost action
frost wedging
exfoliation
exfoliation domes
spheroidal weathering
spheroidal boulders
joints
abrasion
dissolution
carbonatization
hydration
oxidation
particle size

colloids
clay mineral
kaolinite
montmorillonite
illite
hydrous aluminum silicates
hematite
limonite
iron oxides
bed load
traction load
suspension
differential erosion
soil
humus
pedology
soil horizon
A horizon
B horizon

C horizon
fragipan
claypan
hardpan
ironpan
leaching
zone of leaching
accumulation
zone of accumulation

mature soil
immature soil
pedalfers
pedocals
podsol
laterites
bauxite
paleosols

NOTES

Sec. 5.1: Energy Source

Be aware that there are only two types of energy, namely, potential and kinetic. However, the energy may be expressed in numerous forms, such as thermal (heat), chemical, electrical, mechanical, nuclear, etc. Thermal and mechanical energy are intimately associated with the weathering process. For example, the grinding or abrading effect of wind-blown sand on rock surfaces is the result of the kinetic energy of the sand grains acting in a purely mechanical fashion. On the other hand, the expansion and contraction of mineral grains in a rock is a function of the thermal energy gained and lost by its molecules and again results in a purely mechanical effect that may, over a period of time, weaken and break down the rock. Thermal energy is a key element and driving force in promoting both the mechanical disintegration and chemical alteration of rock materials.

Sec. 5.2: Types of Weathering

It is important that you understand that mechanical and chemical weathering actively cooperate with one another to break down and decompose rock. They may be conveniently discussed as separate phenomena, but one process never operates to the exclusivity of the other. One type may dominate but never totally exclude the other.

You may think of mechanical weathering as preparing the raw materials for chemical weathering to operate at greater efficiency. Since mechanical weathering breaks down materials to a smaller and smaller size, the particles present a greater and greater surface area for exposure to moisture and air. Chemical reactions are increased not only by the addition of thermal energy (heat), but also by a decrease in particle size, since the increased surface area allows for greater contact with a fluid reacting medium. A simple example should clarify this point. You probably have had the experience of adding either one teaspoon or lump or granulated sugar to your coffee or tea. Note that it is not uncommon to find a few pieces of undissolved sugar left from the lump, but the granulated variety is readily dissolved by your drink. The surface area of each grain of granulated sugar is in contact with the fluid, while only the outer grain surfaces are in contact in the lump.

Also note the difference between exfoliation domes and spheroidally weathered boulders. The boulders are not merely small scale replicas of the domes. The domes form by the purely mechanical process of joint expansion that results from a release of confining pressure of overlying rock. The spheroidal boulders derive the required pressure from the chemical weathering of the rock where new minerals of greater volume set up stresses in the rock. Note also that certain rocks are more likely to undergo spheroidal weathering than others. Do you think a clean quartz sandstone is a good candidate to produce a spheroidally weathered boulder?

The chemical weathering of minerals is an important section. You should know what minerals are most likely to undergo chemical weathering, what new minerals and other products they form, what is the role of climate in the chemical weathering of these rocks, and what minerals are the most resistant to chemical weathering. Similarly, you should be able to contrast the weathering of such common igneous rocks as granite and basalt based on a knowledge of their composition.

Sec. 5.3: Rates of Weathering

This section now allows you to consider weathering from the standpoint of equilibrium between a mineral and its environment of formation. The farther a mineral is removed from its original environment (high temperature and pressure), the more readily it will decompose in a new environment (low temperature and pressure). The case is clearly made by comparing the rates of weathering of minerals in the Bowen's Reaction Series. Note that the earlier formed minerals (olivine, pyroxene) are the least stable at surface conditions (far out of equilibrium with their crystallization environment), while the later minerals formed at lower temperatures (quartz and muscovite) are the most stable at surface conditions. Do you see why it would be very unlikely to find quartz and olivine in a sedimentary rock like sandstone? In Chapter 6 (Metamorphism) you will see that the weathering products are easily altered when their environment is changed by increases in temperature and pressure during the metamorphic process.

Sec. 5.4: Rates of Erosion

It is easy to confuse weathering with erosion. Keep in mind that weathering describes the mechanical and chemical breakdown of rock at or near the surface of the earth, while erosion refers to the removal of the weathering products by a transporting medium (water, wind, ice) or directly by gravity.

Note also that just as rocks weather at different rates, the rate at which rocks are eroded is also a function of the rocks' stability and resistance in a given environment. As you might expect, resistant rocks tend to form ridges or steep scarps, while weaker rocks tend to floor valleys and form gentle slopes.

Sec. 5.5: Soils

Keep in mind that rock type may be a significant factor in the type of soil developed, but climate, topography, and the amount of time a soil has been developing also have a direct effect on soil types.

Note that soil horizons, while generally recognizable, may be quite variable in their thickness and depth. Soil horizons develop in an evolutionary-like sequence from the surface downward. Thus, the A and B horizons develop before the C horizon. The extent of horizon development is indicative of the degree of soil maturity.

Do not neglect to study Fig. 5.21. This is an excellent example of the chemical stability of the common igneous minerals. Notice the rapid increase of the clay mineral kaolinite at the expense of the feldspars (orthoclase and plagioclase). The greater stability of quartz and orthoclase (the last minerals to crystallize from a magma) is reflected in their initial increase in percentage as they accumulate in the soil. However, even so stable a mineral as quartz is susceptible to some degree of chemical alteration over an extended period of time.

PROGRAMMED REVIEW

1. _____ is the process of change that takes place in surface or near-surface material in response to air, water, and living matter. (68)

   weathering

2. The average rate at which radiant energy is received by the Earth from the sun is called the _____. (68)

   solar constant

3. _____ and _____ are the two general types of weathering. (68)

   mechanical
   chemical

4. The process by which rock is broken down into smaller fragments by physical forces without a resultant change in composition is known as _____. (69)

   disintegration
    (mechanical or
    physical
    weathering)

5. Rapid changes in temperature may be enough to bring about _____ weathering as a result of _____ and _____ of the minerals in a rock. (69)

   mechanical
   expansion
   contraction

6. If temperature change does bring about disintegration of rock, it is probably the result of the rock's minerals expanding and contracting at _____ rates. (69)

   different or
    varying

7. _____ is the process of mechanical weathering caused by repeated cycles of freezing and thawing. The _____ of water during the freezing cycle is the driving force of energy for the process. (69)

   frost action
   expansion

8. The forces set up by the expansion of water during freezing may dislodge fragments from a rock's surface in a process called _____. (69)

   frost wedging

9. Frost action would be most effective in _____ (moist, dry) and _____ (warm, cool) regions whose bedrock is highly _____. (69)

   moist
   cool
   fractured

10. _____ is a mechanical weathering process in which curved plates of rock are stripped from a larger rock mass by the action of physical forces and results in a rather distinctive landform of dome-shaped hills called _____. (69)

exfoliation
exfoliation domes

11. Plants play a role in mechanical weathering when _____ in rock crevices exert sufficient force to dislodge rock fragments. (70)

roots

12. _____ is a process of mechanical weathering where particles are transported by water, ice, or wind and wear away bedrock. (70)

abrasion

13. Another term for chemical weathering is _____. Unlike mechanical weathering, the weathered material _____ composition during the process. (71)

decomposition
changes

14. Feldspar minerals weather to _____ minerals when undergoing decomposition. (71)

clay

15. In the process called _____, natural fluids enter rock and leave no solid residue behind if the rock material is soluble in the fluid. (71)

dissolution

16. If ground water is tested for its dissolved salt content and if found to be very high in sodium and chlorine ions, you may possibly conclude that the ground water may have percolated through a deposit of the mineral _____. (71)

halite

17. When carbon dioxide is the active agent in the weathering process, a type of reaction called _____ results. In this reaction, _____ is dissolved in water to produce the _____ ion. (71)

carbonatization
carbon dioxide
bicarbonate

18. Unlike the role water plays in dissolution, in _____ water combines chemically with other molecules. (71)

hydration

19. In the process of _____, _____ in the presence of water commonly reacts with certain minerals to form oxides. (71)

oxidation
oxygen

20. The rate of a chemical reaction will increase at a given temperature if the particle size of the particle size of the reactants _____(increases, decreases). This is the result of the _____ (increase, decrease) in surface area of the particles exposed during a chemical reaction. (71)

decreases
increase

21. Chemical weathering is enhanced where _____, _____, and _____ are at a maximum. Therefore, one would expect the greatest degree of chemical weathering to take place in the _____ zone and the least in _____ regions. (72)

moisture
temperature
vegetation
equatorial
   (tropical)
desert

22. _____ weathering is similar to exfoliation except the spalling of rock is the result of chemical rather than mechanical weathering. (72)

spheroidal

23. Of all the common rock-forming minerals, _____ has the most stable surface temperature and pressure. The least stable of the rock-forming minerals are the _____. (76)

quartz
ferromagnesian
   (mafic)

24. As a general rule, the earliest minerals to crystallize from a melt are the _____ (least, most) stable at surface conditions, while the later formed minerals are the _____ (least, most) stable. (73, 76)

least
most

25. In the chemical weathering of feldspars, _____ and _____ play a very important role as agents to convert the feldspars to _____ minerals. (73)

water
carbon dioxide
clay

26. Since clay minerals contain water in their crystalline structure, the chemical process called _____ must play an important role in their formation. (73)

hydration

27. Clay minerals fall into three major groups. These are: _____, _____, and _____. (74)

kaolinite
montmorillonite
illite

28. The clay minerals are like the micas in that they are built up of silicon-oxygen tetrahedra linked together structurally in _____. (74)

sheets

29. _____ and _____ seem to be two major factors that determine which type of clay mineral will be produced when feldspars are weathered. (74)

climate
rock type

30. Some silica is dissolved in the weathering of feldspars, but most is released as finely divided quartz particles of _____ size. (74)

colloidal

31. Ferromagnesian minerals also produce clays when weathered, but the presence of iron also results in the production of various _____. A reddish form is called _____, and a yellow-brown, rust-like product called _____ is very common and is often responsible for the coloration of soils. (75)

oxides
hematite
limonite

32. Most of the chemical weathering products of the   sedimentary
    crystalline rocks are found in the _____
    rocks. (75, 76)

33. The rate of chemical weathering seems to be in   Bowen's reaction
    the reverse order of their formation as expressed   olivine
    in the _____ series. Because of this relationship,
    it would be most unlikely to find quartz and _____
    in the same sedimentary rock. (76)

34. The weathering process is the response of materials   equilibrium
    that were once in _____ within the Earth's crust
    to new conditions at or near contact with air,
    water, and living matter. (76)

35. Although weathering is largely a surface phenomenon,   expand
    highly jointed rocks may _____ (expand, contract)
    at depths of several hundred meters when erosion
    strips away overlying material. (77)

36. A rock such as limestone or marble would not make   moist (humid)
    a very good tombstone in a _____ climate because   calcite
    it is composed of _____ which is a very _____   soluble
    material under these conditions. (77)

37. The major agents of erosion are _____, _____,   water
    _____, and _____. (78)   wind
                                                             ice
                                                             gravity

38. A stream carries material in _____, as well as   solution
    in the solid state in the form of sediments. (78)

39. Coarse-grained sediments are commonly transported   bed load
    by streams as _____, while fine-grained materials   (traction
    are usually transported by _____. (78)   load
                                                             suspension

40. One way to measure the rate of erosion of a   drainage
    region is to calculate the amount of stream load   basin
    (all the material it is carrying in solution and
    as solids) for the region's _____. (79)

41. _____ is the process by which different rock   differential
    masses or different sections of the same rock mass   erosion
    erode at different rates. These unequal rates are   composition
    usually caused by variations in the _____ of
    rocks. (79)

42. Quartzite is a tough, hard rock, while limestone   ridges
    in all but very dry climates is relatively weak.   valleys
    If one were to traverse an area whose bedrock is
    made of these rocks, you would expect the quartzite
    to form _____ and the limestone to predominate
    in the _____. (80)

43. The surface accumulation of sand, clay, and decayed plant material that sustains life is called _____. The science of this surface accumulation is known as _____. (81)

soil
pedology

44. Although bedrock does exert some influence on the type of soil that develops, it seems that _____, _____, and type of vegetation in an area might be more important factors in the formation of soils. (81)

climate
topography

45. Since the composition and physical appearance of a soil varies with depth, it has been convenient to subdivide the different zones into what are called _____. The lowermost of these zones is called the _____, and it is successively overlain by the _____ and _____. (82)

soil horizons
C horizon
B horizon
A horizon

46. The greatest degree of weathering would be found in the _____, while the least amount of weathering would characterize the _____. (82)

A horizon
C horizon

47. The B horizon is also known as _____ because mineral matter is deposited here by percolating waters from the A horizon and capillary action that draws water from the underlying C horizon. (82)

zone of
    accumulation

48. A dense subsurface layer called _____, sometimes develops in the B horizon that is almost impermeable to fluids. If this layer is densely packed but not cemented, it is called _____. When cemented, it is known as _____. When the cementing agent is an iron oxide, it is referred to as _____; and when cemented by carbonates, it is given the Spanish name _____. (82)

fragipan
claypan
hardpan
ironpan
caliche

49. The process in which soluble materials are removed from the A horizon and percolated to lower levels is known as _____. Because of this phenomenon, the A horizon is also called _____. (82)

leaching
zone of
    leaching

50. The rate of soil weathering _____ (increases, decreases) with depth. (83)

decreases

51. An _____ soil lacks well-developed horizons and tends to grade into the parent material, while a _____ soil displays fully developed horizons. (83)

immature
mature

52. A convenient way to subdivide soil types has been developed on latitudinal position. _____ and _____ are characteristic of the middle latitudes, while _____ are confined to the latitudes of _____ climates. (83-85)

pedalfers
pedocals
laterites
tropical

53. The _____ soils show accumulations of clays and _____ in the B horizon, but very little in the way of the soluble _____ of calcium and magnesium. Soils of this type are usually associated with _____ and _____ climates under well-developed forest vegetation. (83)

pedalfer
carbonates
temperate
humid

54. Because of the accumulation of iron oxides in the B horizon of pedalfer soils, they are usually _____ to _____ in color. (83)

yellow
reddish-brown

55. A soil produced from a granite in a temperate climate should contain an abundance of _____ in the B horizon, as well as grains of _____ which would undergo very little alteration. If iron oxides were present, the soil should have a _____ to _____ coloration. (84)

clay
quartz
yellow
reddish-brown

56. The _____ is an ashy-gray or gray-brown soil of the pedalfer group. (84)

podsol

57. Soils which tend to accumulate calcium carbonate are known as _____. This major soil group is found at temperate latitudes where the temperature is relatively _____ (high, low), the rainfall is _____ (high, low), and the vegetation is _____ (lush, sparse). (84)

pedocals
high
low
sparse

58. The production of _____ minerals is low in pedocal soils because the _____ climate inhibits the chemical weathering of the _____ minerals. (85)

clay
arid (dry)
feldspar

59. Tropical soils rich in hydrated alumina and iron oxides are called _____. (85)

laterites

60. In some tropical soils, a hydrous aluminum oxide called _____ may develop. This mineral is the ore of aluminum. (85)

bauxite

61. A buried or fossil soil called a _____ is a useful indicator of past environments. (85)

paleosol

62. A more recent soil classification scheme known as the United States Soil Classification System is based on variations in _____, _____, _____, and _____. (86)

precipitation
temperature
vegetation
drainage

SELF-TESTS

Part A: True-False Statements

Each of the following statements is either true or false. Encircle either T or F for each item.

1. Weathering and erosion are synonymous terms for destructive processes working at the surface of the earth. T F

2. The water behind a dam may be said to possess potential energy. T F

3. A slowly moving glacier possesses a high degree of kinetic energy. T F

4. The energy required to drive the weathering process is derived largely from the heat escaping from the earth's interior as radioactive minerals decay. T F

5. A rock being subjected to forces that break it down to smaller pieces without changing its composition is undergoing disintegration. T F

6. The expansion and contraction of rock material is an example of decomposition. T F

7. Frost action and frost heaving are examples of chemical weathering. T F

8. Spheroidally weathered boulders result from chemical weathering. T F

9. Decomposition is enhanced by warm temperature, moisture, and large particle size. T F

10. Chemical weathering would be most active in a hot, dry climate. T F

11. Feldspars are among the most resistant minerals to chemical weathering. T F

12. The greatest amount of carbon dioxide is concentrated in soils. T F

13. Ferromagnesian minerals weather chemically to produce hydrous aluminum silicates and iron oxide. T F

14. Carbonic acid ionizes to hydroxyl and bicarbonate ions. T F

15. Limestones and marbles are among the more soluble of the common rocks. T F

16. You should expect extensive differential weathering and erosion in areas composed of rocks of uniform composition and structure. T F

17. Hornblende is a more stable mineral than olivine at surface conditions. T F

18. It is possible to map the distribution of rocks by the soils that overlie them. T F

19. A well-defined soil profile would be least likely to   T   F
    develop in a pedalfer.

20. The A horizon often develops a high concentration of clay   T   F
    and iron oxides.

Part B: Multiple Choice Items

Each of the following can be completed or answered correctly by choosing
only one of the selections. Encircle the letter a, b, c, or d, designating
your choice.

1. A distant planet lacks an atmosphere, has little or no moisture
   present at its surface, and undergoes a diurnal temperature change of
   300 degrees Celsius. You may conclude that

   a. extensive chemical weathering would characterize this planet.
   b. mechanical weathering may operate, but very little chemical
      weathering.
   c. it is unlikely that any type of weathering would occur.
   d. we would find no evidence of past weathering at its surface.

2. A type of mechanical weathering that requires daily freeze-thaw
   conditions to break rock into angular fragments is

   a. exfoliation.   c. spheroidal weathering.
   b. frost action.   d. frost heaving.

3. Which of the following rocks would most likely weather to a spheroidal
   boulder?

   a. sandstone   c. granite
   b. limestone   d. marble

4. When vegetation is found associated with bare rock surfaces, it is
   concentrated along joints and fractures. This is because

   a. the potential energy of the rock is concentrated along fractures.
   b. the greatest heat is liberated along fractures.
   c. fractures offer the greatest access to air and moisture.
   d. burrowing organisms can enter rock only along fractures.

5. In the relationship between volume, particle size, and surface area,
   as the particle size decreases,

   a. the surface area decreases and the volume remains the same.
   b. the surface area decreases and the volume increases.
   c. the surface area increases and the volume increases.
   d. the surface area increases and the volume remains the same.

6. During the weathering of feldspars, all of the following are produced
   except

   a. clay.   c. soluble carbonates.
   b. iron oxide.   d. colloidal silica.

7. Which of the following minerals does not belong in association with the others?

   a. kaolinite
   b. anorthite

   c. illite
   d. montmorillonite

8. Fresh basalt is a dense, dark gray to black fine-grained rock. The surface of a basalt outcrop exposed to the atmosphere for a few years will almost certainly look very different. The exposed surface would probably

   a. be very light in color due to the production of sodium rich clays.
   b. be very pinkish in color due to the weathering of calcium feldspars.
   c. be very rust colored from the weathering of ferromagnesian minerals.
   d. be very granular from the solution of its more soluble components.

9. Given a source area of acidic and basic igneous rocks weathering in a moist, temperate climate, if you were to examine the sediments of the area streams, you would find very few grains of

   a. orthoclase.
   b. albite.

   c. olivine.
   d. quartz.

10. You would expect differential erosion to proceed most rapidly in a region underlain by

   a. flat-lying sedimentary rocks of uniform composition.
   b. folded rocks of variable composition.
   c. crystalline rocks of uniform composition.
   d. plateau basalts.

11. Which factor probably exerts the greatest influence on soil development?

   a. type of bedrock
   b. climate

   c. topography
   d. soil dwelling organisms

12. You would expect the greatest concentration of iron oxides in the

   a. A horizon.
   b. B horizon.

   c. C horizon.

13. A typical pedalfer soil is

   a. rich in carbonates.
   b. rich in hydrous aluminum oxides.
   c. always developed in warm, dry climates.
   d. none of the choices describe a pedalfer.

14. Tropical soils are typically referred to as

   a. paleosols.
   b. pedalfers.

   c. podsols.
   d. laterites.

15. Which of the following rocks would be most likely to develop an economic bauxite deposit?

    a. granite   c. marble
    b. sandstone   d. limestone

SUGGESTED ESSAY QUESTIONS

The items below represent the type of discussion question to which you might be expected to respond. Try writing a response to these, and then discuss your work with another student.

1. Discuss the role of climate on chemical and mechanical weathering.

2. Why is a sandstone or a limestone not very likely to produce a spheroidally weathered boulder?

3. What factors control the rate of chemical weathering?

4. Name at least four major mineral components of a granite and describe what happens to each as the rock weathers in a moist, temperate climate.

5. Quartz and olivine are mutually exclusive in both igneous and sedimentary rocks. Why do you think this is so?

6. Limestone is not a very resistant rock; yet under certain conditions, it may develop into a prominent escarpment or a ridge. Under what conditions might this happen?

7. Why is a sequence of folded sedimentary rocks more likely to show the results of differential erosion than a sequence of horizontal ones?

8. Discuss the role of water in the weathering of feldspars.

9. Describe the development of a mature soil profile.

10. Suppose a granite bedrock is found in a semiarid region with dry summers and in a moist, temperate region with considerable spring and summer rainfall. How might the soils derived from the bedrock and their soil profiles differ?

ANSWERS TO SELF-TESTS

Part A:				Part B:		
1. F	6. F	11. F	16. F	1. b	6. b	11. c
2. T	7. F	12. T	17. T	2. b	7. b	12. b
3. T	8. T	13. T	18. T	3. c	8. c	13. d
4. F	9. F	14. F	19. F	4. c	9. c	14. d
5. T	10. F	15. T	20. F	5. d	10. b	15. a

CHAPTER 6

ORIGIN AND OCCURRENCE OF SEDIMENTS AND SEDIMENTARY ROCKS

OVERVIEW

Unlike the igneous rocks which comprise 95% by volume of all crustal rocks, the sedimentary rocks account for only 5% of all crustal rocks. However, if one considers their abundance as a percentage of rocks exposed at the surface of the earth, we find that the sedimentary rocks constitute approximately 75% of the total. On the latter basis alone, the sedimentary rocks become a very important rock group. Yet, sedimentary rocks offer the student of earth history considerably more than a shear quantity of surface exposures. Since the sedimentary rocks house the remains of past life (fossils) and contain many features that lend themselves to a study of ancient environments, it should be no surprise that most of what we know of earth history is derived from studies of these rocks.

The chapter begins with a rather extensive look at how sedimentary rocks are formed. Under consideration here are such factors as the source of sediments, methods of sediment transport, and how sediments are deposited. Mineral composition and texture, key parameters in the study of any rock are then discussed in some detail. Unlike the igneous rocks which crystallize from a melt, most sedimentary rocks are deposited as discrete particles and must be bonded together by some natural process. This process, known as lithification, is then described, as well as those factors that may alter sediments or rock after their formation. The common sedimentary rock types are then classified, and the more unique features (mudcracks, ripple marks, etc.) associated with sedimentary rocks are then described. The concept and importance of the sedimentary facies is considered, and the chapter closes with a historical look at the geosynclinal concept and the more modern association of sedimentation related to plate tectonics.

LEARNING OBJECTIVES

After studying this chapter, you should be able to:

1. Understand why it is difficult to arrive at a precise definition of a sedimentary rock.

2. Describe the major characteristics of all sedimentary rocks.

3. Relate the relative abundance of sedimentary rocks to the igneous and metamorphic rocks.

4. Describe how sediments are transported and deposited.

5. Distinguish between rocks of detrital and chemical origin.

6. Define environmental terms like: marine, fluvial, eolian, and lacustrine.

7. Describe the origin of the major minerals found in sedimentary rocks.

8. Understand the significance of texture in the description of sedimentary rocks.

9. Describe the various processes by which sediments are lithified.

10. Describe and classify the major sedimentary rocks.

11. Describe the basic features of sedimentary rocks and how they reveal the rocks' past depositional history.

12. Understand the concept of the sedimentary facies.

13. Describe the influence of plate tectonics on sediments.

KEY TERMS AND CONCEPTS

detrital sedimentary rocks
chemical sedimentary rocks
biochemical sedimentary rocks
fluvial environment
eolian environment
lacustrine environment
sedimentation
precipitation
clastic or detrital texture
sieving
nonclastic texture
particle size
Wentworth Scale
particle shape
roundness
sphericity
sorting

diagenesis
authigenic minerals
dissolution
cementation
replacement
compaction
desiccation
crystallization
clay
silt
sand
gravel
conglomerate
breccia
tillite
quartz arenite or quartzose
sandstone

66

lithic sandstone or graywacke
arkose
mudrock or pelite
shale
limestone
dripstone or travertine
oolite
dolostone or dolomite
tufa
evaporite
gypsum
anhydrite
rock salt or halite
cryptocrystalline silica
chert
carbonate factories
carbonate compensation depth
diatomite
chalk
coquina
coal
peat
lignite
bituminous coal
anthracite coal
bedding planes

parallel bedding
laminated bedding
cross or false bedding
foreset beds
graded bedding
turbidites
disturbed or mottled bedding
ripple marks
oscillation ripple marks
current ripple marks
sole marks
mudcracks
nodules
concretions
geodes
osmosis
fossil
sedimentary facies
geosyncline
miogeosyncline or miogeocline
eugeosyncline or eugeocline
convergent plate boundary
divergent plate boundary
transform plate boundary
volcanic island arcs

NOTES

Sec. 6.1: Formation of Sedimentary Rocks

Be sure you make a clear distinction between deposits of detrital and
chemical origin. Also keep in mind that mixtures do occur, but one type
will predominate.

Note that the term sedimentation means deposition. However, the process is
more than a single act. A source area undergoing weathering and erosion is
required to supply the sediment; a transporting medium is needed to remove
the sediments from the source area; and, finally, the sediment must be
brought to a place where it may be deposited. Areas receiving sediments
are commonly referred to as basins and may represent a variety of
environments (river bottoms, lakes, swamps, ocean - near-shore and offshore, etc.). You can imagine that great variability exists between source
areas, transport media, and basins of deposition. All the variability is
reflected in the types of sediments produced and the subsequent variety of
sedimentary rocks.

In your study of the igneous rocks, you found that certain rocks contained
a distinctive suite of minerals. Because the mineral components in
sedimentary rocks are derived from a variety of source areas and deposited
in different types of basins, we do not expect to find the characteristic
mineral suites associated with the igneous rocks. However, note that only
three minerals, clay, quartz, and calcite, are by far the most abundant.
Also note that, in the case of detrital rocks, the cementing agent is often

different than the grains that make up the rock.
Be aware that most clays are derived from the weathering of feldspars, and that kaolinite and illite are the most common of the clay minerals found in shales and mudstones.

Since quartz is such a common component of detrital sedimentary rocks, you should know what accounts for its great abundance. A quick review of the stability of the common igneous minerals at surface conditions (see Ch. 5) would be worth the extra effort. Note also the distinction between discrete quartz grains, quartz (silica) in solution or colloidal form, and the cryptocrystalline varieties of quartz.

When you think of the mineral calcite in a sedimentary rock, you should immediately make the association to the rock limestone. Calcite is the predominant mineral component of limestone. Note that the calcium is derived by solution of calcium bearing rocks (even other limestones) and is later precipitated as the carbonate by organic and inorganic processes to form the limestone rock.

With reference to the minor constituents of sedimentary rocks, note the following: calcite and dolomite are intimately associated; abundant fresh feldspars and micas indicate a rapid mechanical type weathering of rocks in the source area; iron oxides are primary coloring agents in rocks and may be common as natural cements in detrital rocks; and, halite and gypsum are the most abundant rocks produced by the evaporation of highly concentrated saline solutions. Note also that each mineral will precipitate only when the proper saline concentration is reached.

As in the igneous rocks, the term texture is again used in describing the size, shape, and arrangement of particles that make up the rock. The term clastic texture should always be associated with rocks of detrital origin. However, be aware that chemical and/or biochemical rocks may also show a clastic texture if they are composed of cemented shell fragments and other organic debris.

Note that when a grain-size is specified (see Wentworth Scale), it is expressed as the diameter measurement of a perfect sphere. Since the sedimentary particles are not perfect spheres, the measurement is an extrapolation of the grain's diameter if it were a true sphere. One point to keep very clear in your mind is the distinction between clay as a mineral species and clay as a size term. Clay minerals are clay-size, but not all clay-size particles are clay minerals. To a lesser degree, this confusion also arises with the term sand. Don't assume that all sand is quartz. Sand is a size term and should not arbitrarily be used as a synonym for the mineral quartz.

The lithification process is variable and is partially controlled by the type of sediment being lithified. The cementation process is most common in coarse-grained sediments with their interconnected pores. The lack of interconnected pores allows for very little lithification by cementation in the finer grained sediments. Most fine-grained deposits are lithified by compaction, desiccation, and post-depositional crystallization.

Sec. 6.2: Types of Sedimentary Rocks

You should become familiar with Table 6.2. Note that all detrital rocks have a clastic texture.

Of the detrital sedimentary rocks, note that all sandstones fall into a sand-size range (1/16 mm to 2 mm in diameter), but the composition can be quite variable. It may range from a very pure, clean quartz sandstone (orthoquartzite) to a very hard, dirty, impure rock like the graywacke. As you will see in later chapters, these compositional differences are indicative of very different origins and depositional histories. You should also be aware of the distinction between mudstone and shale. They are the same particle size, but the former rocks are more blocky and massive in appearance. Note also that determining the precise composition of a shale or mudstone is very difficult because of their extremely small particle size.

The biochemical rocks must be composed of the remains of once-living organisms. Note that limestones are by far the most abundant of the biochemical rocks and most are of marine origin, although nonmarine limestones are known. Note also the two distinctive environments of limestone or carbonate production in the modern oceans. First, there are the extensive limestone banks found in the warm, shallow tropical seas that are supersaturated with calcium carbonate. The other environment is found in deep, off-shore areas and does not yield lithified carbonate deposits, but rather is an accumulation of microscopic shells that form a soft ooze. It is also significant that, while covering vast areas of the ocean basins, these calcareous oozes are restricted to a maximum depth of 5 km since the carbonate shells are soluble in very deep, cold waters. Chalk and coquina are also limestones.

Coal is the most common nonmarine organic sedimentary rock. Note that coal formation is a sequential process. Do you see why some geologists consider coal to be a metamorphic rock?

Sec. 6.3: Features of Sedimentary Rocks

From reading this section you can see that identifying sedimentary rock is only a first step in the interpretation of the rocks' geologic history. By studying the features found within the rock (also referred to as sedimentary structures), the geologist can learn a great deal about the conditions under which the deposit was laid down. Note that laminar or parallel bedding is indicative of a low energy (non-turbulent) environment, whereas cross-bedding usually indicates a high energy (turbulent) environment. Try to tie the various structures to their environment of formation. Note also the significance of fossils as indicators of past environments, life, and their role in the subdivisions of the geologic column and time.

The concept of the sedimentary facies can be confusing, and it has taken on many meanings in geology. In the context used in this text, facies represents different types of sediments (and their resulting rocks) forming at the same time but in different depositional environments. Study Fig. 6.17 carefully and that should clarify the meaning of sedimentary facies as previously described.

Sec. 6.4: Plate Tectonics and Sedimentation

Keep in mind that the geosyncline is not a single long, linear basin, but actually two parallel belts. The sediments that accumulate in each belt or trough are quite different and reflect differences in the source areas, as well as the environment of the basin itself.

The inner, shallow water belt of the miogeosyncline is associated with divergent continental margins, while the outer, deeper water belt of the eugeosyncline is characterized by volcanics (island arcs) that form along convergent plate boundaries.

PROGRAMMED REVIEW

1. Sedimentary deposits formed by the accumulation of debris derived from the weathering and erosion of existing rocks are called _____ sedimentary rocks. (90)

   detrital

2. Sedimentary accumulations that develop from the precipitation of dissolved mineral matter by inorganic processes or indirectly through the biologic activity of living organisms are classified as _____ sedimentary rocks. (91)

   chemical

3. Any sedimentary rock that is composed entirely of the skeletal remains of organisms is referred to as a _____ rock. (91)

   biochemical

4. Although sedimentary rocks may be subdivided into the categories listed above, many of these rocks are _____ of the major types. (91)

   mixtures

5. A sedimentary rock often reveals information about its environment of deposition. These depositional environments may be from the sea or _____; streams or _____; by wind or _____; and lakes or _____. (91)

   marine
   fluvial
   eolian
   lacustrine

6. The general process by which rock-forming material is laid down or deposited is known as _____. (92)

   sedimentation

7. _____ is the most common agent or transporting medium of sediments. (92)

   water

8. Deposition of sediments will take place when there is a decrease in the _____ of the transporting medium. In the case of a fluid agent like a stream, deposition will occur when there is a decrease in the stream's _____. (92)

   energy
   velocity

9. _____ is the chemical process by which dissolved material is converted into a solid and separated from the liquid solvent. (92)

   precipitation

10. _____, _____, _____ and minor amounts of   clay
    _____ type minerals predominate in the _____   quartz
    sedimentary rocks. (93)   feldspar
                                                              ferromagnesian
                                                              detrital

11. A non-detrital rock like limestone is composed   calcite
    mostly of _____. (93)

12. _____, _____, _____, and _____ are common   calcite
    cementing materials in the detrital sedimentary   dolomite
    rocks. (93, 96)   silica
                                                              iron oxide

13. _____ and _____ are two important minerals   halite
    that precipitate by the evaporation of highly   gypsum
    saline seawater. _____ will precipitate at   gypsum
    about three times the salinity of normal seawater,   halite
    but _____ will not form until the salinity is
    about ten times that of normal seawater. (94)

14. The term _____ means broken or fragmental and   clastic
    is used to describe the _____ of the detrital   texture
    sedimentary rocks. (94)

15. The _____ of individual particles in a detrital   size
    rock is a very useful factor in its classification.   Wentworth Scale
    The _____ is a classification scheme based on
    this parameter. (94)

16. _____ is the most rapid method of separating   sieving
    a heterogeneous mixture of sediment into a range
    of particle sizes. (94)

17. Most sedimentary particles have an irregular   spheres
    shape, but they are treated as _____ for
    measurement purposes. (94)

18. _____, _____, _____, _____, _____, _____,   clay
    and _____ are descriptions given to particle   silt
    fragments listed in order of increasing size.   sand
    (94)   granule
                                                             pebble
                                                             cobble
                                                             boulder

19. A _____ texture would describe those sedimentary   non-clastic
    rocks whose grains interlock like the _____   crystalline
    texture exhibited by the igneous rocks. (95)

20. Unlike the igneous rock textures, the grain sizes   fine-grained
    of the non-clastic sedimentary rocks are usually   medium-grained
    not described in technical terms. Rather, in order   coarse-grained
    of increasing grain-size, they are simply referred
    to as _____, _____, and _____. (95)

71

21. The range of grain sizes present in a detrital rock is known as _____. A rock that has a very restricted or narrow range of particle sizes would be called _____, while one with a very wide range in grain-size is referred to as being _____. (95)

sorting
well-sorted
poorly-sorted

22. _____ and _____ are measures of particle shape. (96)

roundness
sphericity

23. A particle with a flat, flake-like habit such as mica may be very well rounded but not _____ in shape. (96)

spherical

24. Stream-transported particles of sand-size and larger tend to become _____ (more, less) rounded and _____ (more, less) spherical with increased transport. Smaller particles like silts and clays usually maintain a more _____ shape and a less _____ appearance because of the lack of grain abrasion. (96)

more
more
angular
spherical

25. Post depositional change in a sediment or sedimentary rock of a physical, chemical, or biologic nature is known as _____. (96)

diagenesis

26. The post depositional changes must occur at temperature and pressure that is _____ enough to prevent those changes associated with _____ to occur. (96)

low
metamorphism

27. _____ minerals form as a result of diagenetic change. (96)

authigenic

28. Diagenetic changes may result in the production of voids in rock by the process of _____; the filling in of voids or pore space by _____; and the nearly simultaneous _____ of one mineral by another. (96)

dissolution
cementation
replacement

29. _____ is the process that converts unconsolidated sediment into consolidated, coherent rock. (96)

lithification

30. The reduction of pore space volume by the pressure resulting from the accumulation of overlying sediments is called _____. _____ size sediments are most susceptible to this process. (96)

compaction
clay

31. Another process called _____ removes fluids from the pore spaces of sediments, but _____ rather than pressure is the driving force. (96)

desiccation
evaporation

32. Sediments of a _____ grain-size are very susceptible to cementation because of relatively large interconnecting spaces between the particles. (96)

coarse

33. One way to classify the sedimentary rocks is to subdivide them based on the origin of their contained sediment. Under this method, two major categories exist: _____ and _____. (97)

detrital
chemical

34. The fragmental rocks are subdivided on the basis of their _____, while the other major category may be subdivided on the basis of its _____. (97)

grain-size
composition

35. The chemical rocks may also be split on the basis of their method of formation into _____ and _____. (97)

inorganic

36. A detrital rock composed of gravel-size particles is called a _____ if the grains are rounded and a _____ if they are angular. (97)

conglomerate
breccia

37. All detrital rocks whose grain-size falls between 1/16 and 2.0 mm are known as _____. These rocks may be further subdivided based on their composition into _____, _____, and _____. (98)

sandstones
quartz arenite
  (quartzose ss)
arkose
graywacke
  (lithic ss)

38. The composition of a sandstone is often a guide to its maturity. That is, rapid burial would not allow time for extensive decomposition of the unstable minerals, while extensive transport and erosion cycles would winnow out the unstable and concentrate on the stable minerals. On this basis, a high concentration of quartz and few other minerals would characterize a _____ (mature, immature) sandstone such as a _____. _____ and _____, which have a high percentage of feldspars and ferromagnesian lithic fragments, are _____ (mature, immature) rocks. (98)

mature
quartz arenite
arkose
graywacke
immature

39. Fine-grained detrital rocks (less than 0.004 mm in diameter) are termed _____ or _____. If they are massive or blocky in appearance, they are called _____; _____ if they are very thinly layered and easily split into fissile slabs. (98)

mudrocks
pelites
mudstones
shales

40. Freshwater limestones of inorganic origin are called _____ or _____ if formed in caves by evaporation or _____ if formed by precipitation of calcium carbonate in streams and around springs. (98)

dripstone
travertine
tufa

41. _____ are spherical shaped grains of calcium carbonate that have been deposited in shallow marine waters around a mineral grain or shell fragment that acts as a nucleus. (98)

oolites

42. _____ is a carbonate rock that seems to have been formed by the replacement of calcite by solutions rich in _____. (99)

dolomite
    (dolostone)
magnesium

43. Quartz also occurs in sedimentary rock in a _____ variety or form which lacks a true crystalline structure. It occurs as nodules of _____ in chalk and other limestones. (99)

cryptocrystal-
    line
flint (Chert)

44. Most biochemical limestones are produced in _____ (warm, cold), _____ (shallow, deep) marine waters. (100)

warm
shallow

45. Carbonate sediments found in the ocean basins are referred to as calcareous _____ and are composed of the shell remains of _____ organisms. Since calcium carbonate is soluble in very cold, deep waters, these deposits are not found at a depth of greater than 5 km. The depth at which the carbonate shells dissolve is called the _____ depth. (100)

oozes
pelagic
carbonate
    compensation

46. Another type of deep oceanic ooze is composed of the silicious remains of pelagic plants called _____. Rocks composed of these organisms are called _____. Their carbonate equivalent would be the _____. (100)

diatoms
diatomite
chalk

47. _____ is a biochemical rock composed of the remains of macroscopic or large shell fragments. (100)

coquina

48. _____ is the most abundant of the nonmarine biochemical rocks, and it is derived from the partial decomposition of _____. (100)

coal
plants

49. _____ and _____ are the most abundant of the sedimentary rocks. (101)

mudstone
shale

50. Sedimentary rocks are separated into a series of layers by _____ planes along which the rocks tend to easily separate. If the bedding planes are relatively widely spaced, they are called _____, but if the layers are closely spaced the bedding planes form _____ layers. (102)

bedding
parallel
laminated

51. In _____ bedding, the bedding layers were originally laid down at some angle to the horizontal. This type of bedding is often characteristic of a _____ (high, low) energy depositional environment associated with channel deposits and sand dunes. This type of bedding may also occur in a _____ (high, low) energy environment like a delta where fine sand and silt may be deposited at relatively steep angles (approaching 30°) where they are given the special name of _____ beds. (103)

cross (false)
high
low
foreset

52. When a poorly-sorted mixture of sediments is rapidly deposited, the sedimentary particles will vary from very coarse at the bottom to very fine at the top of the bed. Bedding of this type is said to be _____. (103)

graded

53. If the bedding in the original sediments has been distorted physically by slumping of the sediments or biologically by the action of burrowing organisms, the bedding is said to be _____ or _____. (103)

disturbed
mottled

54. _____, _____, and _____ are characteristic environmental features found on bedding plane surfaces. (103)

ripple marks
mudcracks
sole marks

55. _____ preserved in sedimentary rocks are often excellent indicators of the current conditions at the time of deposition. If they are very symmetric, they are called _____ and are characteristic of a gentle back-and-forth movement of water. If they are asymmetric with a gentle backslope and a steep foreslope, they are called _____ and show that the current moved in a preferred direction (the foreslope is on the leeside). (103)

ripple marks
oscillation
  ripples
current ripples

56. Mudcracks develop in _____ (fine-grained, coarse-grained) sediments and can only form if the sediments are exposed to the _____. (103)

air

57. Mudcracks have a characteristic _____ shape when viewed from above. (103)

polygonal

58. Unlike ripple marks, mudcracks, and sole marks, sedimentary structures like _____, _____, and _____ could have formed only _____ (during, after) the original sediment was deposited. (104)

nodules
concretions
geodes

59. _____ are usually sphere-like in shape and in cross-section show a concentric layering, while _____ are irregular in shape and usually are composed of a different mineral than the rock in which it has formed. (104)

concretions
nodules

60. It is not uncommon for _____ to coalesce into   nodules
    distinctive bands along the bedding planes of   chert (flint)
    the rock. This is quite common in the _____
    found in limestones. (104)

61. Crystals, usually of silica, lining the hollow   geode
    cavity in a rock and projected inward toward its   osmosis
    center define a _____. These crystals develop
    when fluids of unequal concentration are slowly
    mixed as they pass through a silica gel-like
    membrane lining the inside of the cavity. This
    process is known as _____. (104)

62. Any direct or indirect evidence of past life   fossil
    preserved in rock is called a _____. (105)

63. A good first approximation of the environmental   reddish
    conditions of deposition of a rock can be made   nonmarine
    on the basis of color. It is generally inferred   blackish
    that _____ colored rocks had their origin in
    _____ (marine, nonmarine) environments, while
    _____ colored rocks commonly were formed under
    the reducing conditions present in poorly
    oxygenated waters such as lagoons or deep basins.
    (108)

64. The most important sources of color in the   iron oxides
    sedimentary rocks are the _____, which give the   organic
    rocks their shades of yellow, brown, and red.
    _____ matter tends to give the rocks a gray to
    blackish color. (108)

65. The term _____ defines an accumulation of   sedimentary
    deposits that exhibits specific characteristics,   facies
    reflecting a particular depositional environment,   time
    and grades laterally into other sedimentary
    accumulations formed at the _____ but exhibiting
    different characteristics. (108)

66. A sandstone grading upward into a shale _____   would not
    (would, would not) be an example of a facies as   could not
    defined above since the two rocks _____ (could,
    could not) have been deposited simultaneously. (108,
    109)

67. The overwhelming bulk of sedimentary rocks shows   shallow
    evidence of having been formed in _____ (deep,
    shallow) water environments. (109)

68. A large sediment-filled basin of elongate shape is called a _____. The innermost belt of this basin is known as the _____ and is characterized by _____ (shallow water, deep water) deposits, while the outer belt contains an abundance of _____ and _____ (shallow, water, deep water) sediments and is known as the _____. (110)

geosyncline
miogeosyncline
 (miogeocline)
shallow water
volcanics
deep water
eugeosyncline
 (eugeocline)

69. According to modern plate tectonic theory, the shallow water sediments of the geosyncline are probably associated with thick sedimentary accumulations developing along _____ continental margins and the deep water sediments are found in areas of _____ island arcs, probably at a _____ plate boundary. _____ plate boundaries are marked by numerous basins that are later filled by thick sequences of sediments similar to those found along the San Andreas fault zone. (110)

divergent
volcanic
convergent
transform

SELF-TESTS

Part A: True-False Statements

Each of the following statements is either true or false. Encircle either T or F for each item.

1. Stratification or layering is a characteristic feature of sedimentary rocks.   T   F

2. Approximately 95 percent of the outer 15 km of the earth is composed of sedimentary rocks.   T   F

3. Rivers transport most of the sediment delivered annually to the oceans.   T   F

4. A mixture of fragmented shell material and other skeletal debris constitute a detrital sediment.   T   F

5. The salt left behind after a saline body of water evaporates constitutes a chemical sediment.   T   F

6. Most limestones form in a marine environment.   T   F

7. A sand dune is a good example of a lacustrine deposit.   T   F

8. As a stream loses its velocity, some of its coarser-grained particles will be deposited.   T   F

9. Calcite is by far the most common detrital mineral.   T   F

10. Silica occurs in sedimentary rocks in several crypto-crystalline forms.   T   F

11. The mineral dolomite is most often found associated with quartz. T   F

12. When micas and feldspars are found in the same sedimentary rock, they were probably liberated from their source rocks by mechanical rather than chemical weathering. T   F

13. All rocks of detrital origin have a clastic texture. T   F

14. Chemical sedimentary rocks do not develop clastic textures. T   F

15. Rock salt or halite would have a crystalline texture. T   F

16. Compaction is the most important lithification process in coarse-grained detrital rocks. T   F

17. If a sandstone contains quartz and calcite, the calcite is probably a cementing agent. T   F

18. Ripple marks are most often formed in fine-grained sediments. T   F

19. A local concentration of cementing material that has lithified into a sphere or disk shape is called a nodule. T   F

20. The eugeosyncline contains deep-water sediments and interstratified volcanics. T   F

Part B: Multiple Choice Items

Each of the following can be completed or answered correctly by choosing only one of the selections. Encircle the letter a, b, c, or d, designating your choice.

1. As you trace a sedimentary bed in a lateral direction, you note that it gradually changes from a limestone to a shale. From this you may conclude

   a. the rocks are fossiliferous.
   b. the rocks indicate a change in depositional environment.
   c. the age of the rocks must be continually changing.
   d. you are looking at rocks derived from geosynclinal sediments.

2. A metamorphic rock contains a few fossils. You may confidently conclude

   a. the rock was originally sedimentary.
   b. the fossils predate the metamorphism.
   c. the original rock could not have been igneous.
   d. all of the above are valid conclusions.

3. A vertical sequence of sedimentary rocks exhibits laminar bedding. Which of the following sedimentary features might you possibly find on some of the bedding planes?

    a. ripple marks
    b. mud cracks
    c. graded beds
    d. cross beds

4. Current directions can most easily be deciphered if the rocks contain

    a. graded beds.
    b. asymmetrical ripple marks.
    c. sole marks.
    d. laminar bedding.

5. Which of the following depositional environments would least likely contain cross bedding?

    a. off-shore sand bars
    b. lake basins
    c. sand dunes
    d. stream channel sand bars

6. Unlike most igneous rocks, the average sedimentary rock has a high oxide percentage of

    a. iron.
    b. potassium.
    c. sodium.
    d. calcium.

7. Which of the following rocks does not belong in association with the others?

    a. coal
    b. chalk
    c. anhydrite
    d. coquina

8. Dolomites are most often formed by

    a. direct precipitation from seawater.
    b. the replacement of calcium by magnesium from hydrothermal solutions.
    c. the replacement of calcium by magnesium rich solutions circulating through limestones.
    d. the replacement of magnesium by calcium from hydrothermal solutions and other calcium enriched solutions.

9. A detrital rock composed of grains ranging from 1/16 mm to 2 mm in diameter is called a

    a. conglomerate.
    b. sandstone.
    c. shale.
    d. mudstone.

10. On the basis of texture, which rock does not belong with the others?

    a. coquina
    b. chalk
    c. gypsum
    d. siltstone

11. A sedimentary rock is described as an arkose. You may conclude that it

    a. is detrital.
    b. contains feldspars and quartz.
    c. was derived from a granitic source.
    d. all of the above describe an arkose.

12. A conglomerate is most likely to be lithified by

    a. desiccation.
    b. cementation.
    c. compaction.
    d. crystallization.

13. Which of the following minerals is not an abundant component of sedimentary rocks?

    a. quartz
    b. clay
    c. chert
    d. calcite

14. Which of the following may not be a biochemical rock?

    a. coal
    b. chalk
    c. diatomite
    d. limestone

15. Small spheroidal sand-sized grains composed of calcite are most often found in

    a. sandstones.
    b. limestone.
    c. shales.
    d. mudstones.

SUGGESTED ESSAY QUESTIONS

The items below represent the type of discussion question to which you might be expected to respond. Try writing a response to these, and then discuss your work with another student.

1. If the weathering of a variety of rocks is allowed to go to completion, only a very few "end products" will remain. What are these mineral products, how might they be transported, in what type of environment might they be deposited, and what rock might each produce?

2. What is stratification, and how does it develop in sedimentary rocks?

3. Discuss the origin of detrital and chemical sedimentary deposits.

4. Why do living organisms play such an important role in the origin of the sedimentary rocks?

5. Discuss lithification as a function of the size of sedimentary particles.

6. Contrast clastic and non-clastic texture in sedimentary rocks.

7. Suppose you came across a sequence of sedimentary rocks that were tilted to a vertical position. If they contained graded beds and mud cracks, would you be able to tell the top of a rock layer from the bottom?

8. Under what conditions might the following sedimentary structures develop?

   a. laminar bedding   c. graded bedding
   b. cross bedding   d. disturbed bedding

9. What can ripple marks, mud cracks, and sole marks tell you about a rock's environment of deposition?

10. What is a sedimentary facies, and why is it an important concept in understanding sedimentary rocks?

ANSWERS TO SELF-TESTS

Part A:				Part B:		
1. T	6. F	11. F	16. F	1. b	6. d	11. d
2. F	7. F	12. T	17. T	2. a	7. c	12. b
3. T	8. T	13. T	18. F	3. b	8. c	13. c
4. F	9. F	14. F	19. F	4. b	9. b	14. d
5. T	10. T	15. T	20. T	5. b	10. c	15. b

CHAPTER 7

METAMORPHISM AND METAMORPHIC ROCKS

OVERVIEW

Since metamorphic rocks are so wide-spread and because metamorphic
processes apparently exist throughout the crustal zone and may, in fact,
result in the creation of extensive resource minerals, it is reasonable to
expect that in any study of geology the student should devote ample time
and effort in acquiring an understanding of metamorphism. In this chapter
the authors begin by defining the metamorphic process and the environmental
conditions under which the metamorphism will occur. The major agents of
the process and the types of metamorphism they produce are then considered.
A significant section is presented on the metamorphic facies, associated
mineral assemblages, and their role and significance in the interpretation
of the degree of metamorphic intensity. As was the case for the other rock
types, the basic classification of the metamorphic rocks and the
characteristics of the specific metamorphic rock types is then presented.
The chapter closes with a very important section on the origin of granite
and a brief look at geothermometry.

LEARNING OBJECTIVES

After studying this chapter, you should be able to:

1. Describe the concept of metamorphism and discuss the major factors
    involved in metamorphism.

2. Distinguish between metamorphic change and diagenetic change.

3. Distinguish between lithostatic pressure and directed pressure.

4. Describe the two major types of metamorphism: contact and regional.

5. Describe the metamorphic facies and its role in the development of regional metamorphic zones.

6. Distinguish between contact and regional metamorphic minerals.

7. Describe the nature of metamorphism as it occurs at the three types of plate boundaries.

8. State the characteristics that distinguish the foliated from the non-foliated metamorphic rocks.

9. List and be able to identify the common metamorphic rocks.

10. Contrast the magmatic and the metasomatic formation of granite.

11. Describe the relationship between metamorphism and geothermometry.

KEY TERMS AND CONCEPTS

metamorphism
agents of metamorphism
heat
pressure
lithostatic pressure
directed pressure
chemically active fluids
contact metamorphism
cataclastic metamorphism
regional metamorphism
aureoles
metamorphic facies
pressure-temperature fields
contact metamorphic minerals
regional metamorphic minerals
realm of diagenesis
index minerals
isograds
high-grade metamorphism
medium-grade metamorphism
low-grade metamorphism
foliation
non-foliated (granular) metamorphic
  rocks

foliated metamorphic rocks
rock cleavage
slate
phyllite
schist
gneiss
amphibolite
marble
quartzite
mélange
convergent-boundary metamorphism
divergent-boundary metamorphism
transform-boundary metamorphism
magmatic granites
granitization
metasomatic granites
migmatites
granitic front
simatic front
metasomatism
magmatist
granitizationist
geothermometer
conodonts

Sec. 7.1: Metamorphic Processes and Metamorphic Changes

It is important to realize that metamorphism occurs in solid rocks and that a plastic condition is considered to be a solid state of matter. Although pressure, heat, and chemically active fluids are the prime agents of metamorphism, heat is thought by many scientists to be the major factor. Note the distinction between uniform or lithostatic pressure and directed pressure. You will see this more fully developed when the metamorphic rocks are described, as pressure plays a significant role in the textural components of these rocks. Finally, note the importance of water in its role as a chemically active fluid.

Sec. 7.2: Types of Metamorphism

Contact metamorphism creates a set of minerals which differ from those created in regional metamorphism. Be sure to know these minerals. Notice that contact metamorphism involves alterations due to heat and chemically active hydrothermal solutions, whereas regional metamorphism occurs due to pressure and heat, usually from overlying rock layers and, not infrequently, from the effect of nearby magma bodies, excluding metamorphism within a contact zone.

Keep in mind the distinction between metamorphic zone and metamorphic facies. A particular zone indicates the intensity of metamorphism, and certain minerals, called index minerals, may occur within that zone. For example, chlorite indicates a low-grade metamorphism, whereas sillimanite is indicative of a high-grade metamorphism. On the other hand, a metamorphic facies is a group of minerals which may occur within a given zone and which indicates that all numbers of this group formed under the same conditions of heat and pressure. For example, a specific facies will contain chlorite, which suggests a low-grade metamorphism, plus other minerals such as muscovite, albite, and quartz. These four minerals constitute a particular facies.

Sec. 7.3: Metamorphic Rocks

There are many differently appearing rocks which may be classified as metamorphic. Study the example of the portion of the White Mountains described in this section.

The major types of metamorphic rocks are presented and described in this section. The type of foliation, along with the corresponding cleavage, serves to classify many metamorphic rocks. Be able to describe and identify the type of cleavage associated with each rock. Although marble is fairly easy to identify, quartzite can be difficult. Notice how it can be distinguished from sandstone. When reading this section, you should try to have some typical metamorphic rock specimens in front of you. This will make your study more efficient.

Sec. 7.4: Metamorphism and Plate Boundaries

Convergent boundary metamorphism involves descending slabs of lithosphere material. Temperature and pressure apparently are the major factors involved in these regional metamorphic processes. Pay particular attention to Figure 7.11 and be able to reproduce and label it.

Divergent boundary metamorphism involves rising magma and eventual outpourings of basaltic lava, resulting in contact metamorphic processes. Transform boundaries create fractures and faults through which magma may rise, creating volcanoes in oceanic regions. Such relative plate movements will result in enough heat and pressure to form metamorphic minerals.

Sec. 7.5: Origin of Granite

Granitization is a metamorphic process, and a class of rocks referred to as migmatites seems to offer evidence for this process of metasomatism. Notice that migmatites have the composition of granite.

The origin of a particular granite is still a controversial question.

Sec. 7.6: Geothermometers

Some geological mechanisms indicate that certain temperatures had to exist for the specific mechanism to take place. These mechanisms are known as geothermometers. The formation of coal is an example of a geothermometer.

PROGRAMMED REVIEW

1. _____ is a set of processes involving the application of heat, pressure, and chemically active fluids that alter rocks by changing their texture, mineral composition, or both. (114)

   metamorphism

2. _____ is considered to be the most important agent of the metamorphic process. (114, 115)

   heat

3. The addition of heat _____ (increases, decreases) the rate of chemical reaction and allows new minerals to develop, as well as imparting to the rock _____ (larger, smaller) crystal growth and _____ (coarser, finer) texture. (115)

   increases
   larger
   coarser

4. _____ commonly acts to _____ (increase, decrease) the space occupied by the mineral grains in a rock and to _____ its mineral alignment. (115)

   pressure
   decrease
   reorient

5. Unlike rocks at surface temperatures and pressures which are brittle, rocks at depth respond to the increased heat and deforming forces by behaving like a _____ substance. (115)

   plastic

6. Rocks that are confined by an equidimensional or uniform set of forces are said to be under _____ pressure. If the deforming forces are not uniform, the rock is under a _____ pressure. This type of pressure tends to produce a layered appearance called _____ in metamorphic rocks. (115)

lithostatic
directed
foliation

7. _____ is the most important fluid in the metamorphic process. These fluids react more readily with _____ (coarse, fine) grained rocks because they expose _____ (greater, lesser) surface area to the reacting fluids. (118)

water
fine
greater

8. _____ solutions or fluids released in the solidification of magma often percolate beyond the margins of the magmatic body and react with the surrounding rock. (115)

hydrothermal

9. The temperature increases during metamorphism cause minerals containing water in their molecular structure to become _____. (116)

dehydrated

10. _____ and _____ are the major types of metamorphism. (116)

regional
contact

11. A third type, called _____ metamorphism, is associated with the faulting and folding of rocks. These activities cause rock to be broken into coarse-grained fragments or pulverized by grinding into fine-grain material. Rock of the former type is called _____, and that of the latter is known as _____. (116)

cataclastic
fault breccia
mylonite

12. The alteration of a rock at or near its boundary with an intruding magma is the result of _____ metamorphism and is due largely to the _____ associated with the magma. The alteration may sometimes be traced, with decreasing intensity, to a zone a few hundred meters from the contact. This altered zone is called an _____. (116)

contact
heat
aureole

13. _____ metamorphism is always associated with the very large scale effects that result from episodes of mountain building. (117)

regional

14. Because of the directed pressures and intense heat associated with the mountain building process, rocks altered under these conditions are commonly _____ (foliated, non-foliated) and contain characteristic suites or assemblages of newly formed _____. (117)

foliated
minerals

15. An assemblage of minerals that reached equilibrium during metamorphism under a specific range of temperature and pressure defines the _____. (117)

metamorphic
facies

16. Any changes that take place in rock that occur below the temperatures and pressures of metamorphism are referred to as _____ changes. (118)

diagenetic

17. Carbonate rocks such as limestone and dolomite are very reactive when subjected to thermal changes. The calcite of the limestone and any of its silicate impurities may combine to form the mineral _____. The calcium magnesium carbonate of the dolomite and its silicate impurities may form the mineral _____. (119)

wollastonite
diopside

18. Regionally metamorphosed rocks may be subdivided into a series of zones based on certain minerals known as _____ minerals. These minerals allow for the drawing of boundary lines on maps called _____ that separate the zones on the parameters of _____ and _____. We can say that, within each zone, the rocks have experienced the same _____ of metamorphism. (119)

index
isograds
temperature
pressure
grade

19. _____, _____, _____, _____, _____, and _____ are key regional metamorphic minerals listed in increasing grade of metamorphism. (119)

chlorite
biotite
garnet
staurolite
kyanite
sillimanite

20. Based on the temperatures and pressures that develop during regional metamorphism, the intensity or degree of metamorphism may be referred to as _____, _____, and _____. (119)

low-grade
middle-grade
high-grade

21. Suppose you were examining the rocks of a regionally metamorphosed area. In one section you find a group of rocks containing kyanite, garnet, muscovite, and quartz. As you move to another area, you no longer find kyanite and garnet but now start finding chlorite along with muscovite, biotite, and quartz. From this information, you may conclude that you have left a _____ zone and entered a _____ zone. This would indicate that the _____ of the metamorphism is _____ (increasing, decreasing). (120)

middle-grade
low-grade
grade
decreasing

22. While the composition of a metamorphic rock is an important parameter, most metamorphic rocks can be quickly classified on their _____. On this basis, they are subdivided into two groups: _____ and _____. (121)

texture
foliated
non-foliated

23. Because the layered metamorphic rocks contain
    minerals of a flat-flaky (micas) and blade-like
    (kyanite) crystal habit, they tend to break
    along parallel planes in what is referred to
    as _____. (121)   rock cleavage

24. _____, _____, _____, and _____ lists the   gneiss
    foliated metamorphic rocks in decreasing order   schist
    of metamorphic grade or degree of metamorphism.   phyllite
    (121)   slate

25. _____ is a fairly common foliated rock composed   amphibolite
    of the mineral hornblende and plagioclase. (123)

26. _____ is a foliated metamorphic rock that is   phyllite
    fine-grained with a characteristic silky sheen   slate
    and somewhat wavy or irregular rather than flat
    surface. This rock is the result of a slight
    increase in grade of metamorphism of a _____.
    (121)

27. All schists are dominated by clearly visible   platy (flaky)
    minerals like the micas, talc, and chlorite.   schistose
    All these minerals have a _____ crystal habit
    and are responsible for giving the rock its
    characteristic _____ cleavage. (122)

28. The _____ is a foliated metamorphic rock that   greenschist
    owes its characteristic green color to the   chlorite
    presence of the minerals _____ and epidote.
    (122)

29. All _____ are a granular but foliated metamorphic   gneisses
    rock with a characteristic banded appearance. If   ferromagnesian
    rocks of this type are derived from igneous rocks   micas
    such as gabbro or diorite, the foliation is due
    to the _____ minerals found in these rocks. If
    the rock is derived from clay-rich rocks like
    shale, the foliation would be the result of the
    formation of minerals like _____ from the clays.
    (122)

30. The non-foliated metamorphic rocks usually result   mono
    from the alteration of _____ mineralic rocks
    such as quartz arenites and limestones. (123)

31. _____ is the result of the metamorphism of a   marble
    limestone or dolomite. Rocks of this type exhibit   coarser
    a _____ (finer, coarser) grain size than their
    parent rock. (123)

33. The metamorphism of a quartz arenite will result   quartzite
    in the metamorphic rock known as a _____. (123)

34. When a quartz arenite is metamorphosed, the
    resulting rock shows an _____ (increase, decrease)
    in pore volume, and, when broken, it tends to break
    _____ (around, through) the constituent grains.
    (123)

    decrease
    through

35. The non-foliated metamorphic rocks are essentially
    _____ mineralic, but any _____ present in the
    parent rock may result in a variety of colorations,
    as well as the production of a few accessory
    minerals. (123)

    mono
    impurities

36. Where crustal plates are subducted at convergent
    plate boundaries, the sediments tend to consist
    of a _____ of fine-grained deep-sea facies, along
    with exotic blocks of varying ages and sizes. (124)

    mélange

37. Where a thick wedge of sediments has accumulated
    between a continental block and its oceanic edge,
    a downwarping of the wedge may result in a _____
    grade of metamorphism. If any plutonic activity
    develops, one would expect the subsequent intrusions
    of magma to alter the adjacent rocks by _____
    metamorphism. (124)

    low
    contact

38. When a lithospheric slab is subducted, one would
    expect the degree of metamorphism to _____
    (increase, decrease) as the plate descends.
    Because of this, minerals such as sillimanite
    and kyanite should form in the _____ (deepest,
    shallowest) part of the descending plate, while
    minerals like chlorite should form at the _____
    (deepest, shallowest) sections of the plate. (124)

    increase
    deepest
    shallowest

39. Extensive deposits of economically valuable
    minerals may form along divergent plate
    boundaries, where the upwelling of basaltic lavas
    may result in the _____ metamorphism of adjacent
    rock. The seawater may also react with the rising
    magma to produce _____ solutions, which may
    penetrate fissures in rock and produce extensive
    mineralization. (124)

    contact
    hydrothermal

40. A transform plate boundary where plates slide
    past each other might be a good place to look
    for the effects of _____ metamorphism. (125)

    cataclastic

41. Two schools of thought exist on the origin of granite. At their extremes, one school contends that all granite is the result of the crystallization of magma. This is representative of the _____ origin of granite. The other school believes that granite is the result of a process that alters non-granitic rocks into granite without going through a magma phase. This is representative of the _____ origin of granite. (125)

magmatic
metasomatic

42. The _____ is a term applied to rocks whose average composition is that of granite and was apparently formed when magma squeezed in between the layers of _____. (125)

migmatite
schist

43. If migmatites are traced laterally, they tend to lose their _____ character and grade directly into _____. It appears that this gradational change may be the result of fluids reacting with or perhaps ions migrating through solid rock to change the rock to a granite. This is referred to as the theory of _____ and is thought to be the extreme result of the process known as _____. (125)

schistose
granite
granitization
metasomatism

44. To make a rock into a granite requires the addition of such elements as sodium and potassium and the removal of elements like iron, calcium, and magnesium. The limit to which migrating ions have deposited sodium and potassium is called the _____. The limit to which the migrating ions are supposed to have removed the iron, calcium, and magnesium is called the _____. (125)

granitic front
simatic front

45. At the present time, most geologists agree that some granite is definitely of _____ origin and some is of _____ origin. The major topic of debate lies in the quantity to attribute to each. (125)

igneous
  (magmatic)
metasomatic

46. Any mechanism that can be used to determine the Earth's temperature at a specific time and place is known as a _____. The various _____ minerals used to determine metamorphic grade and a group of fossils of unknown affinity called _____ are typical examples of these temperature indicators. (126)

geothermometer
index
conodonts

47. Any minerals that have formed at temperatures above _____ are considered to be the result of the metamorphic process, while those minerals that develop below this temperature are the result of _____ change. (126)

200° C
diagenetic

Part A: True-False Statements

Each of the following statements is either true or false. Encircle either T or F for each item.

1. Most metamorphic processes are accompanied by extensive remelting of rock. T F

2. During metamorphism, the bulk composition of a rock remains essentially unchanged. T F

3. A clean quartz sandstone may be expected to undergo pronounced changes in composition during metamorphism. T F

4. Minerals formed by the process of contact metamorphism are a function of magmatic temperature and composition and the nature of the intruded or host rock. T F

5. Extensive and complete metasomatic replacement by hydrothermal fluids during contact metamorphism should increase with distance from the contact zone. T F

6. A pure quartz sandstone will most likely produce a greater variety of minerals during contact metamorphism than an impure limestone. T F

7. Regionally metamorphosed rocks contain minerals such as kyanite, sillimanite, olivine, and chlorite that are not found in igneous and sedimentary rocks. T F

8. Regional metamorphic zones are identified by the presence of certain diagnostic metamorphic minerals called index minerals. T F

9. An assemblage of minerals that reached equilibrium during metamorphism under a given set of conditions defines a metamorphic facies. T F

10. A granular textured metamorphic rock will most likely exhibit a good rock cleavage. T F

11. Rock cleavage develops when platelike and elongated mineral grains are arranged in parallel to subparallel layers due to heat and deforming pressures during regional metamorphism. T F

12. The banded appearance of gneisses is due to the alternation of light and dark colored mineral grains. T F

13. Quartzite may be distinguished from a well-indurated sandstone by the absence of pore spaces and the breaking of the rock across rather than around the grains. T F

14. Melting and subsequent magma production are most likely   T   F
    to occur along a divergent plate boundary like a
    mid-ocean ridge.

15. Descending lithospheric slabs retain their mechanical   T   F
    competence until thermal equilibrium is reached with
    the surrounding mantle.

16. The Red Sea represents the initial phase of a converging   T   F
    plate-island arc boundary.

17. Some investigators believe that many granitic bodies are   T   F
    not the product of crystallization from a magma.

18. Granitization is a metasomatic process.   T   F

19. The average composition of a migmatite is basaltic.   T   F

20. The removal of ferromagnesian minerals from a rock and   T   F
    their replacement by sodium and potassium will make a
    rock more granite-like in composition.

Part B: Multiple Choice Items

Each of the following can be completed correctly by choosing only one word
or phrase. Encircle the letter a, b, c, or d designating your choice.

1. The metamorphic process occurs

   a. within the zone of weathering and cementation.
   b. within the zone of melting.
   c. below the zone of weathering and cementation and outside the zone
      of melting.
   d. anywhere from the surface of the earth to the base of the
      lithosphere.

2. The agents of metamorphism are

   a. diagenesis and heat.
   b. heat, pressure, and pore fluids.
   c. heat, pressure, and chemically active fluids.
   d. tectonism and seismic activity.

3. When one mineral is changed into another of different composition by
   the removal, addition, or substitution of ions, the process is
   referred to as

   a. tectonism.   c. metasomatism.
   b. isomorphism.   d. hedonism.

4. Assume you are in an area of regionally metamorphosed rocks and are close to a large igneous intrusion but beyond the zone of contact metamorphism. If you were to walk about one kilometer further away from the intrusion, you would most likely be in

   a. unchanged sedimentary rocks.   c. low-grade metamorphic rocks.
   b. high-grade metamorphic rocks. d. middle-grade metamorphic rocks.

5. Which of the following minerals is important in the determination of metamorphic grade?

   a. quartz   c. kyanite
   b. albite   d. biotite

6. Which of the following statements is not true of the rock phyllite?

   a. derived from the metamorphism of slate
   b. a silky sheen on fresh surfaces
   c. is more coarse-grained than slate
   d. has the characteristic mineral assemblage of the granulite facies

7. Which of the following statements is unrelated to amphibolite?

   a. product of the regional metamorphism of relatively pure limestones
   b. a rock of medium- to high-grade metamorphism
   c. may be derived from impure calcareous sediments
   d. may be derived from regional metamorphism of ferromagnesian igneous rocks

8. A rock is described as being unfoliated, coarse-grained, essentially monomineralic, and relatively soft (its grains are easily scratched by a knife blade). The rock is most probably

   a. quartzite.   c. marble.
   b. gneiss.   d. rhyolite.

9. Contact metamorphism along plate boundaries is associated with

   a. zones of low heat flow.
   b. zones of medium heat flow.
   c. zones of high heat flow.
   d. All three choices are quite probable.

10. Mineralization along plate boundaries is mostly the product of

    a. hydrothermal fluids.   c. migmatization.
    b. granitization.   d. magmatic fractionation.

11. Granitization refers to the

    a. conversion of non-granitic rocks into granite.
    b. magmatic origin of granite.
    c. emplacement of batholiths.
    d. permeation of rock by hydrothermal solutions.

12. An aureole zone of maximum width would most likely be associated with the intrusion of a

    a. sill.   c. batholith.
    b. dike.   d. lopolith.

13. Which of the following materials does not belong in association with the others?

    a. wollastonite   c. diopside
    b. sillimanite   d. corundum

14. If calcium, iron, and magnesium were added to and sodium and potassium were removed from a rock, the resulting rock would

    a. be more granitic in composition.
    b. be less granitic in composition.
    c. be very close to a sandstone in composition.
    d. be very close to a quartzite in composition.

15. The limit to which migrating ions are supposed to carry calcium, magnesium, and iron is known as the

    a. granitic front.   c. simatic front.
    b. basaltic front.   d. sialic front.

SUGGESTED ESSAY QUESTIONS

The items below represent the type of discussion question to which you might be expected to respond. Try writing a response for these and then discussing your work with another student.

1. Distinguish between the following:

    a. metasomatism – hydrothermal fluids
    b. regional – contact metamorphism
    c. sedimentary – metamorphic facies
    d. greenschist facies – granulite facies
    e. metasomatic – magmatic granite
    f. granite front – simatic front

2. Contrast the metamorphism of a shale and a quartz sandstone in regional metamorphism.

3. Contrast contact and regional metamorphic processes.

4. Contrast mineral and rock cleavage.

5. Distinguish between the following rock pairs:

    a. marble – quartzite   c. phyllite – slate
    b. schist – gneiss   d. amphibolite – schist

ANSWERS TO SELF-TESTS

Part A: 1. F   6. F   11. T   16. F   Part B: 1. c   6. d   11. a
              2. T   7. T   12. T   17. T   2. c   7. a   12. c
              3. F   8. T   13. T   18. T   3. c   8. c   13. b
              4. T   9. T   14. F   19. F   4. b   9. c   14. b
              5. F   10. F   15. T   20. T   5. c   10. a   15. c

CHAPTER 8

GEOLOGIC TIME

OVERVIEW

The extremely long time intervals involved in geological processes can best be described by the concepts of relative and absolute time. Before actual or absolute time measurements were available, geologists devised two relative scales, one expressed in rock units and the other in time periods. The rock unit scale is called the geologic column, and it lists the order in which the rocks of the planet were formed. The time scale is called the geologic time scale, and it lists the time intervals, or periods, in chronological order also. The name of a specific rock unit (in the geologic column) is also the name of a specific time interval (in the geologic time scale).

Absolute time determinations became possible with the advent of radioactive dating techniques. These measured times were then used to refine the geologic time scale and to give quantitative meaning to the original relative time intervals.

LEARNING OBJECTIVES

After studying this chapter, you should be able to:

1. Define relative and absolute time, and make the distinction between them.

2. Define the law of superposition and the law of faunal succession.

3. Explain how correlation of rock units may be achieved.

4. State examples using the law of superposition, fossils, and faunal succession in the correlation of rock.

5. Describe the phenomenon of radioactivity.

6. Define an unconformity, and describe the major types.

7. Describe what is meant by each of these processes: alpha decay, beta decay, electron capture.

8. List some common radioactive elements, their half-lives, and mode of decay.

9. Describe how carbon-14 is created and how it is used in radioactive dating.

10. Describe how the combustion of coal and nuclear explosions have affected carbon-14 dating.

11. Describe the graph which shows the relationship between carbon-14 dates and dates derived from tree rings.

12. Describe how varves are used to give absolute time data.

13. Define and contrast the geologic column and the geologic time scale.

14. State the entire geologic column, including eras, systems, and series.

15. State the entire geologic time scale, including eras, periods, and epoch, and the duration of each.

16. Explain how radioactivity is used to give absolute time dates to the geologic time scale.

17. Describe how the law of crosscutting relationships is used to give absolute dates to rock units.

18. Explain how magnetic particles within rocks can be used to create a magnetic stratigraphic column.

KEY TERMS AND CONCEPTS

geologic time
relative geologic time
absolute geologic time
law of superposition
overturned sequence
law of crosscutting relationships
law of faunal succession
correlation
physical correlation
fossil correlation
William Smith
Georges Cuvier

Alexandre Brogniart
unconformity
angular unconformity
disconformity
nonconformity
geologic column
geologic-time scale
erathem
system
series
era
period

epoch
radioactivity
Henri Becquerel
half-life
alpha decay
beta decay
electron-capture decay
radiocarbon dating
Willard F. Libby

cosmic rays
carbon-14
fission-track dating
varves
magnetostratigraphy
normal polarity
reversed polarity
polarity epochs
polarity events

NOTES

Sec. 8.1: Relative Time

Establishing the sequence of geologic events is of prime importance when trying to understand geological processes. Consequently, the idea of relative time, in contrast to absolute time, is very useful. You do not have to know the actual age of a phenomenon in order to understand how it was formed, but one usually does have to know the chronological order involved in the formation of the phenomenon. Both the geologic column and the geologic time scale are relative scales.

Notice that the law of superposition is not easily used if the rock layers have been turned over. Also, the correlation of sedimentary rocks based on physical features cannot be used in every case. Widely separated rock outcrops are difficult to correlate. There are also limitations in the use of fossils as a correlation technique, especially in situations involving a horizontal change in the fossil assemblage. Different fossil assemblages, separated from one another, are found in the same rock formation.

Sec. 8.2: The Geologic Column

This is a scale table which lists the relative order of formation of the world's sedimentary rock units. The rock units are divided into eras, systems, and series. No time units are involved. This scale is based on the law of superposition and the fossil record. Since the rock unit divisions do rely on the differences in fossil assemblages, accumulating information about fossils has tended to make these divisions less distinct. That is, if the fossil record indicates a gradual change, then it becomes difficult to separate rock units on the basis of fossil differences.

Note the significance of the absence of deposition or record of geologic activity in a region that is indicated by the unconformity. Study the Grand Canyon section, and refer to Fig. 8.4 to familiarize yourself with the types of unconformities and their interpretation.

Sec. 8.3: Absolute Time

The concept of half-life is basic to understanding the nature of radioactive decay. Table 8.2 should be studied carefully, as it illustrates the idea of half-life. Notice that it is the ratio of lead to uranium which is used in the actual age determinations. The three methods of radioactive decay result in changes in either the atomic number and atomic mass or in both. Notice that, in beta decay, the loss of an electron is the same as the gain of a proton. In electron-capture decay, the atomic number decreases by one, which is the same as losing a proton. In carbon-14, note the significance of its even distribution throughout the earth's atmosphere and the fact that it cannot be replaced within the organic material after the organism dies. An interesting aspect about carbon-14 is its variation from actual dates as shown by Fig. 8.7. Also, if its percentage has been altered by man's activities--coal burning and nuclear explosions--then carbon-14 dates would not be as valid.

Keep in mind that radioactive dating techniques can be applied successfully to sedimentary rocks only if the appropriate radioactive elements are present. These elements are usually in abundance in igneous rocks only and, therefore, most dates pertain to igneous rocks.

Sec. 8.4: The Geologic Time Scale

This is a chronological table which divides the earth's prehistory into conveniently labeled time periods. It is based on and derived from the geologic column. The names of these periods are the same as the names of the rock systems. This, too, is a relative scale and has no time units involved. The periods are arranged according to their relative age. Absolute dates, from radioactive dating, can be correlated with the time scale. The technique for accomplishing this is illustrated in Fig. 8.10 and Table 8.4. This is an excellent example and should be studied thoroughly.

Sec. 8.5: Magnetostratigraphy

Stratigraphy is that branch of geology that deals with the study, interpretation, and correlation of stratified (i.e., lava flows, pyroclastics, etc.) and sedimentary rocks. Therefore, any technique that enhances stratigraphic knowledge makes a significant contribution to the study of Earth history. Notice that, beyond the physical or geophysical evidence for magnetic reversals, the interpretation of this phenomenon requires the establishment of a repetitive pattern and correlation with the standard geologic-time scale. Also note that, as in most geologic events, the evidence becomes more difficult to interpret the further back you go into geologic time.

PROGRAMMED REVIEW

1. The arrangement of geologic events in chronologic sequence without regard to the actual number of years defines the concept of _____. (130)

   relative time

2. The fundamental principle used to determine if one sedimentary rock is older than another is the _____. Using this principle, it has been determined that, in any sequence of sedimentary rocks that have not been _____, the topmost is the _____ (youngest, oldest) and the lowermost layer is always the _____ (youngest, oldest). (130)

   law of super-
   position
   overturned
   youngest
   oldest

3. If one geologic feature cuts across or through another, it must be _____ (older, younger) than that feature. This concept defines the law of _____. As an illustration of this principle, assume a sedimentary rock is cut by a basalt dike and the sedimentary rock and the dike are also faulted. The relative ages of the rocks and events listed from oldest to youngest is _____, _____, and _____. (130, 131)

younger
crosscutting
  relationships
sedimentary rock
dike intrusion
faulting

4. Since no area on Earth has all rocks and events covering all of Earth history, a continuous sequence can only be pieced together by tying the relative age sequence of one region to that of another. This type of ordering of events defines the process called _____. (131)

correlation

5. Assume you are in an area where an exposed cliff face shows from base to top a limestone, coal seam, and a sandstone. If you move to another locality that is not too far away and find the same sequence exposed, you may assume that these sequences are of equivalent age. To reach this conclusion, you have just made a _____ correlation. If you move to another area, again not too far away, and find the same ordered sequence now overlain by a shale, you may conclude that the shale is _____ (older, younger) than the other rocks. You made your determination of the age of the shale using the law of _____. (131)

physical
younger
superposition

6. When areas become too far apart and when facies change, the correlation by physical methods cannot be used. If we are dealing with sedimentary rocks, you must depend on _____ to make correlations. (131)

fossils

7. Rocks containing the same fossil assemblages are considered to be the _____, even if separated by very great distances. (132)

same age

8. We also know that groups of fossil organisms have succeeded one another in a definite and discernible order, and each geologic time period can be recognized by the fossils found in rocks of that age. This is known as the principle of _____. (132)

faunal
succession

9. A buried erosion surface separating two rock masses, of which the older was exposed to erosion for a long period of time before the deposition of the younger, is called an _____. This feature marks a period in the history of a region when _____ was not taking place. (132)

unconformity
deposition
  (sedimenta-
  tion)

10. Depending on the structural relationships and the type of rock on each side of an unconformity, three principle types are recognized. These are _____, _____, and _____. (133)

angular
  unconformity
disconformity
nonconformity

11. Suppose you are examining a cliff face with a series of sedimentary layers whose bedding surfaces appear to be almost parallel. On close examination, you find that the fossil evidence indicates a large gap in time between a limestone and an overlying shale. This describes a type of unconformity known as a _____. (133)

disconformity

12. Now assume you are looking at a cliff face that exposes a set of steeply tilted sedimentary rocks that are overlain by a sequence of horizontal sedimentary beds. This describes an _____. (133)

angular
  unconformity

13. In a nonconformity, the rocks on one side of the unconformity would be _____ but _____ on the other. (133)

crystalline
  (igneous or
  metamorphic)
sedimentary

14. The chronologic sequence of sedimentary rocks from all over the world that is pieced together using the concept of superposition and _____ succession is called the _____. The major divisions in this theoretical sequence were originally placed where there was a _____ change in the _____ content between adjoining strata. (135)

faunal
geologic column
sudden
fossil

15. The largest subdivision of the geologic column is called the _____ and, listed in chronologic sequence based on superposition, it is composed of the _____, _____, _____, and _____. These rocks are broken down further into a _____ and a still finer subdivision called a _____. (135)

Erathem
Precambrian
Paleozoic
Mesozoic
Cenozoic
System
Series

16. When referring to Oligocene rocks, one knows that one is in that part of the geologic column comprising the _____ System of the _____ Erathem. (135)

Tertiary
Cenozoic

17. Dinosaur fossils could only be found in rocks of the _____ Erathem and the _____, _____, and _____ Systems. (135)

Mesozoic
Triassic
Jurassic
Cretaceous

18. The _____ System of the _____ Erathem marks the first abundant fossil record and is characterized by marine _____. (135)

Cambrian
Paleozoic
invertebrates

19. _____ time defines the expression of Earth
    events in terms of actual units of elapsed
    time such as years. A method of making these
    measurements became available with the discovery
    of _____. (136)

    absolute
    radioactivity

20. The rate at which a radioactive element decays
    is a _____ value and is expressed in terms
    called a _____. (136)

    constant
    half-life

21. Assume a given radioactive element will
    spontaneously decay over a period of one million
    years. Based on this rate, if the original
    amount of element was 10.0 grams, you would
    expect that after one million years there would
    be _____ grams of the original element and after
    two million years there would be _____ grams of
    original material. (136)

    5.00
    2.50

22. A radioactive element decays in one of several
    ways. If the nucleus of a radioactive atom loses
    two protons and two neutrons also equal to the
    nucleus of the _____ atom, the process is called
    _____ decay. Some radioactive elements decay by
    losing an _____ or _____ particle from one of
    the neutrons of the nucleus. This is known as
    _____ decay. In a third type of decay called
    _____, the nucleus changes by picking up an
    _____ from the space around the atom's nucleus.
    (137)

    helium
    alpha
    electron
    beta
    beta
    electron capture
    electron

23. The _____ method has proved very useful for
    the dating of geologic events that are less than
    50,000 years old. In this method, _____ rays
    bombard _____ in the upper atmosphere, causing
    a _____ to be knocked out of the nitrogen
    nucleus. The loss of the proton changes the
    atomic number, and therefore the element, from
    seven to _____ and forms the isotope carbon-14.
    (137)

    carbon-14
      (radiocarbon)
    cosmic
    nitrogen
    proton
    six

24. _____ dating is a method of absolute determination
    that can work over a very wide range of time.
    (139)

    fission-track

25. Most radioactive minerals suitable for absolute
    dating come chiefly from _____ rocks. However,
    the mineral _____ found in some sedimentary
    rocks formed in a marine environment contains a
    radioactive isotope of _____ that has been very
    useful in determining when the sediments were
    deposited. (139)

    igneous
    glauconite
    potassium

26. Certain types of sediments called _____ represent
    a single year of deposition. These types of
    sediments are the characteristic deposits left in
    extinct _____ lakes. Except for very recent time
    (a few thousand years) and in only a few areas,
    these types of deposits do not give _____ time
    data in terms of number of years before the present,
    but can only reveal the amount of time for the
    _____ to be deposited. (139, 140)

    varves
    glacial
    absolute
    sediments

27. When referring to the geologic column, one is
    describing _____ units. When referring to the
    geologic-time scale, the subdivisions mark
    _____ units. (140)

    rock
    time

28. The _____, _____, and _____ are considered to
    be the time equivalents of the _____, _____,
    and _____, which describe the major subdivisions
    of rock units in the geologic column. (140)

    Era
    Period
    Epoch
    Erathem
    System
    Series

29. We may say that Cretaceous fossils represent the
    life that existed during Cretaceous _____, and
    they have been fossilized in Cretaceous _____.
    (140)

    time
    rock

30. Estimates for the age of the Earth were made by
    such methods as Biblical genealogy, rates of
    _____, _____ of the oceans, rates required for
    organic _____, and careful measurements on the
    energy of a _____ body. However, it was not
    until the discovery of _____ that a method for
    accurate and reliable dating could be developed.
    (141, 142)

    sedimentation
    salinity
    evolution
    cooling
    radioactivity

31. The oldest rocks on Earth have been dated at more
    than _____ years. Dates from meteorites suggest
    an age for the solar system (and the Earth) of
    slightly greater than _____ years. (142)

    3 billion
    4.5 billion

32. Rocks and sediments containing _____-bearing
    minerals may be used to determine the _____ of
    the Earth's magnetic field at the time of their
    formation. Investigations have shown that the
    Earth's magnetic field changes from what is today
    a _____ polarity to _____ polarity in a geologic
    instant of time (around 2,000 years). (144)

    iron
    direction
    normal
    reverse

33. A _____ marks the interval of time during which   polarity epoch
    the direction of the Earth's magnetic field is   polarity events
    oriented in a single predominant direction (either
    normal or reversed). Certain of these time frames
    are marked by polarity switches (normal to reverse
    and back to normal) for relatively short durations.
    These are called _____. (144)

34. The correlation of changes in the Earth's magnetic   magnetic
    field with the geologic-time scale to fix these   stratigraphy
    events in Earth history is called _____. (144)

SELF-TESTS

Part A: True-False Statements

Each of the following statements is either true or false. Encircle either
T or F for each item.

1. The law of superposition can only be used when the layers   T   F
    of rock are vertical.

2. The process of correlation can be used to relate a rock   T   F
    in one area to a rock layer in another area.

3. If two rock layers in different areas contain the same   T   F
    type of fossils, then the two layers must be parts of
    the same layer.

4. A relative time scale consists of arranging events or   T   F
    durations in a chronological order.

5. An element is radioactive if its nuclei spontaneously   T   F
    disintegrate, forming new elements.

6. Radioactive decay means that any element will decompose   T   F
    if exposed to radioactive material.

7. The rate at which a given radioactive element decays   T   F
    depends on the temperature and pressure.

8. The existence of pleochroic halos in biotite prove that   T   F
    radioactivity occurs only in silicate minerals.

9. Alpha decay occurs when a radioactive nucleus emits the   T   F
    nuclei of helium atoms.

10. Beta decay, the emission of an electron from a radioactive   T   F
    nucleus, increases the atomic number of the substance by
    one.

11. A radioactive element may decay by acquiring an electron   T   F
    from outside the nucleus.

12. The half-life of carbon-14 is about a million times   T   F
    greater than that of uranium-238.

13. Carbon-14 is radioactive and is created when cosmic rays   T   F
    hit a nitrogen-14 nucleus.

14. The distribution of carbon-14 is almost constant.   T   F

15. Carbon-14 will decay into nitrogen-14 by beta decay.   T   F

16. Glauconite is a substance which occurs in sedimentary   T   F
    rocks and contains radioactive potassium.

17. The geologic column shows the relative age of a series   T   F
    of rock units or layers.

18. In the geologic column, the Mesozoic Era is divided into   T   F
    the Cretaceous, Jurassic, and Triassic Periods.

19. Absolute time measurements derived from radioactive   T   F
    techniques cannot be applied to the geologic time scale
    since the measurements are taken from igneous rock
    material.

20. The term "polarity events" refers to the reversal of the   T   F
    earth's magnetic poles--north for south and south for
    north.

Part B: Multiple Choice Items

Each of the following can be completed correctly by choosing only one word
or phrase. Encircle the letter a, b, c, or d, designating your choice.

1. In a series of sedimentary rocks,

    a. the top layer is always the youngest.
    b. the bottom layer is always the oldest.
    c. the top layer could be the youngest.
    d. the bottom layer is never the youngest.

2. A rock layer in one locality can be shown to be related to a rock
   layer in another locality by

    a. discovering fossils in each layer.
    b. identifying a sequence of shale, limestone, and sandstone in each.
    c. using radioactive dating techniques to show that the layers are
        about the same age.
    d. identifying the same physical features in both layers.

3. Which of the following dating techniques cannot yield absolute dates?

    a. tree rings   c. varves
    b. carbon-14   d. uranium-238

4. A radioactive element is one which

    a. decomposes into subatomic particles.
    b. can be chemically decomposed into new elements.
    c. decays into protons, neutrons, and electrons.
    d. decays into new elements spontaneously.

5. The amount of a given radioactive material decaying within any period of time

    a. is constant.   c. increases.
    b. decreases.   d. depends on the pressure.

6. If a radioactive material has experienced four half-lives, the amount of radioactive material remaining is what fraction of the original?

    a. 1/4   c. 1/8
    b. 1/2   d. 1/16

7. The half-life of uranium-238 is

    a. 4.5 million years.   c. 4.5 years.
    b. 4.5 billion years.   d. 4.5 thousand years.

8. A neutron hitting a nitrogen-14 nucleus will most likely result in the formation of

    a. nitrogen-15.   c. carbon-14 and a proton.
    b. nitrogen-14 and a proton.   d. carbon-14 and an electron.

9. When an organism dies, the amount of carbon-14 it contains

    a. decreases immediately to zero.
    b. remains the same.
    c. decreases.
    d. increases.

10. The phrase "radiocarbon years" is used to indicate

    a. that carbon-14 was used as a dating technique.
    b. dates determined since 1850.
    c. that carbon-14 dates do not always represent the actual dates.
    d. that the tree ring dates agree with the carbon-14 dates.

11. Which of the following is not a characteristic of the geologic column?

    a. includes igneous rock sequences
    b. divides the world's sedimentary rocks into groups called systems
    c. rock series arranged in chronological order
    d. names assigned to various groups of sedimentary rocks

12. Which one of the following groups does <u>not</u> contain related or similar terms?

    a. Triassic, Jurassic, Cretaceous
    b. Paleozoic, Tertiary, Cenozoic
    c. Precambrian, Cenozoic, Mesozoic
    d. Eras, Systems, Series

13. Which of the following pertains to the geologic time scale?

    a. absolute time periods   c. series
    b. epochs   d. Precambrian system

14. About how long is the Precambrian Era?

    a. 4 billion years   c. 100 million years
    b. 500 million years   d. 10 billion years

15. Magnetostratigraphy is the technique which

    a. arranges the rock units of the geologic column according to the strength of their magnetism.
    b. correlates igneous rock units into the geologic column.
    c. has been used to prove magnetic pole reversals.
    d. is used to correlate reversals in the earth's magnetic poles with the geologic time scale.

SUGGESTED ESSAY QUESTIONS

The items below represent the type of discussion question to which you might be expected to respond. Try writing a response to these and then discuss your work with another student.

1. Explain the law of superposition, and describe its limitations.

2. Explain how it would be possible to correlate two rock units from different areas if both the physical features and fossil assemblages are different.

3. How does the existence of pleochroic halos support the assumption that radioactive decay rates have not changed over the long geologic times involved?

4. Describe a few of the problems involved in using the carbon-14 technique.

5. How is carbon-14 created, and what happens to it after a long time?

6. What is the geologic time scale?

7. Explain in detail, with an example, how radioactive dates from igneous rocks can be used to refine the geologic time scale.

ANSWERS TO SELF-TESTS

Part A:	1. F	6. F	11. T	16. T	Part B:	1. c	6. d	11. a
	2. T	7. F	12. F	17. T		2. d	7. b	12. b
	3. F	8. F	13. T	18. F		3. c	8. c	13. b
	4. T	9. T	14. T	19. F		4. d	9. c	14. a
	5. T	10. T	15. T	20. T		5. b	10. c	15. d

CHAPTER 9

DEFORMATION

OVERVIEW

Evidence is presented for the movement of the earth's crustal rocks. These
movements may be small or rapid, horizontal or vertical, small or great.
As a result of such movements, the rocks are changed, either in shape or
dimensions or both. Such deformation of the rocks can be analyzed in terms
of the forces acting on the rocks and the inherent strength of the rocks.
In addition to the actual deformation of rock units, large masses of rock
experience deforming forces, which result in the creation of a number of
structural features which are readily observable. All continents possess
basic similarities in their major surface features, such as mountains and
plateaus, which in themselves reveal all of the structural features created
by the deforming forces.

LEARNING OBJECTIVES

After studying this chapter, you should be able to:

1. Define each of the following: stress, strain, shear, rigidity,
    viscosity, strength, brittle, ductile.

2. State the difference among the concepts of tension, compression, and
    shear.

3. Compare and contrast electric and plastic deformation.

4. Describe the role of time in the interpretation of deformation from
    laboratory experiments.

5. Define the following terms: dip, strike, axial plane, fold axis, fold limbs, fold plunge.

6. Describe the mechanism of folding.

7. Make representative sketches of each of the following structures: anticline, syncline, monocline, dome.

8. Relate the relative ages of rocks in a fold structure in relation to the fold axis.

9. Distinguish between a symmetrical and asymmetrical fold structure.

10. Distinguish between overturned and recumbent fold structures.

11. State the difference between a fault and a joint.

12. Define the term joint system, and state the factors that control its development.

13. Define the following terms: dip-slip fault, strike-slip fault, transform fault, hanging wall, foot wall.

14. Make a sketch of each of the following fault types: normal, thrust, left lateral, right lateral, overthrust.

15. Sketch and explain how a graben and horst are formed.

16. Describe and contrast slow and abrupt crustal movements.

KEY TERMS AND CONCEPTS

deformation
volume deformation
stress
unit stress
strain
unit strain
yield point
elastic deformation
plastic deformation
brittle deformation
retardation of recovery
viscosity
viscous
tensional stress
compressional stress
shear stress
strength
yield strength
tension strength
compression strength
shear strength
isostasy

level of compensation
structural geology
dip
strike
folds
concentric folding
flow folding
monocline
anticline
syncline
dome
basin
fold limbs
fold axis
axial plane
fold plunge
symmetrical fold
asymmetrical fold
overturned fold
recumbent fold
joint
joint system

fault
dip-slip fault
strike-slip fault (transcurrent)
normal fault
thrust (reverse) fault
left-lateral strike-slip fault
right-lateral strike-slip fault

graben
horst
transform fault
slow crustal movement
creep
abrupt crustal movement

NOTES

Sec. 9.1: Stress, Strain, and Strength of Rocks

Stress can be of three types: tension, compression, and shear. All three
result in deformation or strain. As Fig. 9.2 illustrates, elastic strain
occurs below the yield point of a material. In that region, the strain is
directly proportional to the stress, and the object will eventually recover
its original size and shape. Beyond the yield point, the deformation is
plastic, and it increases in this region with no increase in stress.
Plastic deformation involves shear stress and a flow of material. Notice
that the slope of the graph in Fig. 9.3 is defined as viscosity. If the
slope is greater, the viscosity is greater. Two objects of different
viscosities may have the same flow rate if the more viscous one has a
greater stress acting on it. The strength of rocks is defined in terms of
the stress experienced by the rocks. Note the difference in brittle and
ductile rocks, and keep in mind that at depths a brittle rock becomes
ductile. The confining pressures due to depth are important in
interpreting the behavior of rock masses. Note also the emphasis placed on
the factor of time in the data from stress-strain experiments on rock
materials. It is very difficult to extrapolate the effects of geologic
time in the short duration of a laboratory experiment.

Sec. 9.2: Features of Plastic Deformation

Dip and strike are used to describe the orientation of individual outcrops
and of structural features. The strike and dip are always perpendicular to
one another. Study Figs. 9.5-7 for a good representation of the
geometrical relationships. Study Figs. 9.9-11 in order to acquire an
understanding of the spatial relationships among plunge, axis, axial plane,
and fold limbs. Figs. 9.14-15 and Table 9.1 present the gist of the
material on folds and should be studied thoroughly. A little hint for
determining the relative ages of the rocks in a fold if they are
sedimentary: All you must do is "walk" in the dip direction, and you will
go from older to younger rocks. Thus, in an anticline, the rocks dip away
from the axis. Therefore, the oldest rock is in the axial region, and, as
you move away from the axis, the rocks must get progressively younger in
age.

Sec. 9.3: Features of Brittle Deformation

In dealing with faults, it is most important to realize that the motion
involved is relative. If both sides of a fracture move by the same amount
and in the same direction, it must be classified as a joint, not a fault.
A fault is classified on the basis of the kind of motion along the fault
plane. This is illustrated in Fig. 9.19. Know it well. Notice the

distinction between a horst and a graben (both normal faults) can be made in terms of the dip angles of the fault surfaces. A graben has the faults dipping toward one another. In a horst, the faults dip away from one another. Notice also the similarities and difference between the strike-slip (transcurrent) fault and the transform fault.

Sec. 9.4: Deformation of the Earth's Crust

Any rocks that have undergone a change in size, shape, and position (called displacement) are considered to be deformed rocks. Although both abrupt and slow movements of the earth's crust are discussed, most of this chapter has dealt with very slow movements of the crustal rocks. The term creep is used here for very slow movements of rock. The abrupt or sudden movements will be the topic of the following chapter.

PROGRAMMED REVIEW

1. Any change in volume, shape, or displacement of a part of the Earth's crust is called _____. (148)

   deformation

2. When rocks are subjected to _____, there is a change in their shape but no change in volume. (148)

   shearing

3. In _____ deformation, the rock retains its original shape, but there is a change in the rock's density. (148)

   volume

4. Any application of a deforming force that tends to change the dimensions of a rock is known as a _____. This is expressed mathematically as the ratio of the total force applied per unit area and is referred to as the _____. (148)

   stress
   unit stress

5. Any resultant change in a rock as a result of the applied stress is described as the _____. The _____ is the fractional change in the material's length, width, or height. (148)

   strain
   unit strain

6. Graphs of stress v. strain from laboratory experiments have shown that for most materials there is a linear relationship between applied stress and resulting strain in the early stages of the deformation. This means that the strain is _____ to the stress. We also know that, if the stress is removed, the strain will return to _____. Any material that behaves in this manner is said to have undergone _____ deformation. (148)

   proportional
   zero
   elastic

7. When the applied stress is increased, a _____ point is reached for a given material. Beyond this point, the removal of the stress will not cause the material to return to its original shape or size. Any substance that behaves in this manner is said to experience a _____ deformation. (148)

yield
plastic

8. For any rock to experience the types of deformation described above, the rock must be under high _____ pressure. (148)

confining
(lithostatic)

9. No rock material under any set of conditions can deform indefinitely. When the rock reaches the breaking point, it will _____. (149)

rupture

10. The resistance a rock offers to elastic deformation is a measure of its _____. (149)

rigidity

11. Unlike a rubber band, when the deforming force on a rock is removed, the recovery of the original shape is not _____, but rather may occur over a very long period. (149)

instantaneous

12. In plastic deformation, a rock will flow under a given stress. The ratio of stress to rate of flow is a measure of the rock's _____. If stress and flow data for a given rock is graphed and the resulting curve is linear (flow is directly proportional to stress and the rate is constant), the rock is described as being _____. (149)

viscosity
viscous

13. Unlike a fluid (deforms at the slightest stress), a solid will not begin to deform until a large stress is applied and does not experience a plastic deformation until a _____ is reached. Because of this, solids are said to possess _____ strength. (149)

yield point
yield

14. When a rock breaks, any differential movement on either side of the break is called a _____. This is an example of _____ deformation. (149)

fault
brittle

15. If a stress results only in a change of shape, it is called a _____ stress. When the applied stress causes a decrease in volume, it is known as a _____ stress. If the deforming force tends to stretch and possibly increase a rock's volume, it is referred to as a _____ stress. (149)

shear
compressional
tensional

16. We must be very careful in the interpretation of laboratory data on the deformation of rock, because, unlike pressure, temperature, and the introduction of fluids, the parameter of _____ is very difficult to reproduce on a laboratory scale. (149)

time

17. The resistance a rock offers to deforming stresses is a measure of its _____. Since a rock may be subjected to three different types of stresses, its resistance to stress is given as a function of _____, _____, and _____. (149)

strength
compressive strength
tensile strength
shear strength

18. The strength of a rock is greatest under a _____ stress and smallest under a _____ stress. In a brittle rock, the _____ strength is much greater than the _____ strength. (149)

compressional
tensional
compressional
tensional

19. As the lithostatic pressure on a rock increases, the difference in magnitude between a rock's compressional and tensional strength _____ (increases, decreases) and the rock becomes less _____ and more _____. (149)

decreases
brittle
ductile

20. As a general rule, the strength of a rock increases with greater _____ and decreases with greater _____. (149)

pressure
temperature

21. The Earth's crust responds to different physical characteristics of rock and the addition or subtraction of rock mass on a regional scale through a process known as _____. (150)

isostasy

22. _____ is a branch of the geological sciences that deals with deformed masses of rock and the stresses that caused the deformation. Major deformational features include _____, _____, _____, and _____. (151)

structural geology
folds
joints
faults
unconformities

23. The geologist determines the spatial orientation of structural features (especially planar ones like bedding planes) by making measurements called _____ and _____. (151)

dip
strike

24. Assume you are standing on a tilted bedding plane surface of a sedimentary rock. Since you are actually standing on the surface, it defines a real plane. Now _imagine_ another plane surface intersecting the real bedding plane surface. Their point of intersection forms a straight line (geometry of intersecting planes). Of course, there are an infinite number of imaginary planes that may intersect the real bedding plane, but there is only one plane that will intersect parallel to the horizon. The line formed by the intersection of the real tilted plane (the bedding plane surface) and the horizontal, imaginary plane is a directional feature (with a compass you can find its bearing) that defines the _____. Now draw a line that will intersect the imaginary line on the tilted bedding plane. Notice that to draw

strike

the line of steepest inclination on the bedding plane, it must intersect your strike line at 90°. This line gives the direction of the tilt or the _____ direction. Also notice that the tilt can only be on the downside direction of the line you just drew. Now imagine the horizontal plane is intersecting the tilted bedding surface (remember the line of intersection is the strike). If you now measure the angle between this horizontal plane and the tilted bed along the dip direction line, you can determine the angle of _____ which is the expression of the _____ of the dip. (151, 152)

dip
inclination
magnitude

25. If a rock is striking north to south (or south to north), its direction of dip may be _____ or _____. (151, 152)

east
west

26. The dip direction of a rock is given as due south. Its strike direction must be _____. (151, 152)

east-west
 (west-east)

27. The magnitude of the dip of a rock is recorded at 90°. This rock would be in a _____ position with respect to the horizon. (151, 152)

vertical

28. Compressive stress will produce a structural deformation in rocks called _____. If this feature is the result of elastic bending of an originally horizontal layer and shows no change in thickness or volume, it is known as _____ folding. When the bending takes place in rocks that are in a plastic state, the feature is the result of _____ folding. (153)

folds
concentric
flow

29. A simple downward flexure of a sedimentary layer describes the fold known as a _____. (153)

monocline

30. When describing the geometry of a fold, the imaginary plane that bisects the fold into nearly equal halves is called the _____ plane. The imaginary line in this plane, drawn along the surface of a single layer where the fold is most pronounced, is called the fold _____. In most folds this line is inclined. The angle that this line makes with the top edge of the axial plane (or conversely with the horizon) describes the _____ of the fold. (153, 155)

axial
axis
plunge

31. The layers of a fold that dip towards or away from the central axis of a fold are referred to as _____. (153)

limbs

32. In an _____ fold, the limbs dip in towards the central axis. If you were to stand in the axial region of the fold and then walk away from the axis, the relative age of the successive layers encountered would be from _____ (older, younger) to _____ (older, younger). (155)

synclinal
younger
older

33. In a _____ fold, the limbs dip away from the central axis. If you were to stand in the axial region of the fold and then walk away from the axis, the relative age of the successive layers encountered would be from _____ (older, younger) to _____ (older, younger). (155, 156)

anticlinal
older
younger

34. If the limbs of a fold dip at approximately equal angles on each side of the central axis, the fold is said to be _____. If the limbs dip at unequal angles from the central axis, the fold is described as being _____. (157)

symmetrical
asymmetrical

35. When seen in map view, an anticlinal fold is a long, narrow type of structure. If a map view shows an almost circular structure where the limbs dip outward from the center in all directions, the structure is called a _____. In this structure the oldest rocks are found at the _____ (center, margin) and the youngest rocks at the _____ (center, margin). This should not be surprising, because, if you walk in the direction of the dip, you must always go from _____ (older, younger) to _____ (older, younger) rocks. (156, 157)

dome
center
margin
older
younger

36. If the limbs are tilted beyond the vertical and both limbs dip in the same direction, the fold is said to be _____. If the axial plane of the fold is nearly horizontal, the fold is described as being _____. (156)

overturned
recumbent

37. In brittle deformation, rocks are broken, producing a fracture surface or plane. If no movement takes place on either side of the fracture, the fracture is called a _____. If there is a slippage or displacement along the fracture surface, the structure is called a _____. (157)

joint
fault

38. The terminology used in the description and
    classification of faults is based largely on
    the relative movements of rock masses on the
    opposite sides of the fault. If the displacement
    is along the dip direction (dip of the fault
    plane), the fault is a _____. The relative
    movement of the blocks on either side of the
    fault plane may be up or down. If the fault
    plane is tilted at some angle to the horizontal,
    you could imagine yourself standing on the
    dipping surface of the fault plane. The block
    under your feet is called the _____, while the
    block on the opposite side of the fault plane
    is called the _____. (159)

    dip-slip
    footwall
    hanging wall

39. In a dip-slip fault where the hanging wall moves
    down relative to the footwall, the fault is called
    a _____ fault. When the hanging wall appears to
    have moved up relative to the footwall, the fault
    is referred to as a _____ fault. The _____ is
    largely the result of horizontal compressive
    stress, while the _____ is when the vertical
    stress is greater than the horizontal. (159)

    normal
    reverse
    reverse fault
    normal fault

40. The _____ fault has the same relative movements
    as the reverse fault, but the angle of the fault
    plane is usually much less than _____ degrees.
    (159)

    thrust
    45

41. A tensional stress that forms a series of related
    normal faults that causes a large block of the
    earth's crust to drop between two steep
    escarpments whose faces are actually dipping
    fault planes is called a _____. If the central
    block moves up so that it stands above the
    bounding normal fault planes, it is called a
    _____. (159)

    graben
    horst

42. In some faults, the displacement is along the
    strike direction of the fault plane. This type
    of movement defines the _____ fault, also
    called a _____ fault. (159, 160)

    strike-slip
    transcurrent

43. Imagine you are standing on a distinctive, flat
    rock surface at the edge of a fault. If you
    step across the fault, you are in a different
    type of rock. To find the same rock on the
    other block, you must move to the _____ or
    _____. Because of this strike-slip, faults
    are designated as being _____ or _____, which
    are terms that describe the type of movement
    and its direction. (159, 160)

    left
    right
    left-lateral
    right-lateral

44. Many large zones of the earth's crust are the result of large scale faulting. The most spectacular system of continental normal faulting that produced an extensive linear trench over 6,000 km long is found in _____ and is called the _____ zone. In the _____ Province of the western United States, a series of tilted fault blocks are the products of normal faults. (160)

Africa
African rift
Basin and Range

45. _____ faults are usually associated with folding and are common in the Alps, southern Appalachians, and the Rocky Mountains. If the dip of the fault plane is low and the displacement very large (several kilometers), it is called an _____. (160)

thrust
overthrust

46. A very active fault on the west coast of the United States is the _____ fault that can be traced for over 1000 km. This fault is classified as a _____. (160)

San Andreas
right-lateral
   strike slip

47. Midocean ridges are offset by what are called _____ faults. In this type of fault, there _____ (is no, is considerable) lateral displacement of the ridge crests with time. (161)

transform
is no

48. Crustal disturbances may produce very large horizontal and/or vertical movements. The rate at which these displacements occur is described as being _____ or _____ (time in a geological and historical sense). In a historical context of time, large displacements (horizontal or vertical) are associated with _____ and can be recorded by direct measurement on a characteristic feature of the rock, whose change in position may be recorded through time. The term _____ is used to describe very slow movements that can only be measured by using a variety of very sensitive instruments. (163, 164)

abrupt
very slow
earthquakes
creep

SELF-TESTS

Part A: True-False Statements

Each of the following statements is either true or false. Encircle either T or F for each item.

1. Stress is the force applied to an object divided by the area over which it acts.   T   F

2. Shear is the type of deformation of a material in which the volume changes, but not the shape.   T   F

3. The property of viscosity is related to the plastic deformation of a material. T   F

4. The strength of a material is the total strain it experiences before it is permanently deformed. T   F

5. Mountains tend to attract nearby masses with forces much greater than calculated according to the law of gravitation. T   F

6. Isostasy explains why less dense portions of the crust stand higher than relatively more dense portions. T   F

7. Brittle deformation results in fracturing and faulting. T   F

8. The parameter of time is relatively easy to reproduce on a laboratory scale in rock deformation experiments. T   F

9. Mountains exist today because the earth's crust keeps pushing up the mountains even as they erode. T   F

10. The idea of dip pertains to the angle at which a mountain slopes. T   F

11. An anticline is a fold which always forms mountains. T   F

12. In a syncline, the oldest rocks are in the center of a fold. T   F

13. A dike is a joint which filled with magma. T   F

14. A normal fault is one in which the footwall has moved up relative to the hanging wall. T   F

15. A horst is a ridge separating two normal faults which dip away from one another. T   F

16. An overthrust is a reverse fault in which the upthrown side has slumped or broken off to fall onto the downthrown side. T   F

17. A transform fault is the oceanic crust equivalent to the continental transcurrent fault. T   F

18. In flow folding, the thickness and volume of the folded strata remain the same. T   F

19. Rock layers are dipping to the east. If you walk in an easterly direction, the relative age of the rocks should become progressively older. T   F

20. In an overturned fold, the limbs are tilted beyond the vertical, and both limbs dip in opposite directions, although they may be at different angles. T   F

Part B: Multiple Choice Items

Each of the following can be completed correctly by choosing only one word or phrase. Encircle the letter a, b, c, or d, designating your choice.

1. The deformation of the crustal rocks is

   a. an infrequent occurrence.
   b. constantly occurring.
   c. caused by special events, such as earthquakes.

2. The types of stress are

   a. compression, tension, and shear.
   b. compression, tension, and strain.
   c. rigidity, viscosity, and rupture.

3. Which group pertains to elastic deformation?

   a. above yield point, size recovered, shape not recovered
   b. strain increases with no increase in stress, above yield point, no recovery of shape
   c. original size and shape recovered, rigidity, below the yield point

4. A material is said to be viscous if

   a. the rate of flow of the material is directly proportional to the stress.
   b. it undergoes stress beyond plastic deformation.
   c. it flows easily.

5. The strength of a rock is defined as the

   a. stress at which the rock becomes permanently deformed.
   b. strain at which the rock begins to flow.
   c. force at which the rock fractures.

6. When a rock's tension strength is much smaller than its compression strength, the rock is referred to as

   a. ductile.   b. pliable.   c. brittle.

7. Two common types of structures which large scale normal faulting has created are horsts and grabens. A pair of faults is involved in each case. How do these types of structures differ?

   a. In a graben, the two faults dip toward one another, whereas, in a horst, the faults dip away from one another.
   b. In a graben, the area between the two faults move up relative to the zones beyond the faults, whereas the opposite is true for a horst.
   c. In a horst, the hanging wall moves up to create a large, elongated ridge, whereas, in a graben, the foot wall moves up to create the ridge.

8. A fold is described as being arched with limbs dipping away from the axis at approximately equal angles. This fold must be

   a. a recumbent anticline.   c. a symmetrical anticline.
   b. an isoclinal anticline.

9. Floating isostatic equilibrium usually refers to

   a. the persistence of plastic deformation at depth.
   b. the continual existence of ocean basin formation.
   c. the continued elevation of mountains.

10. The dip and the strike are related such that

   a. the dip must be measured along the strike.
   b. the strike is zero when the beds are vertical.
   c. the dip is perpendicular to the strike.

11. A type of fold with older beds in its center is a

   a. monocline.   c. anticline.
   b. syncline.

12. What type of fold is characterized by the beds on the lower limbs being upside down?

   a. overturned   c. recumbent syncline
   b. recumbent anticline

13. A set of cracks, usually forming hexagonal patterns, and produced in basalt as it cools, is called

   a. columnar jointing.   c. faults.
   b. sheet jointing.

14. A type of fault which connects other major structural features is called a

   a. transcurrent fault.   c. transform fault.
   b. unconformity.

15. A fault that results from a tensional stress is the

   a. thrust fault.   c. strike-slip fault.
   b. normal fault.

SUGGESTED ESSAY QUESTIONS

The items below represent the type of discussion questions to which you might be expected to respond. Try writing a response to these and then discuss your work with another student.

1. Discuss the graph of stress-strain, commenting on the relationships and the significance of elastic and plastic deformation.

2. Describe the importance of the time factor in the deformation of rock materials.

3. Describe and discuss the relationship between the strike and the dip and its importance in defining the orientation of rock structures and their interpretation.

4. Discuss the relationship between a fold axis and the plunge of a fold.

5. Contrast the features formed by plastic and brittle deformation.

6. Explain the difference between a horst and a graben, and describe how they are formed.

7. Describe and contrast transcurrent and transform faults.

ANSWERS TO SELF-TESTS

Part A:
1. T	6. T	11. F	16. F
2. F	7. T	12. F	17. F
3. T	8. F	13. T	18. F
4. F	9. F	14. T	19. F
5. F	10. F	15. T	20. F

Part B:
1. b	6. c	11. c
2. a	7. a	12. b
3. c	8. c	13. a
4. a	9. c	14. c
5. a	10. c	15. b

CHAPTER 10

EARTHQUAKES
AND THE
EARTH'S INTERIOR

OVERVIEW

Earthquakes bring both benefits and destruction to humankind. Their
destructive effects are well-known, and considerable space is devoted to
them in this chapter. In addition, earthquakes have permitted scientists
to accumulate considerable knowledge about the earth's deep interior. The
means of detecting and locating earthquakes is described, along with the
worldwide distribution of earthquakes. Characteristics of the earthquake
itself--depth of occurrence (focus), the point on the earth's surface
directly over the source (epicenter), and the energy involved--are
presented and described, along with the theories designed to explain
earthquakes. Earthquakes cause several types of waves to be emitted, which
are mechanisms for the earthquake energy to be transmitted to great
distances, and the characteristics of the waves are described in detail.
These waves help geologists determine the nature of the earth's interior,
and the evidence is presented for the existence of specific zones within
the earth's interior. Each of these zones is described, as is their
relationship to adjoining zones.

LEARNING OBJECTIVES

After studying this chapter, you should be able to:

1. List and describe some common effects of earthquakes.

2. Describe how a seismic sea wave is formed and how it changes upon
    approaching a shore.

3. Define the following terms: focus, epicenter, isoseismic line, magnitude.

4. Describe the basic characteristics of the Richter scale.

5. State at what depth most foci are located.

6. Indicate on a map the major earthquake zones.

7. Sketch an excellent approximation of the seismic risk map of the U.S.

8. State a brief description of the Alaskan earthquake of 1964.

9. Describe the elastic rebound hypothesis for the cause of earthquakes.

10. Describe the cause of those earthquakes which occur with increased depth.

11. Explain how plate movements can cause earthquakes.

12. Explain the significance of seismic gaps.

13. Describe in detail, with a sketch, how a seismograph works.

14. Describe in detail the types of body waves.

15. Describe the surface waves generated by an earthquake.

16. Use the travel time-distance graph to determine the distance to an earthquake and its time of occurrence.

17. State how an earthquake's epicenter is located.

18. Define: predictor, dilatancy, P, S, L.

19. Explain how a discontinuity is identified.

20. Describe the M discontinuity.

21. Describe in detail the oceanic and continental crusts.

22. Describe how earthquakes might be predicted and possibly controlled.

23. Describe the mantle.

24. Sketch the spatial relationships of the mantle, asthenosphere, lithosphere, and crust, labeling on the sketch pertinent information.

25. Describe the core.

26. Sketch the earth in cross-section, indicating the various zones and the depths and thickness of each.

KEY TERMS AND CONCEPTS

seismology
seismic waves
seismograph
earthquake belts or zones
elastic-rebound hypotheses
aseismic ridge
inertial member (mass)
transducer member
recorder member
body waves
surface waves
P waves (primary)
S waves (secondary)
L waves (surface)
push-pull (compressional) waves
shear waves
oscillation (vibration)
period
particle displacement by a wave
wave energy
time-distance graphs
travel time curves
interval or lag time
focus
epicenter (epicentral area)
earthquake intensity
earthquake magnitude
earthquake energy
Marcalli Scale
Richter Scale

magnitude or index
logarithmic relationship
wave amplitude
wave length
wave speed or velocity
seismic gap
aftershock
seismic sea waves
tsunami
landslide
fault creep
earthquake sounds
earthquake predictors
dilatancy
waste fluid injection
liquefaction
crust
mantle
core
lithosphere
asthenosphere
Mohorovicic discontinuity
Moho
M discontinuity
continental crust
oceanic crust
sialic crust
simatic crust
body wave reflection
body wave refraction

NOTES

Sec. 10.1: Seismology

In this very brief introduction to the study of earthquakes or seismology,
note the importance of a large number of recording stations needed for a
meaningful interpretation of seismic waves. Also note that seismology is
an integral part of geology called geophysics.

Sec. 10.2: Early Instrumental Observations

This section describes a number of early attempts (pre-twentieth century)
to construct instruments which would detect and record the motions involved
in an earthquake.

Sec. 10.3: Modern Seismology

This is a description of the components of a seismograph, how it functions,
and what the instrument records. Notice that for a complete record three
seismographs are required, since the ground vibrations will move up and
down and back and forth.

Sec. 10.4: Earth Waves

Disturbances, generated by an earthquake, consist of two major types: body and surface waves. Notice that the push-pull body wave can travel through any material, whereas a shear wave will only travel through material which can experience a shear stress. Surface waves can travel along the surface of any material.

Sec. 10.5: Records of Earthquake Waves

The records of P, S, and L waves, along with the time-distance graph (travel time curves), are used to locate an earthquake and to determine when it occurred. The differences in the arrival times (the different waves arrive at different times but were all generated at the same time) then permit the distance to the earthquake to be determined by using the travel time graph. Knowing the distance traveled and when a wave arrived at the recording station, the geologists can then calculate the time of occurrence. Notice that the earthquake's epicenter is located by using data from three or more seismic stations.

Sec. 10.6: Interpreting Earthquakes

Some of the terms used to describe earthquakes are foci (focus), epicenter, isoseismic lines, and magnitude. Notice that the focus is not a point but a zone. Likewise, the epicenter is an area. The Richter scale is logarithmic, meaning that a number is ten times the wave amplitude of the preceding number, and 31 times the energy. An 8 Richter scale reading, compared to a 4, indicates an earthquake which is 10,000 times greater in wave amplitude, involving almost a million times more energy.

Sec. 10.7: Cause of Earthquakes

The cause of all earthquakes must be the sudden rupture of earth materials. This may occur near the surface or as deep as the mantle region. The elastic rebound hypothesis assumes the existence of a fault along which stresses act on the material on either side of the fault, resulting eventually in a breaking loose and the material moving to a condition of equilibrium. This hypothesis cannot explain disturbances which occur at such depths that the rocks are plastic. At depths of 20 to 30 km or more, the idea of plastic rupture seems to offer a better explanation. A rock with a high viscosity may deform plastically (flow), but rupture could occur if the stresses act too quickly, not giving the rocks a chance to respond by flow.

Sec. 10.8: Earthquakes Resulting from Plate Movements

Crustal plate interactions result in earthquakes. This occurs as stresses increase to the point where a sudden slipping occurs along plate boundaries. Major earthquakes occur in boundary zones in which the two plates merged or locked, eventually breaking loose from one another with considerable energy.

Sec. 10.9: Effects of Earthquakes

This is a very straight-forward description of some of the effects of earthquakes, both continental and submarine. A major point to remember is that the duration of an earthquake could be as significant as the intensity. An interesting phenomenon is that seismic sea waves are very much higher on a beach than on the open ocean. Also, the distance between crests is very great.

Sec. 10.10: Earthquake Prediction and Control

Within the vicinity of an earthquake, certain physical changes in the rocks may occur before the actual disturbance takes place. These are referred to as predictions. Some of these changes are due to dilatancy, which signifies a weakening of the rocks. These precursors may be used to predict the magnitude and time of an earthquake. Except for minor earthquakes and in a limited case, no control over earthquakes has been achieved.

Sec. 10.11: Structure of the Earth

Knowledge about the earth's interior has been achieved by the study of earthquake waves. They have proven to be very useful in locating discontinuities. Since wave speeds are dependent on the type of material (solid, liquid, and gas) and the density of the material, scientists can infer from the wave data something about the nature of the earth's interior. Notice the three major zones--crust, mantle, and core--can also be divided.

PROGRAMMED REVIEW

1. The scientific study of earthquakes is called _____. (170)

   seismology

2. In the study and interpretation of earthquake data, it is essential to develop a firm foundation in the natural science discipline of _____. Because of this, the study of earthquakes is a specialty of the branch of geology known as _____. (170)

   physics
   geophysics

3. Early investigators of seismic activity devised several types of devices to detect and record the occurrence of earthquakes. Any instrument used to detect seismic waves is called a _____, and the written record is known as a _____. (171)

   seismograph
   seismogram

4. All modern seismographs consist of three basic parts: _____, _____, and _____. The _____ component is a suspended weight that is constructed to move freely in only one direction. This large mass will (when damped) _____ (remain at rest, oscillate) when seismic waves pass by. The _____ is any type of device that picks up the relative motion of the mass and ground. (172)

   inertia member
   transducer
   recorder
   inertia (mass)
   remain at rest
   transducer

5. Since the ground motion occurs in all directions, it is necessary to have _____ seismographs at a recording station. The station may then record the _____, _____, and _____ components of the ground motion. (172)

three
vertical
north-south
east-west

6. The inertial member is set to oscillate for a short time (5 s) or a longer time range (up to 60 s), but the ground vibration is much _____ (longer, shorter). The time for the inertia member (or the ground) to complete one oscillation defines its _____. (173)

shorter
period

7. Part of the energy released when earth materials rupture travels away in the form of _____. During an earthquake, two distinct types are produced. If they travel through the interior of the earth, they are called _____. If they are transmitted only along the outer surface, they are known as _____. (173)

waves
body waves
surface waves

8. The waves that travel through the interior of the earth are composed of two types: _____ and _____. The _____ type travel through solids, liquids, and gases. Any particles moved as the wave passes through a material vibrate _____ (parallel, at right angles) to the direction of travel. The _____ type will not travel through a _____, and the particles vibrate _____ (parallel, at right angles) to the direction of travel. (173)

push-pull
shear
push-pull
parallel
shear
gas
at right angles

9. In any type of wave motion, _____ is being transmitted through a material, but the particles of the medium _____ (are, are not) moving along with the wave. That is, they may _____ as the wave passes, but their net displacement must equal _____. (173)

energy
are not
vibrate
  (oscillate)
zero

10. Because seismic waves travel at different velocities, they reach a given recording station separately. The first to arrive is called the _____ wave; the second is the _____ wave; and the third is the _____ wave. They are symbolized _____, _____, and _____, respectively. (174)

primary
secondary
large
P
S
L

11. The first waves to reach the seismograph are of the _____ (push-pull, shear) type, and the second to reach it are of the _____ (push-pull, shear) variety. Their speed is a function of the _____ of the material they travel through. (174)

push-pull
shear
density

12. Many measurements have shown that there is a relationship between the travel schedules for P-, S-, and L-waves. These are most conveniently expressed on a _____ plot or graph. However, these relationships and their predictive values are limited to distances of less than _____ km. Beyond this distance, the P-waves are _____ (early, late), and the S-waves _____ (are early, are late, are not recorded). This would seem to indicate that the interior of the earth is _____ (uniform, not uniform) in its composition and physical state. (174)

time-distance
11,000
late
are not recorded
not uniform

13. The point within the earth where a rupture of rock results in an earthquake is called the _____. An area on the surface of the earth directly above this point is designated as the _____. The focus depths of earthquakes have been recorded to almost _____ km, but about 75 percent occur at less than _____ km. (175)

focus
epicenter
700
75

14. Assume a recording station receives a P-wave at 12 h 30 m 10 s and the S-wave is recorded at 12 h 34 m 10 s. By referring to Fig. 10.9 in your text and making the necessary calculations, you may conclude that the lag time for the waves is _____ and the seismograph station is _____ km from the quake. For you to locate the position of the quake, you would need the travel-time data from at least _____ stations. (176)

04 minutes
3,200 km
two

15. Determination of the intensity of an earthquake has been based on rather crude and subjective features. The United States Geological Survey uses a scale (subsequently refined) developed by _____ consisting of _____ degrees of intensity based on the construction of manmade structures and their behavior during a quake. When enough data are acquired, they are plotted on a map and the points are contoured using _____ which connect points of equal intensity. (177)

Mercalli
12
isoseismic lines

16. Unlike the scale described above, a more quantitative method based on the amplitude of actual seismic records was developed by Gutenberg and _____. This scale assigns a number or _____ value as a measure of the quake's energy at its focus. The scale magnitude increases _____, so that each increase in whole numbers is _____ times the wave amplitude of the prior number. This scale also allows for estimates of the _____ of energy released in terms of explosive equivalents of TNT or tonnage of atomic explosives. (178)

Richter
magnitude
logarithmically
ten
amount

17. Most earthquakes tend to occur in _____, and many are associated with _____. The greatest area of earthquake activity is found around the borders of the _____. Many quakes have their foci aligned along mountain chains. A very active belt of this type is found in the _____ zone from western Europe to southeast Asia. Narrow belts are also associated with _____ systems in the midocean regions. (181)

belts (zones)
active volcanoes
Pacific Ocean
Mediterranean-
    trans-Asiatic
ridge

18. The immediate cause of an earthquake is the sudden _____ of earth materials when distorted beyond the limit of their _____. (182)

rupture
strength

19. The mechanism of _____ is the idea that rocks under stress can store energy as they are deformed and release the energy when they _____. (183)

elastic rebound
rupture

20. Most earthquakes and volcanic activity are associated with the interaction along lithospheric plate boundaries. However, regions such as the Hawaiian Islands and certain other ridge systems in the oceanic crust experience extensive volcanic activity but very little seismicity. These regions of oceanic crust are known as _____. (184)

aseismic ridges

21. Along some plate boundaries, there are fault zone regions which experience little seismic activity for many years. These regions are called _____ and may mark sections where stresses are building up towards a major quake. (189)

seismic gaps

22. The vast majority of earthquakes recorded each year are too small to have any significant geological or physically damaging effects. However, the secondary effect of _____ has been and will continue to be the greatest hazard to a populated, modern city such as San Francisco. The type of materials and construction used in buildings can often be chosen and designed to withstand relatively large magnitude quakes. However, the substrate on which the buildings sit is very important to their stability. In quake areas, it is always best to build on _____ and never on _____ materials. (189)

fire
bedrock
unconsolidated

23. Earthquakes of equal magnitude acting on identical structures and bedrock may produce widely different effects, depending on the _____ of the quake. (189)

duration

24. Submarine earthquakes may set up extremely large
    swells at sea called _____ or _____. In deep
    ocean waters they have extremely long _____
    lengths and _____ (small, large) amplitudes.
    When they approach the shallows of a coast,
    there is a large decrease in their _____ and a
    very large increase in their _____. (189)

    seismic sea
      waves
    tsunami
    wave
    small
    wave length
    amplitude

25. In regions where there are many hills with steep
    slopes or soil conditions that are sensitive to
    vibrations, earthquakes are often the cause of
    _____. (191)

    landslides

26. Unlike earthquakes that result in large vertical
    and/or horizontal displacements of the surface,
    _____ is a slow, periodic movement of land on
    opposite sides of a fault. (192)

    fault creep

27. Structures built on water saturated soils or
    loose sediments are prone to failure during a
    quake, due to _____ rather than the actual
    ground shake. In this process, the unconsolidated
    sediments behave like a _____ and cannot support
    the structures. (192)

    liquefaction
    liquid

28. Ground vibrations that disturb the air and produce
    sound in the range of human hearing are referred
    to as _____. (193)

    earthquake
      sounds

29. Any long-term or short-term effects that have
    been associated with a following earthquake are
    called _____. A well-known precursor has been
    the strange behavior of _____ prior to the
    quake. (193)

    predictors
    animals

30. Another precursor is the marked change in the
    _____ of seismic waves due to the phenomenon
    of _____, which occurs in rocks prior to rupture.
    (193)

    velocity
    dilatancy

31. A blending of historic, stratigraphic, and the
    more accurate data from modern measurements lends
    itself to a _____ analysis of the information
    and predictions based on the probability of a
    quake occurring in known earthquake zones. (193)

    statistical

32. The control or modification of earthquakes is a
    long sought after but as yet not attainable goal.
    One idea is to trigger small quakes along fault
    zones of great stress and prevent the occurrence
    of a major quake. This may be accomplished by
    injecting _____ along the fault zone to reduce
    the _____ resistance across the fault. (193)

    fluids
    frictional

131

33. Most of our knowledge of the earth's interior comes from an analysis of the behavior of _____ and _____ waves. The velocity of these waves increases with increasing _____ of the material. It is also known that waves moving from one type of material may be _____ or _____ at their boundary or interface. The boundary along which these changes take place is called a _____. (193, 194)

body
surface
density
reflected
refracted
discontinuity

34. On the basis of data gathered from seismological studies, the earth has been divided into three major zones: _____, _____, and _____. (194)

crust
mantle
core

35. A Yugoslavian seismologist noticed that P- and S-waves traveling through the crust encountered a boundary that caused some of their energy to be _____ towards the surface and a noticeable increase in _____ for those waves that crossed this boundary. This worldwide change in the behavior of P- and S-waves marks this boundary as the _____. (195)

reflected
velocity
Mohorovicic
   discontinuity
   (Moho)

36. Seismic data has revealed the crust of the earth to be _____ (thickest, thinnest) under the continents and _____ (thickest, thinnest) under the ocean basins. We also know that the oceanic crust is composed exclusively of _____ rock, the continental crust is divided into an upper, middle, and lower series of layers of _____, _____, and _____ composition respectively. (195)

thickest
thinnest
simatic
sialic
mafic
simatic

37. The rock of the mantle must be _____ because it transmits S-waves and is more _____ than crustal rocks, as indicated by an increase in the velocity of body waves traveling through it. The velocity of P-waves in the mantle also changes. This has led to its subdivision into a _____ and _____ mantle. These changes may be due to _____ or possibly to a change in the _____ of the material. (195)

solid
dense
lower
upper
composition
elasticity

38. The _____ is the rigid outer layer of the earth that includes the crust and the _____. The _____ is the zone within the earth's mantle that is particularly _____ in its behavior. (196)

lithosphere
upper mantle
asthenosphere
plastic

39. Analysis of seismic records indicates that the
    core is composed of an _____ and _____ zone.
    The outermost layer is _____ (thicker, thinner);
    and because S-waves do not penetrate this zone,
    it must behave like or actually be in a _____
    state. P-waves penetrate this outer layer, but
    they _____ at the boundary, indicating a change
    in composition. The P-wave velocity _____
    (increases, decreases) in the inner core, and
    other geophysical evidence indicates that it
    is in a _____ state. The specific gravity of
    the inner core is very _____ (high, low) when
    compared to mantle and crustal rock. Studies
    on the composition of meteorites and other
    geophysical investigations indicate that the
    inner core is composed primarily of _____ and
    about eight percent _____, and smaller amounts
    of _____. Oxygen, sulfur, silica, and carbon
    may be present in very small amounts. (196)

inner
outer
thicker
liquid
refract
increases
solid
high
iron
nickel
cobalt

SELF-TESTS

Part A: True-False Statements

Each of the following statements is either true or false. Encircle either
T or F for each item.

1. The duration of an earthquake could be just as important   T   F
   as the intensity in causing damage.

2. Fault creep is the very slow opening of a crack in the   T   F
   earth's rocks due to an earthquake.

3. The focus of an earthquake is the precise point which   T   F
   marks the source of an earthquake.

4. No earthquakes have been detected at depths below 700   T   F
   kilometers.

5. The Richter scale assigns to each earthquake a magnitude   T   F
   number which indicates the depth of occurrence.

6. Most of the energy released by earthquakes is confined to   T   F
   a zone stretching from Burma to the Alps, called the
   Mediterranean and Trans-Asiatic zone.

7. The probability of an earthquake occurring is less in   T   F
   western New York State than in southern California.

8. In the Alaskan earthquake of 1964, which had its epicenter   T   F
   on land, the greatest loss of life was due to the seismic
   sea wave.

9. The cause of all earthquakes must be due to movement along   T   F
   faults.

10. Earthquakes which occur at considerable depths can be   T   F
    explained by the sudden flow of rocks in the plastic state.

11. The interaction of two crustal plates results in a   T   F
    continuous series of earthquakes along the plate boundaries.

12. A seismic gap is a zone in which two plates have become   T   F
    locked, permitting stresses to build to very high levels.

13. A modern seismograph consists of three major components: T   F
    an inertia component, a recorder, and a pendulum.

14. A push-pull wave is a type of surface wave generated by   T   F
    an earthquake.

15. A shake, or shear, wave can only move through substances   T   F
    which resist change in shape.

16. S-waves travel at about two-fifths the speed of P-waves   T   F
    in any given material.

17. S- and L-waves are body waves.   T   F

18. At seismic recording stations which are at distances from   T   F
    the epicenter greater than 11,000 km, no S-waves are
    recorded.

19. A discontinuity is a boundary which separates oceanic   T   F
    and continental crust.

20. The mantle is a thick zone which separates the crust and   T   F
    the core of the earth.

Part B: Multiple Choice Items

Each of the following can be completed correctly by choosing only one word
or phrase. Encircle the letter a, b, c, or d, designating your choice.

1. During an earthquake, at which one of the following locations would
   you prefer to be?

   a. focus
   b. epicenter
   c. open ocean
   d. sunbathing 3000 km away from epicenter

2. A seismic sea wave is caused by

   a. volcanic eruptions.
   b. tsunamis.
   c. rupture of rocks in the ocean basin.
   d. submarine landslides.

3. An area which experiences earthquakes with very deep foci (100 to 700 km) is

    a. western South America.   c. eastern United States.
    b. western United States.   d. Australia.

4. Which of the following is not a typical earthquake effect?

    a. fires   c. landslides
    b. liquefaction   d. sonic boom

5. The focus of an earthquake is

    a. the zone to which the energy of the earthquake is transmitted.
    b. the area where the actual disturbance originates.
    c. the area on the earth's surface directly above the source of the earthquake.
    d. almost always at depths greater than 700 km.

6. An earthquake's magnitude is a number

    a. indicating the amount of energy released by an earthquake.
    b. which predicts the amount of damage done by an earthquake.
    c. indicating the relative size of the earthquake waves.
    d. which designates the relative size of the areas affected.

7. Most of the earthquakes which occur every year are of what magnitude range?

    a. 5.0 to 9.0   c. 2.5 to 2.9
    b. 3.0 to 5.0   d. less than 2.5

8. How many major earthquake belts or zones are there on the planet?

    a. 1   c. 3
    b. 2   d. 4

9. Which characteristic does not pertain to the elastic rebound hypothesis?

    a. plastic flow
    b. slow deformation and rupture
    c. surface and near-surface faulting
    d. San Andreas fault

10. Seismic gaps occur at certain localities along plate boundaries when

    a. the two plates stop moving.
    b. one plate begins to move over another one.
    c. a severe earthquake occurs.
    d. the plates become locked together.

11. A push-pull type of body wave involves

   a. the up and down motion of rock particles.
   b. disturbance in solids only.
   c. the transport of huge masses of rock.
   d. the compression and rarefaction of rock masses.

12. The distance to an earthquake source can be determined from the travel time curve if

   a. the time at which the P- and S-waves arrived is known.
   b. the time interval between the arrival of the P- and S-waves is known.
   c. the time interval between the arrival of the P- and L-waves is known.
   d. the time at which the L-waves arrives is known.

13. The identification and existence of what phenomenon has permitted geologists to determine an appropriate model of the earth's interior?

   a. mantle   c. discontinuities
   b. density variations   d. dilatancy

14. Which portion of the crust probably extends around most of the earth?

   a. sima layer   c. lithosphere
   b. sial layer   d. asthenosphere

15. Geologists think that the composition of the mantle is different from the crustal rocks because

   a. it has a greater density.
   b. it is under great pressure.
   c. the speed of P-waves increases and no S-waves are transmitted.
   d. the speeds of P- and S-waves increase significantly and suddenly.

SUGGESTED ESSAY QUESTIONS

The items below represent the type of discussion questions to which you might be expected to respond. Try writing a response to these, and then discuss your work with another student.

1. Discuss the various effects of earthquakes which may result in changes to both society and nature.

2. What is the relationship between numbers on the Richter scale and wave amplitudes and earthquake energies?

3. Describe the physical characteristics of a seismograph, and explain how it works.

4. Discuss in detail the travel time-distance curve, explaining how it is used to locate earthquakes and to determine the time of occurrence.

5. Explain how the Mohorovicic discontinuity was discovered.

6. Sketch the spatial relationship which exists among the crust, core, and mantle, including depth and thickness values.

ANSWERS TO SELF-TESTS

Part A: 1. T   6. F   11. F   16. T   Part B: 1. c   6. c   11. d
         2. F   7. F   12. T   17. F   2. d   7. a   12. b
         3. F   8. T   13. F   18. T   3. a   8. c   13. c
         4. T   9. F   14. F   19. F   4. d   9. a   14. a
         5. F   10. F   15. T   20. T   5. b   10. d   15. d

CHAPTER 11

CONTINENTS, OCEANS, PLATES, AND DRIFT

OVERVIEW

The earth's lithosphere consists of huge sections, called plates, which are moving relative to one another. The boundaries between plates are marked by the earthquake zones. The different types of motions between plates result in a set of characteristics for each boundary. The continents and ocean basins are the top sections of the plates, and they, therefore, move also. The ocean basins today are a result of the enlarging of the sea floors; and the distribution of the continents today is a result of the motion of the plates, with the original configuration consisting of one huge continental mass about 200 million years ago. The evidence for the continental motions comes from the directly observable features of the rocks themselves (fossils, structure, glaciation, etc.) and the indirect evidence from geophysics, which involves the magnetism of minerals formed over a period of 200 million years.

LEARNING OBJECTIVES

After studying this chapter, you should be able to:

1. State the approximate ages of the earth's crust and the present ocean basins.

2. State briefly the concepts of continental drift, sea-floor spreading, and plate tectonics.

3. Define the following terms: magnetic dip pole, magnetic inclination, magnetic declination, geomagnetic poles, magnetic equator, Curie temperature.

4. Explain why the earth's magnetism is probably not due to magnetized masses within the earth.

5. Describe the dynamo theory of earth magnetism.

6. Define the following terms: natural remanent magnetism (NRM), thermoremanent magnetism (TRM), depositional remanent magnetism (DRM), virtual geomagnetic poles, normal polarity, reverse polarity, polarity epoch, polarity event.

7. Describe the phenomenon of paleomagnetism.

8. Describe the past variations of the magnetic field's intensity and the geomagnetic pole positions.

9. List the evidence for continental drift.

10. Describe in detail the phenomenon of sea floor spreading and how it relates to continental drift.

11. Explain how the shapes of continents may be considered as evidence for continental drift.

12. Describe how paleomagnetism can be used as evidence for continental drift.

13. Describe how ancient climates can be used to support the theory of continental drift.

14. Describe how ancient plants and reptiles might support the idea of continental drift.

15. Describe how mountain chains, rocks of similar age, and ancient wind deposits may contribute to the idea of continental drift.

16. List the arguments against continental drift.

17. List the six major crustal plates.

18. Sketch and label the structure of the crustal plates.

19. List the three types of plate boundaries, with sketches, and describe each one in terms of structure, earthquake occurrence, and presence of volcanoes.

20. Describe the movement of plates using the idea of convection cells.

21. Describe the plume theory as a mechanism for plate movements.

22. Describe how the material on the sea floor is recycled.

23. List the major events involved in continental drift and sea floor spreading, along with the time of occurrence.

24. Describe how a landmass might split and begin to drift.

25. Describe the significance of microplates in the plate tectonic model for the origin of the continents.

KEY TERMS AND CONCEPTS

shield or craton
continental drift
sea-floor spreading
plate tectonics
Alfred Wegener
Pangaea
Gondwanaland
Gondwana System
paleoclimates
Glossopteris flora
fossil reptiles
Mesosaurus
Lystrosaurus
Vine-Matthews hypothesis
paleomagnetism
Curie temperature
north magnetic (dip) pole
south magnetic (dip) pole
magnetic equator
magnetic inclination
magnetic declination
natural remanent magnetism (NRM)
thermoremanent magnetism (TRM)
depositional remanent magnetism
  (DRM)
secular variations
geomagnetic intensity

geomagnetic reversals
virtual geomagnetic poles
normal polarity
reverse polarity
polarity event
geographic north pole
geomagnetic north pole
pole migration
lithosphere
lithospheric plate
asthenosphere
plate boundaries
divergent
convergent
transform
tensional forces
compressive forces
rift valleys
rifting
convection currents
convection cells
plumes
hot spots
obduction
Benioff Zone
microplates (exotic terranes)
microcontinents

NOTES

Sec. 11.1: Origin and Permanence of the Continents and Ocean Basins

The earth's crust is at least 4.0 billion years old; and, although there is some question as to how it became separated into oceanic and continental components, there is strong evidence to suggest that the volume of continental crust has been rather constant ever since its formation. Even with continental drift, the continents have apparently maintained a constant, relative elevation above sea level.

Note that in sea-floor spreading the floor of the sea does not really spread but is rather created at mid-ocean ridges and "destroyed" at subduction zones. Also note that the geologically young age of the present ocean basins does not preclude the former existence of older ones.

Sec. 11.2: Continental Drift

The development of Wegener's theory is presented using the clearly
observable evidence of the rock record. Note that the apparent fit of
South America and Africa is even better at the edge of the continental
shelves than at the modern coasts or sea level. It is interesting to note
the much greater acceptance of continental drift by southern hemisphere
geologists than their northern counterparts. Remember, the early
observable evidence was most impressive in the southern hemisphere. The
paleomagnetic data is only briefly mentioned. It has been a major factor
in the acceptance of continental drift and will be expanded upon in the
next section. Know it well.

Sec. 11.3: Magnetism and Paleomagnetism

Magnetic and geomagnetic poles are not the same. Note that a magnetic, or
dip, pole is defined operationally--by the response of a magnetized needle.
A geomagnetic pole is the theoretical location of the intersection of the
imaginary magnetic axis with the earth's surface. Note the reasoning
involved with the idea that the geographic and geomagnetic poles coincided
throughout much of geologic time. This is vital to the concept of
continental drift. The theoretical locations of the geographic poles can
be determined by locating the virtual geomagnetic poles. The fact is that
paleomagnetic data from rocks of the same age but from different
observational stations locate virtual magnetic poles at different
positions. The implication here is that the continental masses have moved.

Sec. 11.4: Sea-Floor Spreading

The important factors to consider are the integration of the Vine-Matthews
paleomagnetic hypothesis with sea-floor spreading and the further
corroboration of this phenomenon as given by the age of oceanic crust and
sediments with distance from a ridge axis. Remember, the sea floor does
not really spread, but gives the appearance of spreading as new oceanic
crust is created at the ridges and older crust is destroyed in the
subduction zones. Finally, notice that sea-floor spreading does not
require the continents to plow through solid rock (Wegener's explanation
and a physical impossibility, given the size of the forces needed), but
they are passive riders on the moving lithospheric plates.

Sec. 11.5: Plate Tectonics

The tectonic plates do not consist of either continents or ocean basins.
Some plates may contain both. The motion of these plates includes a
component attributed to the opening up of ocean basins--the creation of new
oceanic crustal material. Note that any given plate extends past the Moho
into the mantle. Table 11.1 gives an excellent summary of the various
plate boundaries and the characteristics to be expected in any of the three
types of plate interaction.

Also note the recent discovery of microplates and their incorporation by
accretion onto the more ancient continental masses. The microcontinents
are like the microplates, being largely of continental lithosphere, but
have yet to be accreted to a major landmass.

1. The idea that landmasses have wandered over the earth's surface defines the phenomenon of _____. (202)

   continental drift

2. _____ is one of the possible mechanisms that causes the continents to change position. During this process, new sea floor is formed at _____ areas, and the older sea floor is _____ into the mantle. (202)

   sea-floor spreading
   midocean ridge
   subducted

3. The concept of _____ pictures the earth's crust as a jigsaw-like puzzle of rigid plates that jostle one another, grow in some places, and decay in others. (202)

   plate tectonics

4. The present ocean basins are geologically _____ (young, old) features with the oldest sediments in the basins dated as _____ in age on the geologic-time scale. Any sediments and oceanic crusts that were older than the time just indicated must have been destroyed and recycled along the earth's _____ zones. (202)

   young
   Jurassic
   subduction

5. The first coherent theory presented for the impermanence of the continents was developed by the German meteorologist _____. His theory took into account the apparent fit between the west coast of _____ and the bight of west _____, as well as the similarities in the overall _____, _____ content of the rocks, and evidence of _____ on continents now widely separated. (203)

   Alfred Wegener
   South America
   Africa
   geology
   fossil
   glaciation

6. He also pictured the existence of a supercontinent called _____ that began to break up during the _____ Era. (203)

   Pangaea
   Mesozoic

7. Much of the evidence for continental drift is based on paleoclimatic reconstructions. An underlying assumption is the fact that modern climatic zones or belts are roughly _____ to and _____ about the equator. If the basic climatic controls have _____ (remained the same, changed), this pattern _____ (should have, could not have) existed in the past. (203)

   parallel
   symmetrical
   remained the same
   should have

8. The rocks of the _____ System found on the Indian peninsula range in age from late _____ to early _____. These beds show striking similarities with many other widely separated regions of the _____ hemisphere. It is felt that these present regions must have been part of a single landmass called _____. (203)

   Gondwana
   Paleozoic
   Cretaceous
   southern
   Gondwanaland

9. The distribution of vast continental-size _____
    deposits in these southern regions is one of the
    most convincing lines of evidence for Wegener's
    theory of continental drift. The present
    geographic continental distribution would place
    the source of the _____ in the southwestern
    part of the Indian Ocean. However, a reconstructed
    Gondwanaland places the source in a landmass that
    was at that time near the _____. (203)

    glacial
    glaciers
    South Pole

10. Another line of evidence is based on the chemical
    sedimentary rock group known as _____ that form
    by precipitation under arid conditions, and the
    biochemical (organic) _____ composed chiefly of
    _____. In both examples, by plotting past
    distributions and comparing them with modern
    climatic zones, the evidence indicates a shifting
    of landmasses. (205)

    evaporites
    limestones or
      reef rocks
    corals

11. The _____ flora is found in rocks in regions of
    the _____ hemisphere that are now separated by
    very large stretches of open ocean. This flora
    is _____ (diverse, uniform) in its composition
    and is very different than the _____ (diverse,
    uniform) modern flora of these regions. This
    again argues for a connection of these now
    separated areas. Two reptiles, _____ and _____,
    also seem to have been incapable of crossing large
    open stretches of ocean, but they too are found in
    southern hemisphere rocks that are presently at
    great distances from each other. (205)

    Glossopteris
    southern
    uniform
    diverse
    Mesosaurus
    Lystrosaurus

12. Some mountain chains that now terminate at modern
    continental margins seem to _____ with other
    mountain belts in terms of age and structure, if
    the modern continents are _____ to their presumed
    positions prior to their _____. (206)

    match
    shifted
    break up

13. Until about 1940, most of the proponents of drift
    were found in the _____ hemisphere. This is not
    surprising, since most of the readily observable
    evidence is contained in those rocks. However,
    in the 1950s, new evidence was being gathered
    from the field of _____ by studying the _____
    of rocks on the ocean floor. These studies have
    shown a very definite pattern of magnetic
    anomalies that show up as _____ and _____
    polarities on either side of a _____ ridge.
    These magnetic patterns are extremely important,
    because they indicate that the process of _____
    spreading is actually occurring and the continents
    may be drifting apart as a consequence of this
    activity. Remember, Wegener postulated that the
    continents literally plowed through oceanic crust,

    southern
    geophysics
    paleomagnetism
    normal
    reverse
    mid-ocean
    sea-floor
    both

but we now know them to be passive riders on
moving plates. These plates include _____
continental and oceanic components. (206)

lithospheric

14. The earth's magnetic field is composed of _____
and _____ components. Of the two, the _____
component is of greatest interest to geologists.
(207)

internal
external
internal

15. The _____ temperature is the temperature at which
materials lose their _____ properties. For
magnetic materials, this temperature ranges from
750°C (pure iron) to 350°C (nickel).
Extrapolating using the earth's _____ of
30°C/km, no earth materials would be magnetic
below 25 km. The magnetic intensity of the
surface rocks is _____ (greater than, less than)
the average intensity of the earth. Based on
this information, the magnetic intensity of the
earth _____ (can, cannot) be due to permanently
magnetized bodies at depth or at the surface.
(210)

Curie
magnetic
temperature
  gradient
less than
cannot

16. Most modern theorists believe the earth's _____
acts as a self-existing _____. While many
complicated processes must occur to generate
the earth's magnetic field, it is believed to
be the earth's _____ that imposes order to the
field. (210)

core
dynamo
rotation

17. If the earth's magnetic field is pictured as a
series of lines of force, a magnet (compass
needle) free to rotate will align itself _____
(parallel to, at right angles to) the field.
Any compass needle will be oriented or inclined
at _____ when positioned directly over the
_____ or _____ poles. Halfway between these
poles lies the _____ equator. If the compass
is placed here, it will maintain a _____
position. From this information, we can see
that the intensity of the earth's magnetic
field increases towards the _____ and decreases
towards the _____. The angle that a compass
needle makes with the surface of the earth is
called _____. (210)

parallel to
the vertical
north magnetic
  (dip)
south magnetic
  (dip)
magnetic
horizontal
magnetic poles
magnetic equator
magnetic
  inclination
  (dip)

18. Because the magnetic poles do not correspond to
the geographic poles, there is in most cases a
divergence between the magnetic poles (to which
the compass needle points) and the geographic
poles (based on the earth's axis of rotation).
This divergence is called _____ and is measured
in degrees _____ or _____ of the geographic
pole. (210)

magnetic
  declination
east
west

19. The magnetism contained in the naturally magnetic
minerals of a rock is referred to as _____. As
a magma cools, magnetically susceptible minerals
(iron, nickel, etc.) acquire a permanent magnetism
as they cool below the _____ point. This
magnetism is oriented _____ (the same, opposite
to) the earth's field at the time of crystallization.
This is called the _____, which remains with the
rock unless it is reheated past the _____. (211)

natural remanent
   magnetism
   (NRM)
Curie
the same as
thermoremanent
   magnetism
   (TRM)
Curie point

20. Sedimentary rocks acquire their remanent magnetism
when susceptible mineral particles orient themselves with the _____ (inclination, declination)
of the earth's magnetic field at the time of their
deposition. This magnetism is known as _____.
(211)

declination
depositional
   remanent
   magnetism
   (DRM)

21. The study and interpretation of a rock's natural
remanent magnetism forms the basis of the field
of _____. (211)

paleomagnetism

22. Measurements made over long periods (secular
changes) have shown that the magnetic declination
and intensity change with time. It is believed
that, as the intensity decreases to zero, there
will be a _____ in the direction of the field.
When this happens, the north-seeking pole of the
compass needle would point toward the _____. We
call the present polarity _____ and a polarity at
180° to this field _____. The succession of these
field changes pieced together forms the basis of a
magnetic stratigraphy when correlated with the
geologic-time scale. We refer to the longer periods
of a given polarity as a _____ and to the shorter
changes as _____. (212)

reversal
south pole
normal
reverse
polarity epoch
polarity event

23. Paleomagnetic studies have shown that the ancient
geomagnetic pole positions must have been _____
(apolar, dipolar) and closely approximated the
earth's axis of rotation and by extension, therefore, the _____. If we look at the present pole
position, we can see that the geomagnetic and
geographic poles _____ (do, do not) coincide.
However, magnetic measurements from recent and
Pleistocene rocks and sediments show pole positions
clustered about the present _____ pole and not the
present _____ pole. Based on an averaging of
measurements over 2,000 year periods, it appears
that any paleomagnetic pole should _____ (have,
have not) coincided with the geographic pole of
the time. A key piece of evidence for continental
drift shows that from the lower Tertiary
(Oligocene) to the present there has been _____
(no significant, significant) shift of the
geomagnetic poles. Prior to Oligocene time, the

dipolar
geographic pole
do not
geographic
geomagnetic
have
no significant

evidence indicates _____ (no significant, significant) magnetic and geographic pole migration. (213)

significant

24. Paleomagnetic data on normal and reverse polarities led to the _____ hypothesis for sea-floor spreading. This is reflected in a mirror image pattern of bands on each side of a _____ ridge. Any magnetic material presently forming or being deposited there should show a _____ polarity. The next band out either side of the ridge should show a _____ polarity. (213)

Vine-Matthews
mid-ocean
normal
reverse

25. Further evidence for sea-floor spreading comes from the age of oceanic crust and sediments with distance from a ridge. The oldest rock and sediment is found _____ (closest to, farthest from) a mid-ocean ridge. Similarly, the thickness of sediments should _____ (increase, decrease) with distance from the ridge. (213)

farthest from
increase

26. There are at least _____ major plates and a host of minor ones, each of which is bounded by a major weakness or flaw. The boundaries of these plates are the loci of present-day _____ and _____ activity. These plates may be comprised of _____ and _____ areas or be restricted to _____ regions such as the _____ plate. (215)

six
earthquakes
volcanic
oceanic
continental
oceanic
Pacific

27. The _____ is the rigid outer layer of the earth, and it includes the crust and _____. This layer rides over the more plastic _____. The _____ marks the boundary between the upper _____ and crust. The crust above this boundary is thinnest in the _____ and thickest under the _____. There is no known rock of _____ (sialic, simatic) composition in the _____ crust, although both are found in _____ crust. (216)

lithosphere
upper mantle
asthenosphere
Moho
mantle
ocean basins
continents
sialic
oceanic
continental

28. The lithospheric plates originate at _____ and spread laterally toward _____ zones. The manner in which these plates move relative to each other defines the type of plate boundary. A _____ boundary would be found along a mid-ocean ridge, while a _____ boundary is likely to be associated with a _____ zone. A _____ boundary defines where one plate moves past another in a nearly parallel fashion. (216-218)

mid-ocean ridges
subduction
divergent
convergent
subduction
transform

29. Divergent boundaries represent conditions of
    _____, while _____ is associated with convergent
    ones. The former are sources of _____ (shallow-
    focus, deep-focus) earthquakes and volcanic
    activity along ridge crests in the oceanic regions
    and along _____ valleys on the continents. _____
    (Shallow-focus, Deep-focus) quakes are most likely
    to be found along the convergent boundaries. (218)

tension
compression
shallow-focus
rift
deep-focus

30. Young mountains are usually the result of
    collisions between _____ plates which cannot be
    _____ because they are too light to be carried
    down to the denser material of the mantle.
    Volcanic activity is _____ (common, rare) under
    these conditions, and deep-focus quakes are
    _____ (common absent). (218)

continental
subducted
rare
absent

31. One possible mechanism to drive the plates from
    oceanic ridges are _____ moving as cells. These
    cells are thought to arise in the mantle, ascend
    below the ridge, and then _____ (diverge,
    converge) as they approach the ridge center. The
    _____ theory suggests the existence of hot spots
    of hot-rising solid mantle zones a few hundred
    kilometers in diameter. Under this hypothesis,
    plate movement is the result of the upward flow of
    the plume, the _____ (outward, inward) radial flow,
    and the return downward flow of the _____. (218)

convection
  currents
diverge
plume
outward
mantle

32. All the evidence indicates that the current ocean
    basins are geologically _____ (old, young)
    features. If the ocean basins existed through
    most of geologic time, the oceanic crust must be
    continuously _____ as new crust is created at the
    ridges. In some subduction zones, part of a plate
    rich in mafic and ultramafic rock may break off and
    ride over another plate during a collision. This
    process, called _____, may place deep-ocean rocks
    at the earth's surface. (222)

young
destroyed
  (recycled)
obduction

33. Based on the plate tectonic model, the major
    features of the ocean basins and landmasses may be
    integrated. For example, in the oceans the ridges
    and their tension-created rifts must represent an
    upwelling of _____ material along the ascending
    currents of adjacent _____. Where the currents
    turn downward in the _____, they carry with them
    crust, upper mantle, and sediments. The deep
    arcuate _____ of the oceans are the surface
    manifestations of these downturned currents. The
    drifting of the continents is the result of the
    constant movement of crustal plates and the creation
    and destruction of _____ crust. In places where
    mantle material is welling up under continents and

mantle
convection cells
subduction zones
trenches
oceanic

they are rifting, we can expect the creation of a   ocean basin
new _____ such as is presently forming in the
modern Persian Gulf. (222)

34. The earthquake belt along the western coast of   trench
South America occurs where the Pacific Ocean   Benioff
crust is dragged into a deep _____ which becomes   Andean
deeper (to 700 km) inland. The foci of the   lithospheric
Andean zone that dips under the South American   plates
continent. The elevation of the adjacent _____
chain is interpreted in part as the result of
underflow of oceanic crust. In summary, we can
see that plate-tectonic theory can account for
mountain ranges, ocean basins, and most surface
features as a result of the interaction and
movement of _____. (223)

35. The recent discovery of _____ or "exotic terranes"   microplates
seems to indicate that some of the larger plates   accretion
grew by the _____ of the "exotic terranes" onto   craton (shield)
a more ancient central mass or _____. Places   microcontinents
like New Zealand, Japan, Madagascar, and parts of   rifting
the Philippines are referred to as _____ and are
the result of the _____ from larger continental
masses. (224)

SELF-TESTS

Part A: True-False Statements

Each of the following statements is either true or false. Encircle either
T or F for each item.

1. The earth's crust is about 4.0 billion years old.   T   F

2. The elevation of the continents relative to sea level has   T   F
varied considerably throughout the last 500 million years.

3. The oldest sedimentary features on the ocean floors are   T   F
of Jurassic age.

4. The south magnetic dip pole is located in the area where   T   F
the south-seeking end of a freely-moving magnetic needle
points directly downward.

5. The magnetic declination is the angle made between a   T   F
magnetic needle and the earth's surface.

6. A geomagnetic pole is located where the magnetic axis   T   F
of the earth's theoretical dipole intersects the earth's
surface.

7. The earth's magnetism can be attributed mostly to the   T   F
   magnetic properties of rocks down to a depth of about
   25 km.

8. The initials NRM stand for "no residual magnetism" and   T   F
   refers to the lack of magnetic fields within any given
   rock specimen.

9. The intensity of the earth's magnetic field could become T   F
   zero.

10. Taken over a long period of time, the magnetic poles and T   F
    geographic poles coincide.

11. Pangaea is the name given by the scientist Alfred Wegener T   F
    to the continent which first revealed a motion.

12. Magnetic anomalies associated with the ocean area can be   T   F
    attributed to the widening of the ocean basins.

13. The age of the rocks near the mid-Atlantic ridge decreases T   F
    as distance from the ridge increases.

14. The study of ancient climates reveals that virtually all   T   F
    of the continents had to exist along the equator until
    very recent times.

15. Although a great deal of evidence suggests the drifting   T   F
    of continents, no evidence involves fossils.

16. The major crustal plates consist of two ocean plates and   T   F
    four continental plates.

17. An ocean-continent plate boundary usually involves ocean   T   F
    trenches and young mountain ranges.

18. The moving crustal plates include only the portion of the   T   F
    earth above the Moho discontinuity.

19. In the convection cell theory for sea-floor spreading,   T   F
    the mid-ocean ridges lie over a region of sinking convection
    cells.

20. The material of the sea floor eventually moves under the   T   F
    continents.

Part B: Multiple Choice Items

Each of the following can be completed correctly by choosing only one word
or phrase. Encircle the letter a, b, c, or d, designating your choice.

1. Which of the following questions is not of primary importance to geology?

   a. How did the crust become separated into oceanic and continental sections?
   b. How did the continents form?
   c. Where was the planet in space when the crust formed?
   d. How did the present ocean basins form?

2. Which of these could be determined by actually observing the position of a magnetized needle?

   a. north geographic pole
   b. north geomagnetic pole
   c. north magnetic pole
   d. virtual geomagnetic pole

3. The earth's magnetic field is probably due to the

   a. magnetic properties of the surface rocks.
   b. solid iron inner core.
   c. existence of electric currents in the outer core.
   d. magnetosphere.

4. The magnetic properties of certain minerals in an igneous rock is referred to as

   a. RTM.
   b. TRM.
   c. DUM.
   d. DRM.

5. Virtual geomagnetic poles are determined by

   a. using a magnetized needle.
   b. locating the paleomagnetic dip poles.
   c. reconstructing the earth's magnetic field at a specific period.
   d. using paleomagnetic data from one observational site.

6. Which of the following pertains to the earth's magnetic field throughout geologic time?

   a. constant in intensity
   b. constant in declination
   c. reversed polarity
   d. constant polarity

7. Paleomagnetic data obtained from rocks of the same age on two continents suggests that the north geomagnetic pole

   a. existed at one position.
   b. was located in the past exactly where it is today.
   c. coincided with the present north geographic pole.
   d. existed at two different positions at the same time.

8. Which of the following does not provide evidence for continental drift?

   a. shape of continents
   b. Pleistocene glaciation
   c. paleomagnetism
   d. similarities of rock ages

9. Magnetic measurements taken at sea have indicated a distinct pattern of normal polarity separated by zones of reversed polarity. These magnetic anomalies are often associated with

   a. submarine mineral deposits.
   b. continental slopes.
   c. ocean ridges.
   d. undersea volcanoes.

10. Sea-floor spreading implies that

   a. the ocean basins are getting thinner.
   b. with increasing distance from the ridges, the rocks are younger.
   c. the oceans of the planet are getting larger.
   d. new crustal material is being formed.

11. Evidence to support the idea of continental drift includes

   a. the existence of ancient mountain ranges.
   b. extensive Paleozoic glacial deposits in areas which today could not support such glaciation.
   c. extensive glaciation which occurred 15,000 years ago.
   d. the absence of marine fossils in certain localities.

12. The outline of the tectonic plates can be determined by the

   a. orientation of the mid-ocean ridges.
   b. distribution of the major mountain chains.
   c. distribution of the world's earthquakes.
   d. continental-ocean boundaries.

13. A convergent plate boundary would not result in the formation of

   a. an ocean trench.
   b. young mountain ranges.
   c. volcanoes.
   d. a rift valley.

14. Which of the following does not pertain to the plume theory?

   a. plate movement mechanism
   b. hot spots several hundred kilometers in diameter
   c. part of flow is radially outward from hot center
   d. convection cells in lower mantle

15. New crustal material is being formed

   a. along the island arc systems.
   b. in young mountain chains.
   c. wherever convection currents move downward.
   d. along mid-ocean ridges.

SUGGESTED ESSAY QUESTIONS

The items below represent the type of discussion questions to which you might be expected to respond. Try writing a response to these, and then discuss your work with another student.

1. Describe the variations in the earth's magnetic field over time, and comment on any expected changes.

2. Explain why geologists don't think that the magnetism in the earth's rocks is the origin of the magnetic field.

3. What is the difference between geomagnetic poles and virtual geomagnetic poles?

4. Why do paleomagnetic readings from the same age rocks from two continents indicate different geomagnetic pole positions?

5. Explain why the ocean basins are geologically young and that the sediment becomes older with increasing distance from the mid-ocean ridge.

6. Describe the evidence involving Paleozoic glaciation which is used to support the idea of moving continents.

7. Briefly describe the system of plates which make up the lithosphere.

8. Describe a continent-continent plate boundary for all three types of boundaries.

9. How does the plume theory explain the movement of plates?

ANSWERS TO SELF-TESTS

Part A: | 1. T | 6. T | 11. F | 16. F | Part B: | 1. c | 6. c | 11. b |
2. F	7. F	12. T	17. T		2. c	7. d	12. c
3. T	8. F	13. F	18. F		3. c	8. b	13. d
4. T	9. T	14. F	19. F		4. b	9. c	14. d
5. F	10. T	15. F	20. T		5. d	10. d	15. d

CHAPTER 12

MASS MOVEMENT
OF
SURFACE MATERIAL

OVERVIEW

The earth's landscapes are modified by the destructive processes of
weathering and erosion. The agents of erosion act to shape the earth's
surface into a collection of sloping surfaces which serve as passageways
for the transport of the debris liberated by weathering and erosion. This
downslope transport of debris is collectively referred to as mass movement.

This chapter will describe the processes responsible for mass movement, the
classification of the variously recognized types of mass movement, and the
significant role played by water and the influence of gravity in initiating
and aiding the process. Since mass movement involves the deformation of
earth materials, you may want to review or refer to Chapter 9, where the
mechanics of deformation are discussed in more detail.

LEARNING OBJECTIVES

After studying this chapter, you should be able to:

1. Describe the concept of mass movement.

2. Explain why mass movement plays such a significant role in altering
    the landscape.

3. Describe the role of gravity as an underlying cause of mass movement.

4. Discuss the direct and indirect role of water in mass movement.

5. Distinguish between rapid, moderate, and slow mass movements.

6. Describe the major types of mass movements.

7. Describe the causative factors of major rock slides.

8. Be able to recognize possible early warning signals in landslide areas.

9. Describe the unique behavior of surface materials at high latitudes and altitudes.

KEY TERMS AND CONCEPTS

role of gravity	frost heaving
unconsolidated deposits	freeze-thaw cycles
interstitial spaces	solifluction
elastic	permafrost
plastic	periglacial
liquid flow	rock glaciers
slide	slump (slope failure)
flow	earthflow
fall	debris slide
heave	mudflow
threshold of stability	talus (slide rock)
slow movements	rock slide (avalanche)
moderate movements	momentum transfer
rapid movements	prehistoric slides
creep	early warnings

NOTES

Sec. 12.1: Factors in Mass Movement

It is important to understand that gravity is the underlying cause of mass movement. However, a material's internal resistance must be overcome before gravity will move it. Therefore, other factors must be operating to augment the role of gravity in the downslope movement of material.

The most significant adjunct to gravity is the role played by water, whether directly or indirectly, in destabilizing slopes. The role of water is extremely varied and may act on slopes by permeating the soil, frost action in colder climates, undercutting slopes by stream erosion, solution, and even the direct impact of raindrops.

The mechanics of the moving material is also a significant factor in mass movement. Be sure you understand the meaning of plastic and elastic deformation.

Sec. 12.2: Slow Movements

Although rapid movements are often spectacular and destructive and readily observable, most materials are transported by slow, imperceptible

movements. Creep is by far the most important slow movement as it operates
on any slope and in any climate. The high latitudes present the unique
condition of soil frozen almost year-round to great depths (permafrost).
Soils under these conditions are greatly affected by thaw conditions and
promote solifluction. Although solifluction is a high latitude phenomenon,
it will happen on a small scale at lower latitudes with even moderate
freezing depths. If you live in a temperate climate, you may have noticed
the effect created by the surface thawing of lawns and fields in the early
spring.

Sec. 12.3: Movements of Moderate Velocity

Notice that the range of velocities given may seem slow, but at the bottom
of the range (1 cm/day) the material would move 3.65 m in one year, and at
the upper end could theoretically travel approximately 320 km in one year.
In each of the movements, note that gravity is still the underlying force,
but the role of moisture (solid or liquid) is a key element in promoting
the movement.

Sec. 12.4: Rapid Movements

The movements represent the most spectacular types from a human perspective
because of the possible great destruction and alteration of landscapes they
may produce. In all cases, whether influenced by human activity or not,
the threshold between stability and instability must be crossed. This
threshold is approached by the combination of factors in the geologic
setting, namely, steep slopes, planes of weakness in the rock (faults,
bedding planes, etc.), and the behavior of the rock to deforming forces
(plastic and elastic). Also note the sensitivity of animals to an
impending rapid movement. You encountered a similar behavior pattern under
the heading of earthquake prediction in Chapter 10.

PROGRAMMED REVIEW

1. The underlying factor in the downslope movement of   gravity
    rock and debris is _____, although _____ is a   water
    major contributing factor to the instability of
    slopes. (228)

2. The most spectacular examples of mass movements   youthful
    are found in _____ (youthful, mature) landscapes.
    (228)

3. Materials moving downslope may behave as _____,   elastic solids
    _____, or _____. (229)   plastic
                                                                  materials
                                                                liquids

4. The rates of movement are classified as _____,   slow
    _____, and _____. (229)   moderate
                                                                rapid

5. It is also possible to consider the movement in
    terms of a dominant type. That is, they may be
    _____, _____, _____, and _____ movements.
    (229)

    slide
    flow
    fall
    heave

6. Some slopes may be very stable, but they are
    always approaching a delicate balance point
    called the _____ between stability and instability.
    (229)

    threshold

7. Most slow movements occur in _____ (consolidated,
    unconsolidated) materials and _____ (do, do not)
    occur at depth. (230)

    unconsolidated
    do not

8. The imperceptible downward movement of surface
    material is called _____. This movement is
    driven by _____ and any element that contributes
    to the weakening of a slope. (230)

    creep
    gravity

9. _____ is comparable to the mechanical weathering
    of frost wedging, except it occurs in _____
    (consolidated, unconsolidated) materials. A
    similar phenomenon known as _____ occurs when
    the ground is _____ (partially, completely)
    saturated with water to a much greater depth.
    This phenomenon occurs most extensively in regions
    of permanently frozen grounds known as _____.
    The boundary between the permanently frozen ground
    and that portion above it that thaws during the
    summer is called the _____. It is this thawed
    zone that is very susceptible to movement. (232)

    frost heaving
    unconsolidated
    solifluction
    completely
    permafrost
    permafrost table

10. Tongues of rock waste that form in high mountain
    valleys and flow as a viscous mass down valley
    are called _____. It appears that _____ ice
    within the mass is responsible for the flow
    ability. On this criterion, _____ (coarse, fine)
    rock debris would be most favorable for the
    development of this feature. (233)

    rock glaciers
    interstitial
    coarse

11. Slump, earthflows, debris slides, and mudflows
    are examples of movements of _____ velocity.
    (234)

    moderate

12. An _____ involves the plastic movement of _____
    (consolidate, unconsolidated) material that _____
    contains excessive moisture. The line at which
    this material pulls away from the slope is marked
    by a(n) _____ (curved plane, abrupt scarp). (235)

    earthflow
    unconsolidated
    abrupt scarp

13. A slope composed of unconsolidated material that
    forms a series of hummocks and intervening
    depressions is probably the result of a _____.
    (235)

    debris slide

14. During _____ the _____ (consolidated, unconsolidated) material moves downward and along a curved plane as if it were an elastic solid. The upper surface of the block is tilted _____ (forward, backward) as it moves. (235)

slump
unconsolidated
backward

15. A _____ is a well-mixed mass of rock, earth, and water that flows down a valley with a consistency of freshly mixed concrete. This type of movement is most common in areas of _____ (steep, gentle) slopes and a _____ (moist, dry) climate. (235)

mudflow
steep
dry

16. A loose accumulation of rock debris at the base of a cliff is called _____. The rock fragments are most commonly produced by _____ weathering processes, with _____ being the most common type. _____ is the agent responsible for the movement of the individual fragments. (235)

talus
mechanical
frost wedging
gravity

17. Unlike the moderate velocity movement described above, a(n) _____ involves the very rapid movement and distant transport (kilometers) of many tons of debris. In this type of movement, the rock debris at the upper part of the slide does not overtake the lower debris but rather collides with the material immediately in front of it and "pushes" it ahead. This transfer of energy through the slide is called _____. (236)

rock slide
  (avalanche)
momentum
  transfer

SELF-TESTS

Part A: True-False Statements

Each of the following statements is either true or false. Encircle either T or F for each item.

1. The energy for downslope movement of material is derived primarily from water.   T   F

2. Surface tension between individual mineral grains generally increases as the moisture content of the pores decreases.   T   F

3. Pore water pressure tends to push grains apart and increase a material's internal resistance.   T   F

4. The impetus needed to initiate a mass movement may be furnished by the gentle activities of burrowing animals.   T   F

5. Rapid movement of a block or blocks of material along a downward curving plane is called a slump.   T   F

6. A key factor in the Gros Ventre slide was the extreme inclination of the sedimentary rock beds dipping into the Gros Ventre Valley.   T   F

157

7. Large rock slides are commonly responsible for the development of lakes.   T   F

8. Rapid earth movements grade imperceptibly into slow ones.   T   F

9. While not restricted to semiarid climates, mudflows commonly develop under these conditions, since slopes are often steep, sudden flash floods may occur, and unconsolidated material is plentiful.   T   F

10. Earthflows involve the plastic movement of unconsolidated material lying on bedrock.   T   F

11. Talus debris can be traced upslope to a line which marks the point at which the debris pulled away from the cliff.   T   F

12. Slow movements are probably responsible for the removal of more material than the more violent movements of rock and soil.   T   F

13. Soil creep is the one type of slow movement that is easily recognized.   T   F

14. Where exposed, tree roots may indicate the creep process as the roots lag behind the "rapidly" moving trunk.   T   F

15. In a very dry soil, the creep process will most likely be enhanced.   T   F

16. Solifluction is a characteristic phenomenon of high latitude soils.   T   F

17. Solifluction is most active during periods of intensive deep freezing of the ground.   T   F

18. Animal behavior patterns may be predictors of impending mass movements.   T   F

19. Momentum transfer is a way in which energy is transferred during slow movements.   T   F

20. A talus slope may completely bury the cliff that produced it.   T   F

Part B: Multiple Choice Items

Each of the following can be completed correctly by choosing only one word or phrase. Encircle the letter a, b, c, or d, designating your choice.

1. The underlying cause of all mass movement is

   a. the influence of gravity.   c. the solution of rock.
   b. the work of water.   d. the regional climate.

2. Water in the pore spaces of unconsolidated materials may

    a. give the material cohesion by increasing its surface tension.
    b. add weight to the material and decrease its stability.
    c. push the grains apart if under sufficient pressure.
    d. all of the statements are correct under certain conditions.

3. A type of rapid movement where material moves down and outward along a curved sloping surface is called

    a. a landslide.   c. creep.
    b. a rock slide.   d. slump.

4. Rock slides are most likely to occur

    a. on broad, sloping coastal plains.
    b. in rugged mountain regions.
    c. at high polar latitudes.
    d. anywhere unconsolidated materials are extensively exposed on slopes.

5. Which of the following mass movements does not belong in association with the others?

    a. debris slide   c. solifluction
    b. mud slide   d. earthflow

6. The Gros Ventre slide was most probably due to

    a. the steepness of the mountain slope.
    b. the excessive soaking of a clay layer which reduced adhesion between it and overlying sandstone layers.
    c. the extensive fault system developed in the valley which served as a plane of weakness.
    d. the extremely steep dip of the rocks into the valley.

7. In the Turtle Mountain slide, the rock unit that was undergoing plastic deformation was

    a. shale.   c. sandstone.
    b. limestone.   d. granite.

8. Which of the following mass movements does not belong in association with the others?

    a. extremely steep slopes
    b. a clay bed which acted as a lubrication plane
    c. folded and faulted rock structure
    d. weak rocks flooring the valley

9. Which of the following mass movements does not belong in association with the others?

    a. slump   c. solifluction
    b. creep   d. rock glaciers

10. Ground that is frozen to great depths at high latitudes is known as

    a. frost heaved.   c. permafrost.
    b. frost wedged.   d. soliflucted.

11. Which of the following rock slides is of prehistoric origin?

    a. Madison Canyon, Montana   c. Blackhawk, California
    b. Elm, Switzerland   d. Turtle Mountain, Alberta

12. Mudflows seem to develop most extensively in

    a. tropical mountain ranges.
    b. very moist, temperate regions.
    c. mountainous, semi-arid regions.
    d. high, moist latitudes.

13. A moving mass of debris with ice filling in spaces between the debris blocks is called

    a. an earthflow.   c. permafrost.
    b. a debris slide.   d. none of the above are correct.

14. A slope built up by an accumulation of rock fragments at the foot of a cliff is called

    a. a slump block.   c. creep slope.
    b. talus.   d. none of the above are correct.

15. Water plays a direct role in moving material downslope during

    a. rain wash.   c. raindrop impact.
    b. solution.   d. all of the above are correct.

SUGGESTED ESSAY QUESTIONS

The items below represent the type of discussion question to which you might be expected to respond. Try writing a response to these, and then discuss your work with another student.

1. Discuss the role of water in the mass movement of material.

2. Distinguish between rapid and slow mass movements.

3. How may mass movements be a factor in the formation of lakes and ponds?

4. What problems might you expect to encounter building a road at high latitudes?

5. Describe the major factors that may initiate rock slides.

ANSWERS TO SELF-TESTS

Part A: 1. F   6. F   11. F   16. T   Part B: 1. a   6. b   11. c
         2. F   7. T   12. T   17. F   2. d   7. a   12. c
         3. F   8. T   13. F   18. T   3. d   8. b   13. d
         4. T   9. T   14. T   19. F   4. b   9. a   14. b
         5. T   10. T   15. F   20. T   5. c   10. c   15. d

CHAPTER 13

RUNNING WATER

OVERVIEW

Running water is the principal agent of continental erosion. The handiwork
of streams may be found in all regions of the world except those presently
covered by glaciers. Even the driest deserts reveal the distinct features
associated with stream erosion.

This chapter subdivides running water into two major categories. Namely,
you will first consider the ultimate source of the water (the hydrologic
cycle) and the unique factors that govern the dynamics of individual
streams. Here you will consider the relationship between precipitation and
stream flow, the mechanics of flow, the dynamic equilibrium that governs
the economy of a stream, the effect of human activity in upsetting a
stream's equilibrium, and how a stream transports and deposits its load.

After considering the factors that govern individual streams, you will
proceed to the second category where the features produced by streams
working in consort will be described. Here you will consider how streams
cut and shape their valleys and the various features that develop as
valleys evolve (waterfalls, rapids, meanders, floodplains, levees, etc.).
You will also study the patterns of streams (as seen in map view) and what
these patterns reveal about the composition and structure of the underlying
bedrock. The chapter concludes with a discussion of the relationship
between the world's major stream systems and plate boundaries.

LEARNING OBJECTIVES

After studying this chapter, you should be able to:

1. Describe the workings of the hydrologic cycle.

2. Discuss the relationship between precipitation and stream flow.

3. Distinguish between laminar and turbulent flow.

4. Describe the factors that control laminar and turbulent flow.

5. Describe the factors that control a stream's velocity.

6. Determine how a stream's discharge is calculated.

7. Discuss the relationships among discharge, stream, velocity, channel depth and width, as they pertain to a single stream when followed from its headwaters to its mouth.

8. Describe the natural phenomenon of floods and how human activity can both control and initiate flood conditions.

9. Discuss the significance of the concept of base level on controlling a stream's activity.

10. Describe the work of running water in terms of sediment transport, erosion, and sediment deposition.

11. Describe how streams cut and modify their valleys.

12. Discuss the significance of dendritic, radial, rectangular, and trellis drainage patterns in relation to bedrock composition and structure.

13. Describe the relationship between stream order and the number of streams, length of streams, and the mean drainage of an area.

14. Describe the development of the following features:

    a. waterfalls and rapids.
    b. erosional and aggradational flood plains.
    c. meanders, cutoffs, and oxbows.
    d. braided streams.
    e. levees and back swamps.
    f. yazoo-type streams.
    g. bank and point bar deposits.
    h. deltas and alluvial fans.
    i. stream terraces.

15. Discuss the relationships among tectonism, stream erosion, and plate boundaries.

KEY TERMS AND CONCEPTS

hydrologic cycle
precipitation
evaporation
transpiration
evapo-transporation
runoff
infiltration
groundwater
laminar flow
streamline flow
turbulent flow
stream velocity
gradient
forward flow
discharge
hydrograph
base flow
lag time
flood stage
bank-full stage
flashy stream
base level
temporary base level
ultimate base level
transportation
load
capacity
competence
solution
suspension
bed load
saltation
terminal velocity
erosion
abrasion
impact
deposition
aggradation
longitudinal profile
cross valley profile

valley walls
flood plain
divide
drainage basin
network
stream order
drainage patterns
dendritic
radial
trellis
rectangular
water gap
superimposed stream
stream piracy
narrow valleys
waterfalls
rapids
broad valleys
aggradation flood plain
meanders
meander scars
cutoffs
neck cutoff
chute
chute cutoff
oxbow lake
braided stream
natural levee
back swamp
overbank deposits
point bar deposits
delta
foreset beds
bottomset beds
topset beds
distributary channels
stream terrace
cut-and-fill terrace
paired terraces
unpaired terraces

NOTES

Sec. 13.1: World Distribution of Water

Note that the vast bulk of the earth's water is in the oceans (97%), while
less than 3% is on the land. Of the approximately 3% on the land, slightly
over 2% is held by the world's glaciers and ice caps. The bulk of the
almost 1% remaining on the land is contained as groundwater (0.6%).
Therefore, all the world's surface waters (streams, lakes, and soil

moisture) constitute less than 0.3% of all the globe's water. These are instructive and rather surprising figures. Check them over in Appendix C.

Sec. 13.2: Hydrologic Cycle

This section, although brief, presents an interesting historical development of the hydrologic cycle. Note how the investigative approaches become more quantitative through historical time. You should concentrate your major effort on Fig. 13.2, where the hydrologic cycle is diagrammatically represented and explained. Be sure you understand the meaning of the terms runoff, infiltration, and evapo-transpiration. The relationship between these variables is quantified by a general equation. You should be able to work the equation by solving for an unknown variable if the others are given.

Sec. 13.3: Stream Flow

The velocity of a stream is an important factor to consider because it plays an important role in the transportation, erosion, and deposition of sediments. While the nature of a stream's channel and discharge (the amount of water) exert their influence on stream velocity, the gradient or slope of the stream bed can be a critical factor. Note that if you follow a stream in longitudinal profile from its headwaters to its mouth, the profile presents a concave up-curve with the steepest gradients confined to the stream's upper reaches and the most gentle gradients near its mouth. This type of curve will hold true for any stream, be it a major river or a tiny rivulet cutting into a dirt slope. Given enough time, a stream will remove (it is always trying to remove) many of the irregularities along its profile as it erodes and cuts its channel.

Pay careful attention to Figs. 13.4 and 13.5. Here you can see how the opposing forces of forward flow and friction create zones of turbulence. Notice that, along straight stretches, the stream's velocity is greatest toward the center of the channel, but the greatest turbulence is along the banks, where friction opposes the forward flow. You would notice the same effect if you took a vertical section from the surface down through the water column to the stream's bed. Again, the greatest turbulence occurs where the water encounters resistance to its forward flow, and this is closest to the stream's bed. Note also that, as the stream swings around a bend, its velocity increases on the outside of the bend, while at the same time the forward flow is opposed by friction from the outside bank. This is a zone of maximum turbulence. Therefore, erosion should be greatest on the outside bend. This is reflected in the asymmetry of the channel where it is deepest and most heavily scoured on the outside bend. Do you see that deposition will be greatest on the inside bend of the stream? You will encounter this phenomenon in Sec. 13.6, where point bar formation is described.

Carefully study the hydrograph shown in Fig. 13.9. This is an important method that will be related to natural and human induced river flooding and its control.

Sec. 13.4: Economy of a Stream

Know the relationship between discharge and velocity, channel width, and channel depth. From the equation, you can see that a stream maintains a balance between the amount of water it carries (discharge) and the variables of velocity, channel depth, and width.

Carefully study Fig. 13.10. This shows a quantitative relationship between discharge and the previously mentioned variables. Note that the relationship is statistically linear (the trend of the data points indicate a straight line graph). As discharge increases, velocity, width, and depth also increase in a regular, orderly fashion. Do you notice the apparent anomaly? Stream velocity is increasing downstream where the gradients are decreasing. You should be able to explain this apparent discrepancy.

With reference to floods, note that they are an expected part of natural stream behavior, and their frequency can be predicted through statistical methods. Study Fig. 13.11, which shows how the predictions are calculated.

Because man is closely associated with rivers and river systems, pay careful attention to the sections relating man's use of flood plains and his attempts to control flooding which are often the natural outcome of his activities.

The concept of base level is an important one as it controls the degree to which a stream may erode its channel. Know the difference between temporary and ultimate base level. Also know what natural agents serve as temporary base levels and why the ultimate base level is not fixed in time. Do not overlook Figs. 13.15 and 13.16.

Sec. 13.5: Work of Running Water

The work done by running water is considered in three phases: (1) transportation of debris, (2) erosion of the stream's channel, and (3) the deposition of stream debris. Know how a stream transports its load. Be able to describe the relationship between particle size, stream competence, and the type of load transport. Although it is considered under the subheading of changes in water quality, note how human activity has drastically upset the natural transport mode of streams.

Do not overlook Fig. 13.19, which relates stream velocity and particle size to erosion, transportation, and deposition of sediments. Note that it takes a greater velocity for a stream to erode (literally to pick up and remove) clay and silt sediments than it does to erode sand-size particles. Also be aware that, once set in motion, it takes very low velocities to transport silt and clay but much higher velocities for a stream to carry sands and coarser particles. The curves also reveal that the fine-grained material will be transported over a much wider range of velocities than the sand and gravel fractions. As you might expect, the sands and gravels are rapidly deposited with decreases in velocity.

Sec. 13.6: Features of Valleys

This is a very descriptive section that outlines the development of valleys as they evolve through the process of stream erosion. You should know what evidence leads to the conclusion that streams cut their own valleys. You should also know what the various branching patterns developed by streams reveal about the underlying bedrock and its structure (study Fig. 13.23 carefully). Be able to contrast the features found in narrow, youthful valleys with those of the more mature, broad valleys.

Quantitatively, the most difficult part of this section concerns the ordering of streams. Your best bet is to concentrate on Fig. 13.24 which clearly shows how the streams of a drainage basin are arranged in a hierarchy. The lower the number, the smaller the stream. Note the tabulation that shows stream order and the number of streams. This is an inverse relationship. That is, as one variable increases (stream order), the other variable decreases (number of streams). This relationship is graphically indicated in Fig. 13.25a. As we might expect, there is a direct relationship between stream order and the corresponding mean or average stream length and drainage area (Figs. 13.25b and c). Note also that the relationship is also linear.

Sec. 13.7: Of Rivers and Continents

Two key points are made here. First, if tectonic activity were nonexistent, all the continents would be reduced to base level in a few million years. Second, the divides of the world's major drainage basins coincide with plate margins.

PROGRAMMED REVIEW

1. Approximately 97 percent of the planet's water is contained in the _____. Of the remaining 3 percent, most is found in the form of _____. (242)

   oceans
   ice

2. The _____ traces the circulation of water through the planet's _____, oceans, and continental waters. (242)

   hydrologic cycle
   atmosphere

3. The greatest quantity of water is returned to the atmosphere by _____ from bodies of water and soil, and by the _____ of plants. Because it is difficult to measure these processes independently, they are generally combined and reported as _____. (244)

   evaporation
   transpiration
   evapo-
     transpiration

4. _____ is any precipitation that reaches streams or bodies of water by moving over the land surface. Some precipitation soaks through the surface in a process called _____ and becomes part of the _____ system. (244)

   runoff
   infiltration
   groundwater

5. The basic equation of the hydrologic cycle is: Precipitation = _____ + _____. (244)

   runoff
   evapo-
     transpiration

6. Studies of stream flow have shown that in some
   cases the particles of water move in different
   layers and do not mix. This is known as _____
   flow. However, this type of flow is very rare
   as any obstructions and changes in stream _____
   will cause the particles to break into swirls
   and eddies that define _____ flow. (244)

   laminar
   velocity
   turbulent

7. The _____ of a stream is measured in terms of
   the distance its water travels in a unit of time.
   This parameter is a function of several factors,
   the most obvious being the _____ or slope of the
   stream bed. (244, 245)

   velocity
   gradient

8. The slope or gradient of a stream bed is expressed
   in terms of its _____ per fixed _____ distance.
   As a general rule, most streams show a(n) _____
   (increase, decrease) in gradient from headwaters
   to mouth. However, this change is not linear.
   Because of this, a lengthwise or longitudinal
   profile of the stream shows that the gradient is
   _____ (steeper, more gentle) at the headwaters.
   A drawn curve of this profile would be _____
   (concave, convex) up toward the sky. (245)

   vertical drop
   horizontal
   decrease
   more gentle
   steeper
   concave

9. The velocity of a stream is altered by the _____
   it encounters with its bed and channel walls.
   Because of this, the velocity of a straight flowing
   stream is _____ (greatest, least) near its center
   just below the surface. If the stream is moving
   around a bend, the change in channel shape and
   volume of water will cause the flow velocity to
   be _____ (greatest, least) on the outside of the
   bend and _____ (greatest, least) on the inside
   of the bend. (245)

   friction
   greatest
   greatest
   least

10. The _____ of the water under gravity and the
    _____ generated by channel bed and walls are two
    _____ (opposing, complimentary) forces acting on
    a stream. Zones of maximum turbulence are created
    where the velocities are the most _____ (similar,
    different). (245)

    forward flow
    friction
    opposing
    different

11. _____ is a measure of the volume of water passing
    a given point per unit of time. This parameter
    usually _____ (increases, decreases) from head-
    waters to mouth. A plot of this parameter as a
    function of time is called a _____, which is an
    excellent method for charting the flow history of
    a stream. On these charts, the _____ flow marks
    the low-water flow stage of a stream that is
    attributable to supply by _____. The highwater
    flow stage is reached _____ (before, after) the
    time of maximum precipitation. This time
    differential is called _____. (245)

    discharge
    increases
    hydrograph
    base
    groundwater
    after
    lag time

12. The discharge of any stream is a function of channel _____, channel _____, and stream _____. Careful measurements from many streams made from headwaters to mouth shows that there is a(n) _____ (increase, decrease) in channel width and depth, and a(n) _____ (increase, decrease) in stream velocity with distance from the headwaters. (247)

depth
width
velocity
increase
increase

13. Floods are a _____ (normal, abnormal) behavior pattern of streams. Because of this, their rate of occurrence _____ (can, cannot) be predicted. Flood control methods are based on _____ water during periods of high runoff and _____ the excess water in a controlled manner. The effect of this type of control is to alter the _____ of a stream, which is the record of its natural flow history. (248)

normal
can
storing
releasing
hydrograph

14. The ultimate effect of urbanization and suburbanization is to alter a natural stream into one that is described as a _____ stream. Streams of this type have a _____ (low, high) base flow and a _____ (high-short, low-long) flood peak. Streams of this type also show a noticeable increase in their discharge during the _____ stage as a result of an increase in channel depth and width due to urbanization. (250)

flashy
low
high-short
bank-full

15. A(n) _____ (increase, decrease) in the vegetative cover of an area would produce effects similar to urbanization. (250)

decrease

16. The lowest point to which a stream can erode its channel is called the _____. A lake acts as a _____ for a stream because, once it is lowered or filled in, the stream will continue to deepen its channel. The ocean or sea level marks the position of the _____ for a stream, since no stream may cut its channel below sea level. Note: Where streams do flow below sea level, their valleys are structurally produced and were not cut by streams. (250, 251)

base level
temporary
  base level
ultimate base
  level

17. The building of a dam across a stream would cause the base level to _____ (rise, fall). The result would be a(n) _____ (increase, decrease) in deposition along the stream's channel. A lowering of the base level would result in _____ (erosion of, deposition in) the stream's channel. (251)

rise
increase
erosion of

18. The work done by water flowing in streams is expressed by the performance of three main functions, namely, _____, _____, and _____. The quantity of available _____ energy in a stream determines the amount and type of work it is capable of doing. (252)

transportation
deposition
erosion
kinetic

19. The total amount of material a stream is carrying at any given amount of time is called its _____. The total amount of material a stream is capable of carrying under any set of conditions defines its _____. The former is usually _____ (more than, less than) the latter. (252)

    load
    capacity
    less than

20. Streams transport material in three ways: _____, _____, and _____. Silt and clay would most probably be transported by _____, while coarse sand and gravel would be carried as _____. It would seem reasonable to expect a larger than normal soluble load for a stream traveling through a region underlain by _____ (sandstones, limestones, shales). (252)

    solution
    suspension
    bed load
    suspension
    bedload
    limestones

21. If a particle such as a sand grain is released in a column of water, it will _____ (increase, decrease) its velocity as it falls through the water until it reaches a _____ velocity. At this point, the force of _____ is in equilibrium with the resistance of the water through which it is falling. The sand grain should now _____ (remain suspended in, move at constant speed through) the water column. Given gravel-size and sand-size particles of similar shape and density, the _____ will attain the greatest terminal velocity and require a greater _____ to keep it suspended in the water column. (252, 253)

    increase
    terminal
    gravity
    move at constant
      speed through
    gravel
    turbulence
      (force)

22. Sand grains are usually transported as part of a stream's _____. However, they are often temporarily suspended for a brief period of time in the water column. This type of transport, unique to sand grains, is called _____. Particles that maintain continual contact with the channel floor during transport are moved forward by _____ or _____, depending upon their shape. (253)

    bed load
    saltation
    rolling
    sliding

23. For a stream to directly lift sediment particles from its channel, there is an intricate relationship between velocity, turbulence, and particle size and shape. Assume clay, silt, find sand, and coarse sand. List these in order of increasing current velocity to directly lift from the channel floor: _____, _____, _____, _____. (253, 254)

    fine sand
    silt
    clay
    coarse sand

24. _____ is the process where the solid particles themselves act as erosive agents as they are transported by a stream. (254)

    abrasion

25. The cross-section of a stream taken at right angles to the trend of its valley is referred to as a _____ profile. This profile usually consists of four basic parts. The sloping walls at the edges of the valley floor that serve as a funnel for surface runoff is called the _____; the ridges that separate one stream valley from another are known as _____; the valley floor that may vary in width but is covered by sediments deposited during flood stages constitutes its _____; and the furrow that contains the stream's water and guides its flow is called the _____. (255)

cross-valley
valley walls
divides
flood plain
channel

26. A _____ is the entire area from which a stream and its tributaries receive their water. The individual streams and their valleys are joined together in a _____. (255)

drainage basin
network

27. The streams of any given network are linked together in a geometrical relationship that allows them to be placed in a ranking _____. Thus, streams (and drainage basins) may be ranked as first, second, third, etc. _____. A single stream without any tributaries would constitute a _____ stream. If this stream joins with another to form a new, larger one, this becomes a _____ stream. The main segment of a system always has the _____ (highest, lowest) order number of the network, and the order number would also describe the _____ basin. (256, 257)

hierarchy
order
first-order
second-order
highest
drainage

28. Relationships between stream order and the number of streams, average length of streams, and average size of drainage area shows that the number of streams _____ (increases, decreases) with increasing order; the average length _____ (increases, decreases) with increasing order; and the average size of the drainage area _____ (increases, decreases) with increasing order. (257)

decreases
increases
increases

29. When seen in map or plan view, a drainage system shows a definite pattern. This pattern is largely controlled by the type of underlying bedrock and structure. A branching pattern similar to the veins in a maple leaf is called _____. This pattern occurs when the underlying bedrock is _____ (uniform, non-uniform) in composition. A bedrock composed of _____ (horizontal, dipping) sedimentary rock or _____ (crystalline, non-crystalline) material would produce this pattern. A _____ pattern could develop on the flanks of a volcano where the

dendritic
uniform
horizontal
crystalline
radial

streams would radiate outward from some high
central area. A _____ pattern might develop
on rock that exercises a structural control on
the streams if the bedrock is cut by a series
of joints or faults at nearly right angles. A
similar pattern called _____ results commonly
when the region is underlain by bands of
resistant and nonresistant rock (folded
sedimentary or dipping sedimentary rocks).
(257, 258)

rectangular
trellis

30. If a region of folded rock is subsequently
overlain by a series of sedimentary layers, a
stream may cut through the sediments and cut a
narrow gorge when it encounters resistant rock
in the folded structure. The narrow gorge would
be called a _____, and the stream that did the
eroding is known as a _____ stream. The
Delaware River on the New Jersey-Pennsylvania
border is an example of this type of stream and
has produced this landform where it cuts through
the Kittatinny Mountains. (258, 259)

water gap
superimposed

31. In the process called _____, one stream increases
its size and valley at the expense of another.
(259)

stream piracy

32. In the early stages of valley enlargement, a
stream is most actively cutting its channel
_____ (vertically, laterally), but in the
latter stages a stream expends most of its
energy to transport its _____ and tends to
erode _____ (vertically, laterally). (259, 261)

vertically
load
laterally

33. A characteristic feature found in steep, narrow
valleys is a _____. This feature may develop
when a stream cutting through _____ (resistant,
nonresistant) rock encounters a _____
(resistant, nonresistant) layer. Through a
period of erosion, this feature will eventually
become a _____. It is interesting to note that
a stream is always working to remove any
irregularities it encounters. As a result, a
stream's longitudinal profile tends to become
_____ and _____ towards the sky. (261, 262)

waterfalls
nonresistant
resistant
rapids
smoother
concave up

34. A characteristic feature of broad valleys is the
flood plain. If produced by lateral cutting and
the gradual retreat of valley walls and composed
of a thin sequence of sediments, it is called a
_____. If composed of a thick sequence of
sediments, it is known as an _____. (263)

erosional flood
  plain
aggradational
  flood plain

35. The broad sweeping bands of a river on a flood   meanders
    plain are called _____. The bend increases in   outside
    size by erosion on the _____ (inside, outside)   inside
    part and deposition on the _____ (inside,
    outside) portion of the bend. (263)

36. As a meander migrates down-valley, different parts   cutoff
    travel at different rates. Sometimes the narrow   scar
    neck of the meander may be cut through, producing   oxbow
    a new channel called a neck _____ and leaving
    behind the large sweeping bend of the meander.
    If this bend is drained of water, it is called
    a meander _____, but, if it retains water, it
    forms an _____ lake. (263)

37. A complex tangle of converging and diverging   braided
    stream channels separated by sandbars form a   overloaded
    _____ stream. This is characteristic of streams
    that are _____ (overloaded, underloaded) with
    sediment. (264, 265)

38. The highest and driest place on many flood plains   natural levees
    is nearest the river where _____ are formed.   back swamp
    Leaving this feature and moving away from the   sand
    river, it is common to find a low-lying marshy   silt
    area known as a _____. If the sediments of the   clay
    flood plain are composed of sands, clays, and   velocity
    silts, an analysis of grain size distribution   coarsest
    from river edge to marshy area should show a
    lateral gradation of _____, to _____, to
    _____. This is the result of the deposition of
    sediments during floods when the river is no
    longer confined to its channel. When the river
    leaves its channel, there is an immediate decrease
    in its _____, resulting in the deposition of the
    _____ (coarsest, finest) sediment nearest the
    river bank. (266)

39. A _____ type river is a tributary stream that   yazoo
    cannot find its way directly to the main stream   natural levees
    channel because of the high _____. (267)

40. Flood plain sediments consist of two basic types.   overbank
    The _____ deposits are composed of fine sands,   flood
    silts, and clays, and are the result of deposition   point bars
    during _____ (slack water, flood) stages. The   slack water
    _____ are coarser sediments of gravel and coarse   inside
    sands that are deposited in the _____ (slack
    water, turbulent zone) on the _____ (inside,
    outside) of a meander. (267)

173

41. Whenever a stream flows into a standing body of   decrease
    water, there is a(n) immediate _____ (increase,   decrease
    decrease) in its velocity and a(n) _____   delta
    (increase, decrease) in its ability to transport   distributaries
    its load. If the proper conditions exist, a   coarse
    stream will build a _____. A series of branching   foreset
    channels or _____ build up this deposit. Under   finer
    the most optimum conditions, the deposits will   bottomset
    form a characteristic pattern of steeply dipping   topset
    _____ (coarse, fine) grained sediments known as
    _____ beds. The _____ (coarser, finer) sediments
    will settle further out on the floor of the body
    of water and are known as _____ beds. As the
    deposit is built further out into the body of
    water, the steeply dipping beds will become
    overlain by sediments called _____ beds. (268)

42. The land counterpart of a delta is called the   alluvial fan
    _____, and it is most characteristic of _____   arid
    and _____ climates. (268)   semiarid

43. A _____ is a relatively flat surface of alluvial   terrace
    deposits running along a valley with a steep bank   cut-and-fill
    separating it from the flood plain. In the type   paired
    known as a _____ terrace, the stream cuts its   unpaired
    way through the aggraded deposits that have
    clogged the valley floor. Sometimes the terrace
    on one side of the valley is matched in elevation
    by one on the opposite side. These are known as
    _____ terraces. If the elevations are not
    equivalent, they are referred to as _____
    terraces. (269)

44. On a global scale, the world's major drainage   plate
    basin divides seem to coincide with _____
    boundaries. (270)

SELF-TESTS

Part A: True-False Statements

Each of the following statements is either true or false. Encircle either
T or F for each item.

 1. In the hydrologic cycle, water may be temporarily stored   T   F
    before being returned to the atmosphere.

 2. Rainfall cannot account for the total flow of rivers.   T   F

 3. After precipitation has fallen on the land, the smallest   T   F
    amount soaks into the ground through infiltration.

 4. The greatest amount of water on the land is contained in   T   F
    glaciers.

174

5. Surface runoff is equivalent to the amount of precipitation.   T   F

6. Laminar flow decreases with increasing velocity.   T   F

7. The gradient of a stream increases from headwaters to mouth.   T   F

8. Stream velocity is a function of stream discharge and gradient.   T   F

9. Discharge decreases downstream.   T   F

10. The velocity of a stream increases towards the outside of a meander.   T   F

11. Zones of maximum turbulence occur where different velocities come into close contact.   T   F

12. If a stream's discharge increases, there must be a corresponding change in channel width, depth, and stream velocity.   T   F

13. A stream's velocity decreases towards its mouth.   T   F

14. Channel depth and width increase downstream, but a stream's velocity decreases.   T   F

15. A hydrograph of a river shows the variation of stream discharge with time.   T   F

16. A flood control dam should increase the lag time between precipitation and flood crest.   T   F

17. The base flow of a hydrograph is a measure of the portion of a stream's flow attributable to groundwater recharge.   T   F

18. The lowest point to which a stream can erode its channel is a function of its base level.   T   F

19. Capacity defines the maximum size particles a stream can transport.   T   F

20. Sand-size particles are most commonly transported by the process of saltation.   T   F

Part A: Multiple Choice Items

Each of the following can be completed correctly by choosing only one word or phrase. Encircle the letter a, b, c, or d, designating your choice.

1. A broad valley is most likely to contain

   a. rapids.
   b. a flood plain.
   c. a flood plain and a meandering stream.
   d. a flood plain, a meandering stream, and a dendritic drainage
      pattern.

2. As the ranking order of a stream increases, the number of streams in
   the order

   a. increases.   c. remains the same.
   b. decreases.   d. is unrelated to the order.

3. A dendritic drainage pattern is most likely to develop on rocks that

   a. are crisscrossed by fractures.
   b. have developed a dome-like structure.
   c. are folded.
   d. are uniform in their resistance to erosion.

4. Water gaps are cut by

   a. braided streams.   c. superimposed streams.
   b. aggrading streams.   d. yazoo-type streams.

5. Streams cutting narrow valleys are most actively

   a. developing flood plains of aggradation.
   b. developing erosional flood plains.
   c. trying to reach base level.
   d. depositing the eroded debris.

6. Broad valleys are characterized by each of the following except

   a. steep stream gradients.   c. flood plains.
   b. meanders.   d. swamps.

7. A cross-section through a meander would show

   a. the greatest depth on the outside bend.
   b. the greatest depth on the inside bend.
   c. a uniform depth across the channel.
   d. none of the above.

8. An abandoned meander is called a(n)

   a. neck-cutoff.   c. oxbow.
   b. chute cutoff.   d. meander scar.

9. A heavily overloaded stream on flood plain may develop

   a. natural levees.   c. stream terraces.
   b. oxbow lakes.   d. a braided pattern.

176

10. Deltas and alluvial fans are similar in each of the following except

    a. development of topset, foreset, and bottomset beds.
    b. being the result of deposition caused by a drop in stream velocity.
    c. in building outward from their point of deposition.
    d. in showing a decrease in grain-size outward from their point of deposition.

11. Distributary channels develop on

    a. topset beds.   c. bottomset beds.
    b. foreset beds.   d. upset beds.

12. A rectangular drainage pattern is most likely to develop on rocks that are

    a. of uniform composition.   c. crisscrossed by fractures.
    b. folded.   d. uplifted into a dome.

13. Gravel would most likely be transported

    a. as bed load.   c. in suspension.
    b. by saltation.   d. in solution.

14. A quartz grain settling through a column of water encounters an eddy current whose velocity just equals that of the sinking grain. This will cause the grain in the water column to

    a. rise.   c. remain suspended.
    b. sink.   d. none of the above.

15. The Jordan River flows into the Dead Sea which lies 396 m below sea level. From your knowledge of base level, it is most likely that the

    a. Jordan River cut its valley from above sea level to its present depth.
    b. Jordan River could not have cut its valley from above sea level to its present depth.
    c. Jordan River will soon cut its valley below the Dead Sea.
    d. Jordan River is probably at the bank-full stage most of the year.

SUGGESTED ESSAY QUESTIONS

The items below represent the type of discussion questions to which you might be expected to respond. Try writing a response to these, and then discuss your work with another student.

1. Describe the mechanics of the hydrologic cycle.

2. Discuss the factors governing laminar and turbulent flow.

3. Streams are trying to attain an equilibrium with their environment. What evidence do we have to support this view?

4. Every stream tries to attain a smooth concave-up longitudinal profile. Why do few, if any streams, attain this state?

5. How do streams transport their load?

6. Discuss the relationship between stream velocity and particle size in relation to erosion by direct lifting.

7. How do drainage patterns give information about the composition and structure of the underlying bedrock?

8. Contrast the development of narrow and broad valleys by streams.

ANSWERS TO SELF-TESTS

Part A: 1. T   6. T   11. T   16. T   Part B: 1. c   6. a   11. a
         2. F   7. F   12. T   17. T   2. b   7. a   12. c
         3. T   8. T   13. F   18. T   3. d   8. c   13. a
         4. T   9. F   14. F   19. F   4. c   9. a   14. c
         5. F   10. T   15. T   20. T   5. c   10. a   15. b

CHAPTER 14

UNDERGROUND WATER

OVERVIEW

Groundwater accounts for the greatest store of water on land, exclusive of glacial ice. In terms of total volume, it is 98-99% more abundant than all the surface waters of the world's lakes and rivers combined. This chapter will develop the basic distribution of groundwater, present a theoretical discussion on the factors that govern its movement and supply, and the actual occurrence and behavior of underground water in nature.

Some of the more common features associated with groundwater are also considered, such as wells, springs, and geysers. A fairly large section is devoted to the development of caves and their related features. The chapter closes with a discussion of the detrimental effects of human activity on groundwater systems.

LEARNING OBJECTIVES

After studying this chapter, you should be able to:

1. Describe the distribution of groundwater in terms of the zones of aeration and saturation.

2. Describe the subdivisions of the zone of aeration:

    a. belt of soil moisture   c. capillary fringe
    b. intermediate belt

3. Discuss the development of and what factors influence the water table.

179

4. Distinguish between porosity and permeability.

5. Explain the significance of the hydraulic gradient, head, and Darcy's Law on the rate of groundwater flow.

6. Discuss the development of springs, wells, artesian water, and geysers.

7. Discuss how groundwater supplies are recharged.

8. Explain how caverns develop and the chemistry involved in the formation of limestone caves.

9. Describe the origin of stalagmites, stalactites, columns, sinkholes, and karst topography.

10. Discuss the effects of human activities on groundwater pollution, saltwater invasion, and land subsidence.

KEY TERMS AND CONCEPTS

groundwater (underground water)
zone of aeration
suspended water
zone of saturation
molecular attraction
attraction by similar molecules
  (cohesive force)
attraction by dissimilar molecules
  (adhesive force)
belt of soil moisture
intermediate belt
capillary fringe
water table
cone of depression
porosity
permeability
aquifer
hydraulic gradient
head
head pressure
spring
perched water table

well
hard water
soft water
artesian water
Darcy's Law
hydraulic conductivity
thermal spring (hot spring)
geyser
groundwater recharge
caves (caverns)
dripstone
calcite (calcium carbonate)
carbonic acid
calcium bicarbonate
stalactites
stalagmites
columns
sinkholes (sinks)
dolines
karst topography
land subsidence
saltwater invasion

NOTES

Sec. 14.1: Basic Distribution

Be sure you understand the difference between suspended water and groundwater. You should also know how molecular attraction holds suspended water in the zone of aeration and how capillary action draws water into the zone of aeration from the underlying zone of saturation.

Because the water table is an irregular surface, be sure you understand how the topography reflects the shape of the water table. Remember, the rate of flow of the groundwater is greatest where the slope of the water table is at its maximum. This usually occurs closer to the valley than the crest of a hill (see Fig. 14.3).

Sec. 14.2: Movement of Underground Water

You must know the difference between porosity and permeability. Many earth materials are extremely porous but have an extremely low permeability. Note the significance of grain-sizes and mixtures on porosity, as well as the porosity of consolidated and unconsolidated deposits.

The permeability factor plays a significant role in the rate of flow. However, the flow rates and paths of groundwater movement are greatly influenced by such factors as topography (see Fig. 14.4) and the hydraulic gradient. You should also know why groundwater follows a curved path, rather than following a vertical or horizontal route. Note that Darcy's Law is simplified to show that, for a material of uniform permeability, the velocity of flow is directly proportional to the hydraulic gradient. Compare the flow rates for groundwater to those for surface streams (Chap. 12). Similarly, note that groundwater flow is basically laminar, while surface flow is turbulent.

Sec. 14.3: Wells, Springs, and Geysers

The prior section dealt with a simple model of groundwater moving indefinitely through uniformly permeable material. In nature, the subsurface conditions negate the simplified model. Rather than move indefinitely, be aware that groundwater will be diverted to a lateral flow when it encounters an impermeable layer. Note that springs develop as the lateral flowing water intersects the ground surface. Note also that the wells are artificial intersections cut from the surface into the zone of saturation. The depth to which a well enters the zone of saturation will determine the productivity of a well in a climate that causes great fluctuations in the water table. Note also that relatively impermeable rocks like granite may produce a sufficient well flow if they are highly fractured. However, the supply will be limited, since the fractures are usually not interconnected and also decrease with depth.

Know the conditions required for the production of artesian water and the difference between thermal springs and geysers.

Sec. 14.4: Recharge of Groundwater

Note that groundwater supplies are directly linked to rainfall. However, be aware that much of the water reaching the earth's surface does not penetrate the zone of saturation, where it can recharge the groundwater supply. If you recall from Chapter 13, the least amount of precipitation infiltrates the ground. Most of it is lost to vegetation, evaporation, and surface runoff. Even if all the precipitation infiltrated the ground, there would be a lag time between recharge and rainfall, since the movement of groundwater is so slow. Note that, in some circumstances, it is necessary to recharge groundwater supplies by artificial means.

Sec. 14.5: Caves and Related Features

Know the chemistry involved in the solution of limestone. You have already studied the solvent involved under chemical weathering (Chap. 5, the ionization of carbonic acid). The double arrows in the equations mean that the reactions are reversible. Note the uncertainty involved in where caves develop in relation to the water table. There is also the problem of how to get groundwater undersaturated, with respect to calcite, to the depths we find caves today.

You should also be familiar with the formation of the most common cave formations (stalagmites, stalactites, and columns). Don't overlook the development of sinkholes and karst topography. If your lab manual has a map of such a region, look it over and try to find surface streams. If you do find any, you will note that they suddenly disappear. Do you know what happens to them?

Sec. 14.6: Some Groundwater Problems caused by Human Use

Note that groundwater is subject to the same types of pollution as surface waters. Land subsidence due to groundwater pumping is usually not noticeable to the general population unless it is associated with sinkholes, where the results can be catastrophic. Be aware that land subsidence is much more noticeable in areas of extensive underground mining.

The saltwater invasion is one of the greatest problems for groundwater supplies. This is particularly true for heavily populated areas that depend extensively on underground water for agricultural, industrial, and general freshwater supply. You should know how this occurs. See Figs. 14.20 and 14.21 as you read the explanation in the text.

PROGRAMMED REVIEW

1. Water contained in the pore spaces, cracks, and crevices of consolidated and unconsolidated material is referred to as _____. (274)

    underground water (subsurface or subterranean water)

2. Water that is held in earth materials that are not fully saturated is called _____. The zone in which it is held is known as the zone of _____. There are two forces operating to prevent the water from moving deeper into the earth. One is an _____ force between the molecules of the water and rock, and the other is a _____ force between the molecules of the water particles themselves.

    suspended water
    aeration
    adhesive
    cohesive

3. The zone of aeration is subdivided into three belts of subzones: belt of _____, an _____ belt, and a _____. (274)

    soil moisture
    intermediate
    capillary fringe

4. Beneath the zone of aeration, the earth materials
   are completely saturated by _____. This lower
   zone is called the zone of _____, and the
   boundary between it and the overlying zone of
   aeration is called the _____. The level of
   this boundary _____ (remains constant, fluctuates)
   with variations in the supply and usage of the
   groundwater. (275)

   groundwater
   saturation
   water table
   fluctuates

5. The water table is an undulating surface that
   _____ (rises, falls) beneath hills and _____
   (rises, falls) when it enters a valley. If the
   water table is deep below a valley, it will
   maintain a relatively _____ orientation. As
   more water infiltrates into the zone of _____,
   the water table will maintain this orientation
   but slowly begin to _____. When the water
   table reaches the elevation of the valley bottom,
   it will continue to rise beneath the _____, but
   maintain a flow towards the valley. The rate of
   flow is determined by the type of materials
   containing the groundwater and the _____ of the
   hill. (275)

   rises
   falls
   horizontal
   saturation
   rise
   hill
   slope

6. The shape of the water table surface will become
   modified by a dimple or indentation called the
   _____ as water is pumped from a well drilled
   below its surface. (276)

   cone of
       depression

7. The total volume occupied by voids or interstices
   of a rock expressed as a percentage defines the
   parameter called _____. This parameter would
   be _____ (greater, lesser) for a sediment
   composed of uniformly sized and shaped sand
   grains than for this same sediment mixed with
   silt and clay. As a general rule, the clastic
   sedimentary rocks would have a _____ (greater,
   lesser) total pore volume or _____ than
   unfractured crystalline rocks. (276)

   porosity
   greater
   greater
   porosity

8. The ability of an earth material to actually
   transmit groundwater defines the property of
   _____. In relating this parameter to porosity,
   consider water-saturated clays and sands. The
   clays would have a _____ (higher, lower)
   porosity, but the sand would transmit the
   groundwater _____ (more quickly, more slowly).
   Pumice is a rock that has a very high porosity
   but a negligible permeability. This is because
   in this rock the pore spaces are not _____. (276)

   permeability
   higher
   more quickly
   interconnected

9. Any permeable material that carries underground water is called an _____. A quartzite would make a good carrier only if it were highly _____. If you were drilling a well through siltstones, sandstones, and limestones, the _____ and _____ would probably be poor water transmitters, but the _____ and possibly the _____ would be good carriers. In the latter case, the high _____ of this rock may increase its _____ and _____ to make it a good carrier. (276)

aquifer
fractured
siltstones
shales
sandstones
limestones
solubility
porosity
permeability

10. Unlike surface waters which characteristically exhibit a _____ flow, most groundwater exhibits a _____ flow. This is because of the low _____ of groundwater. (276)

turbulent
laminar
velocity

11. The slope of the water table is a measure of the groundwater's _____ gradient. The difference in _____ of the water table between any two points divided by the _____ of flow is a numerical expression of this parameter. The elevation of the water table at any given point is called the _____. (277)

hydraulic
elevation
length
head

12. An equation that expresses the velocity of groundwater is known as _____ Law. As a general rule, the velocity is a function of the _____. As this parameter increases, there should be a(n) _____ (decrease, increase) in flow velocity. (277)

Darcy's
hydraulic
  gradient
increase

13. The path followed by groundwater from a hill to a valley is that of a _____. This is because there is a greater head _____ beneath the hill and the flow is always from zones of _____ to zones of _____. (277)

curve
pressure
higher pressure
lower pressure

14. Groundwater is never free to move through uniformly permeable material in an unlimited aerial extension. If the groundwater reaches an impermeable layer or even the water table, it will migrate laterally until it breaches the surface to form a _____. If groundwater percolates through permeable material on a hill but then encounters an impermeable zone that prevents it from reaching the underlying water table, the impermeable zone allows water to accumulate over it, forming what is called a _____ water table, from which a spring may emerge when the water reaches the edge of the hill. (277, 278)

spring
perched

15. A spring is a _____ intersection of the water table and ground surface, but a well is an _____ one. In order to be productive, a well must be drilled into the _____ below the water table. Assume you had the choice of drilling into a fractured granite, buried stream gravel deposit, and well-cemented sandstone. List the aquifers in order of increasing volume of well flow per unit of time: _____, _____, _____. Now suppose you are getting water from a crystalline aquifer but need a greater flow rate (assume no pumping). Is it true or false to expect to attain this increase by drilling deeper into the aquifer? _____. You answered as you did because you knew that the fractures in the aquifer would most probably _____ (increase, decrease) with depth. (278, 279)

natural
artificial
zone of
  saturation
stream gravel
fractured
  granite
sandstone
false
decrease

16. A limestone aquifer would probably yield water described as being _____, because of the high _____ content of the groundwater derived from the soluble limestone. A sandstone aquifer cemented by silica should produce _____ water. (279)

hard
calcium
soft

17. _____ describes the rate at which an aquifer can be expected to yield water. (279)

hydraulic
  conductivity

18. A permeable sandstone crops out in a mountainous region but then dips underground, where it is overlain by an impermeable volcanic ash bed and underlain by an impermeable shale. A well drilled into this aquifer requires no pumping. This type of water system is referred to as being _____. The best example of this system in the United States is the _____ sandstone of _____ age that crops out in the Rockies and Black Hills and underlies the Great Plains. (279)

artesian
Dakota
Cretaceous

19. Any spring that is slightly higher than the ambient air temperature is called a _____. The heat for most of these springs is derived from a _____ source. In some springs, the groundwater circulates so deep that it is warmed by the earth's natural heat, which could be calculated by knowing the earth's _____. Springs in the _____ part of the United States are characteristic of the former and the _____ regions for the latter. (280)

thermal spring
  (hot spring)
  (warm spring)
magma
thermal gradient
western
eastern

20. A _____ is a special type of thermal spring that ejects water intermittently and with considerable force. (282)

geyser

21. The ultimate source of groundwater is controlled   precipitation
    by the quantity of _____ in an area. _____   recharge
    is the term that describes the resupply of water   saturation
    to the zone of _____. (283)

22. Caverns are produced by the _____ of the rock   solution
    _____. Actually, any _____ rock may develop   limestone
    caverns, but they are most common in _____   soluble
    because of their wide aerial extent. Calcite   limestone
    is not very soluble in pure water, but in the   carbonic
    presence of _____ acid, which forms when   carbon dioxide
    _____ dissolves in water, it reacts with the   calcium
    calcite to produce the soluble _____. (283,   bicarbonate
    (284)

23. When calcium carbonate is redeposited in a cavern,   dripstone
    it is called _____. If the formations hang from   stalactites
    the ceiling of the cave like an icicle, they are   stalagmites
    called _____. If the formations develop into a   column
    heavy, postlike formation building up from the   evaporation
    floor, it is called a _____. Sometimes these   carbonate
    two formations join into a single feature called
    a _____. In all cases, the formations form as
    a result of _____ of solutions charged with
    calcium bicarbonate and the subsequent deposition
    of calcium _____. (284)

24. With reference to the water table, there are   above
    conflicting opinions as to where caverns develop.   at
    They may form _____, _____, or _____ the   deep below
    water table. (284)

25. Areas underlain by limestone caverns often reflect   sinkholes
    their presence by surface depressions. These   (sinks)
    depressions are called _____, and an area with   karst
    may of these features is referred to as exhibiting   dolines
    _____ topography. If these depressions contain   collapse
    water, they may be called _____. As a general
    rule, most of these depressions are the result of
    the _____ of surface material into a cavity.
    (286)

26. Human activity can and has produced severe problems pollution
    for groundwater systems. Just like surface waters,   salt water
    groundwaters are subject to _____ from landfills,   invasion
    toxic waste dumps, and septic systems. Extensive   land subsidence
    pumping of groundwater near coastal areas may lead
    to a _____ that will contaminate the aquifers.
    Another problem of excess pumping of groundwater
    is _____, resulting from the compaction of
    sediments that formerly contained water. (287)

Part A: True-False Statements

Each of the following statements is either true or false. Encircle either
T or F for each item.

1. The amount of underground water far exceeds the total of   T   F
   surface water contained in lakes and streams.

2. Water in the zone of aeration partially fills the pores   T   F
   of earth materials.

3. The capillary fringe draws water from the zone of aeration.   T   F

4. The boundary between the belt of soil moisture and the   T   F
   intermediate belt of the zone of aeration defines the
   water table.

5. The level of the water table fluctuates with variations   T   F
   in the amount of water coming from the zone of aeration.

6. As you climb a hill, the water table should also be rising.   T   F

7. A small dimple in the water table formed by the pumping   T   F
   of groundwater into a well defines a cone of depression.

8. A spring is produced when the water table intersects   T   F
   the ground surface.

9. Groundwater is found in the zone of aeration.   T   F

10. Porosity is a measure of a material's ability to transmit   T   F
    groundwater.

11. Permeability is a measure of the percentage of total   T   F
    volume that is occupied by voids in earth materials.

12. A sand composed of uniform grain size has a greater   T   F
    porosity than a mixture of sand and gravel.

13. Any permeable earth material defines an aquifer.   T   F

14. The movement of groundwater defines a broadly looping   T   F
    path that converges toward an outlet.

15. Groundwater flow is usually turbulent.   T   F

16. A water table that drops 15 m in a flow length of 150 m   T   F
    defines a head of 10 percent.

17. According to Darcy's Law, the velocity of groundwater in   T   F
    material of constant permeability increases with increasing
    hydraulic gradient.

18. The tendency of groundwater for lateral flow is the result   T   F
    of the movement of water to an area of higher pressure.

19. A shale layer or zone in a permeable sandstone may result   T   F
    in a perched water table.

20. The quantity of water flowing from a well is independent   T   F
    of its cross-sectional area.

Part B: Multiple Choice Items

Each of the following can be completed correctly by choosing only one word
or phrase. Encircle the letter a, b, c, or d, designating your choice.

1. Pollution of groundwater by microbial activity is most likely in
   aquifers of

   a. sandstone.   c. gravel.
   b. limestone.   d. conglomerate.

2. Land subsidence associated with groundwater may be the result of

   a. the formation of sinks.
   b. compaction of sediments resulting from intensive pumping.
   c. excessive pumping from crystalline rocks.
   d. both (a) and (b) are possible.

3. A karst topography will most easily develop in areas underlain by

   a. unconsolidated sediments.   c. shales.
   b. soluble carbonates.   d. sandstones with silica cement.

4. Groundwater that is heated to a high temperature in a conduit under
   high pressure may develop into a

   a. hot spring.   c. geyser.
   b. warm spring.   d. thermal spring.

5. In crystalline rock aquifers, the water supply may be limited because

   a. their fractures may not interconnect.
   b. there may not be sufficient head.
   c. it may develop a large cone of depression.
   d. they are not very porous.

6. For limestone caverns to form below the water table, it would require

   a. extensive sink development.
   b. groundwater unsaturated with respect to calcite.
   c. groundwater saturated with respect to silica.
   d. the rapid (geologically) development of stalactites and
       stalagmites.

7. The hydraulic gradient is expressed by

a. Q/A.   c. $h_2 - h_1/l$.
b. K.   d. V.

8. In a moist temperate region, you would expect

a. a high water table.
b. a low water table.
c. a very variable water table.
d. a water table that drops under hills and rises in valleys.

9. Water percolating downward through an aquifer and encountering a shale layer would

a. continue through the shale, but at a reduced flow rate.
b. spread laterally in the aquifer above the shale.
c. develop a perched water table.
d. rise vertically into the aquifer.

10. The water table underlying a flat, expansive plain should

a. rise away from the center of the plain.
b. dip inward toward the center of the plain.
c. roughly parallel the surface of the plain.
d. show no relationship to the surface of the plain.

11. The height of water in the capillary fringe is a function of

a. the level of the water table.
b. its depth below the belt of soil moisture.
c. the thickness of the intermediate belt.
d. none of the above.

12. Suspended water is found in the

a. zone of saturation.   c. capillary fringe.
b. zone of aeration.   d. water table.

13. If the recharge of groundwater were to cease, the water table under a hill would

a. rise.
b. drop but still maintain a slight incline.
c. approach the level of the water table in the valley.
d. form a series of depression cones, giving the surface a very irregular slope.

14. Groundwater may flow vertically upward into a stream channel because

a. it is moving to a region of lower pressure.
b. it is being aided by gravity.
c. it is being drawn up by capillary action.
d. the hydraulic gradient reaches its maximum in valleys.

15. Thermal springs in the eastern United States are

    a. warmed by a nearby magma source.
    b. warmed by the regular temperature increases associated with the thermal gradient.
    c. warmed by radioactivity in the rocks.
    d. warmed by the decrease in pressure as the water rises toward the surface.

SUGGESTED ESSAY QUESTIONS

The items below represent the type of discussion question to which you might be expected to respond. Try writing a response to these, and then discuss your work with another student.

1. Describe the features pertaining to underground water you would see in a cross-section from the surface to below the water table.

2. What factors affect the level and shape of the water table?

3. Why do some very porous materials have a very low permeability?

4. Why does groundwater follow broadly looping paths?

5. What features characterize an artesian water system?

6. Discuss the origin of limestone caverns in relation to their formation above or below the water table.

7. What is microbial pollution and saltwater invasion of wells?

ANSWERS TO SELF-TESTS

Part A:					Part B:			
1. T	6. T	11. F	16. F		1. b	6. b	11. d
2. T	7. T	12. T	17. T		2. d	7. c	12. b
3. F	8. T	13. T	18. F		3. b	8. a	13. c
4. F	9. F	14. T	19. T		4. c	9. b	14. a
5. T	10. F	15. F	20. F		5. a	10. c	15. b

CHAPTER 15

GLACIATION

OVERVIEW

Glaciers are the most spectacular agents of erosion. Their handiwork is etched in regions of the globe that, at present, do not contain any active glaciers. Similarly, the widespread glaciations of the relatively recent past modified climates well beyond the furthest advance of the great ice sheets and resulted in significant fluctuations in sea level.

This chapter will consider the requirements for glaciers to develop, their classification, modern distribution, and mechanics of movement. The erosional and depositional features of alpine and continental glaciers are considered in detail (be ready for many new terms).

This chapter closes by tracing the development of the glacial theory and then considers the possible causes of glaciation and extrapolates its possible implications for the future.

LEARNING OBJECTIVES

After studying this chapter, you should be able to:

1. Describe the transformation of snow to glacial ice.

2. Describe the climatic requirements for a glacier to develop.

3. Describe the characteristics of valley glaciers, piedmont glaciers, and ice sheets.

4. Relate the present distribution of glaciers to those of the great Ice Age or Pleistocene Epoch.

5. Describe how a glacier is nourished and how this is related to its advancement, retreat, or stagnation.

6. Distinguish between the zone of fracture and zone of flow and the role each plays in the mechanics of glacial movement.

7. Distinguish between the mechanisms of internal flow and basal slip of a glacier.

8. Distinguish between a cold and warm glacier.

9. Define and describe such features of glacial erosion as:

   a. plucking   g. cirques   m. truncated spur
   b. striations   h. horns   n. rock basins
   c. grooves   i. aretes   o. hanging valleys
   d. polish   j. cols   p. fiords
   e. rock flour   k. tarns   q. asymmetric rock knobs
   f. bergschrund   l. U-shaped valley

10. Define and describe such depositional features as:

    a. drift   l. boulder trains
    b. stratified drift   m. glacial outwash
    c. unstratified drift   n. outwash plains
    d. moraines   o. pitted outwash plains
    e. terminal moraine   p. kettles
    f. recessional moraine   q. eskers
    g. ground moraine   r. crevasse fillings
    h. lateral moraine   s. kames
    i. drumlins   t. kame terraces
    j. drumlin fields   u. varves
    k. erratics

11. Describe the effects of continental glaciation in those areas beyond the main margins of the advancing ice.

12. Historically trace the development of the glacial theory and its proof.

13. Briefly describe the theory of multiple glaciations during the Pleistocene Epoch.

14. Briefly describe and list the evidence for pre-Pleistocene glaciation.

15. Any theory accounting for the cause(s) of glaciation must subscribe to what basic geologic data?

16. Distinguish between long-term and short-term climatic changes and how each is related to the causes of glaciation.

17. Discuss what implications an extrapolation of the possible causes of glaciation may have in the future, and what effects man's activity may add to these predictions.

KEY TERMS AND CONCEPTS

glacier
snowfields
snow line
hexagonal crystals
sublimation
firn (neve)
pressure melting
glacier ice
valley glacier (alpine or
  mountain glacier)
piedmont glacier
ice sheet
icecap
continental glacier
nourishment and wastage
zone of accumulation
zone of wastage
ablation
calving
icebergs
zone of fracture
zone of flow
crevasses
basal slip
surge
cold glacier
warm glacier
plucking (quarrying)
bergschrund
rock flour
striations
grooves
cirque
nivitation
meltwater hypothesis
head wall
horn
arete
col
U-shaped valley
truncated spur
tarn
paternoster lake

rock basins
hanging valley
fiord
rock knobs
drift
unstratified drift
stratified drift
till
clay till
boulder (stony) till
moraine
terminal (end) moraine
recessional moraine
ground moraine
lateral moraine
medial moraine
drumlin
drumlin field
erratic
boulder train
outwash
outwash plain
valley train
pitted outwash plain
kettle
esker
crevasse filling
kame
kame terrace
varve
Little Ice Age
multiple glaciation
long-term cooling
short-term cooling
orbital (Milankovitch) hypothesis
orbital eccentricity
obliquity of the ecliptic
precession of the equinoxes
greenhouse effect
interglacial epoch
superinterglacial
glacial epoch

NOTES

Sec. 15.1: Glaciers

Note that a key part of the definition of a glacier involves movement. The ice must flow, or at least show signs of past flow, to be considered a glacier. A common misconception associates the formation of glaciers with extreme cold. Actually, extremely cold temperatures lower the atmosphere's ability to hold water vapor and may inhibit the formation of the snow necessary for eventual glacial development. A key ingredient in glacier formation is a climate that supports short, cool summers, which prevents the winters' snow accumulation from completely melting.

Note that the transition of snow to glacial ice is a metamorphic process governed by changes in temperature and pressure. In a sense, there is even a "chemically" active fluid in the form of the glacial meltwaters that percolate downward through the snow, where it refreezes on the granules of firn (granular snow) at points where they are not in contact. Be aware that the slippage along shear planes and the plastic flow involved in glacial movement are also part of the metamorphic process. It should be readily apparent that glacial ice is a true metamorphic rock.

The classification of modern glaciers also applies to the glaciers of the past. You should know how to define the major types of glaciers. You should also realize that the distribution of modern glaciers is a function of latitude and altitude. Given the proper conditions, small glaciers are active at low latitudes and even at the equator, but they are found above 5000 meters in altitude.

Whether a glacier advances, retreats, or stagnates is dependent upon the dynamic equilibrium achieved between a glacier's nourishment and wastage. You should know the requirements that determine which phase a glacier will exhibit. Don't overlook Fig. 15.4. This is an excellent longitudinal section through a valley glacier that shows features associated with the glacier's movement, erosion, and nourishment. A note about glaciers in retreat. Glaciers do not literally move backward up-valley. Rather, they melt at their down-valley or snout end, which gives the illusion of retreat or backward movement. A further note concerning glacial stagnation. When a glacier is not in advance or retreat, there is still internal movement within the glacier. The movement takes place along shear planes in the zone of plastic flow, and it is under conditions of stagnation that such depositional features as terminal and recessional moraines develop.

The movement mechanics of a glacier are not completely understood. However, be familiar with the distinction between the zone of flow and the zone of fracture. You should know why crevasses form, why they narrow with depth, and are restricted to the zone of fracture. Be sure you can distinguish between the internal movement of the ice (the result of shearing) and the movement involving the glacier as a whole (basal slip). Another key point is the orientation of the shear planes at the down-valley or terminal end of the glacier. The indication of upward motion shows how debris may be delivered toward the surface of a glacier from its lower reaches and result in the distinct ridges referred to as terminal and recessional moraines (see Fig. 15.18, where this movement is shown in sequential steps).

Sec. 15.2: Results of Glaciation

Like streams, the erosional and depositional features of glaciation leave
very distinctive imprints on the topography. This section describes many
of these features, but it will become overwhelming if you merely try to
memorize the terms. Your best bet is to use the descriptions in
conjunction with the numerous sequential diagrams and pictures that clearly
illustrate these features and their development. Your lab manual should
also be an excellent source for diagrams and topographic maps carefully
selected to show the results of specific types of glaciation. Once you
have seen a map of alpine glaciation, you will never confuse it with any
other agent of erosion. Continental glaciation might not be as distinctive
at first, but, with a little practice, its features (mostly depositional)
will clearly stand out.

You should also make a clear distinction between those features associated
with alpine (valley) and continental glaciation. Table 15.1 will be very
useful in summarizing this material.

Even though the chapter concentrates on the results of glaciation in those
areas directly affected by the ice, be aware that the global effects of
glaciation profoundly altered those regions well beyond the margins of the
ice front.

Sec. 15.3: Development of the Glacial Theory

The development of the glacial theory is a classic example of an
application of the doctrine of uniformitarianism. It should not be
surprising that the testing ground for the theory developed in Switzerland,
where active glaciers and historical records were available for study. You
should be able to trace the historic development of the theory and link its
proof to uniformitarianism.

The question of multiple glaciations is not extensively developed, but,
since glaciation is a global phenomenon, its effects should be reflected in
both the continental and marine environments. The continental evidence is
derived from studies of overlapping moraine deposits and their degree of
weathering in the mid-continent region. It can be shown that in places
older tills, overlain by younger tills, have developed extensive soil
profiles and vegetation patterns that could only have formed during an
interglacial period. The analysis of vegetation patterns from a study of
pollen grains preserved in bogs and lake sediments also show distinct
climatic fluctuations from warm (interglacial) to cold (glacial) during the
past two million years.

The marine evidence is derived largely from an examination of the fossils
preserved in deep-sea sediments, which also show distinct fluctuations in
ocean surface temperatures from warm (interglacial) to cold (glacial) in
temperate regions. See Fig. 15.27.

Sec. 15.4: Extent of Pleistocene Glaciation

As you study this section, you should refer to Figs. 15.28 and 15.29, which
show the aerial extent of continental glaciation in the northern
hemisphere. Note that, in areas to the south of the great ice sheets, the

glaciations are confined to the high mountain regions (Rockies, Sierra Nevada, Alps, Himalayas, etc.)

Sec. 15.5: Pre-Pleistocene Glaciation

Several points to note in this section: Glaciations can be traced well back into the pre-Cambrian (2.2 billion years before present), they are not confined to the northern hemisphere, the evidence for their recognition becomes more difficult with age, and glaciation is used as a line of evidence for the theory of continental drift.

Sec. 15.6: Causes of Glaciation

You should definitely understand that any theory for glaciation must be in accord with the geologic record. Know the four criteria listed.

Note that the causes are subdivided into long-term and short-term effects. The glaciations are believed not to be caused directly by long-term cooling, but rather initiated by one or more of the short-term causes.

Sec. 15.7: Implications for the Future

Predictions about future trends in climatic fluctuations are subject to challenge. Even so, the general trends (see Fig. 15.32) indicate the inevitability of another glacial stage. Note the inadvertent "holding" action that may result from excessive amounts of carbon dioxide released into the atmosphere by human activity. Even the production of a "super-interglacial" period would lead to serious consequences as extensive melting of the polar icecaps would result. The melting of the icecaps would produce a considerable rise in sea level and drown the world's coastal regions.

PROGRAMMED REVIEW

1. A mass of flowing ice formed by the recrystal-   glacier
    lization of snow and moving under the influence of
    gravity defines a _____. (294)

2. In areas where the winter snow accumulation   snowfield
    exceeds the summer melting, a large area of   snowline
    perennial snow, called a _____, will develop.   lower
    The lower limit of this snow accumulation is
    called the _____. The position of this boundary
    would be _____ (higher, lower) in altitude as
    one approaches the polar regions. (294)

3. All snow crystals develop a _____ pattern that   hexagonal
    is a reflection of the internal arrangement of   hydrogen
    _____ and _____ atoms. Snow does not crystallize   oxygen
    from liquid water (rain), but rather condenses   vapor
    directly from water _____ by the process known   sublimation
    as _____. (294)

4. _____ or _____ is the granular type snow that develops after a period of time from an originally light, fluffy mass. During the transformation process, sublimation from _____ (vapor to solid, solid to vapor) occurs. (294)

firn
neve
solid to vapor

5. The melting of ice is enhanced by an _____ (increase, decrease) in pressure. This type of melting is referred to as _____. (295)

increase
pressure melting

6. As pressure on the granular snow or _____ is _____ (increased, decreased), most of the air between the grains is displaced and the granular snow is converted to a solid of interlocking crystals or _____ ice. (295)

firn (neve)
increased
glacial

7. In the transformation of snow to glacial ice, several changes such as an increase in grain size and recrystallization take place. From this, we may conclude that glacial ice is a _____ rock. (295)

metamorphic

8. Glaciers are classified into four principal types. These are _____, _____, _____, and _____. If you were in high mountains like the Andes or the Alps, you would expect to see very large _____ glaciers. By following some of these glaciers to lower elevations, they may join together or coalesce on a broad, flat plane to form _____ glaciers. (295)

valley glaciers
piedmont
  glaciers
ice sheets
continental
  glaciers
valley glaciers
piedmont
  glaciers

9. Any broad, moundlike mass of ice that spreads radially under its own weight is called an _____. If it is a relatively small mass (150 km x 150 km), it is called an _____. If the mass is so large that it covers mountains and parts or all of a major landmass (Antarctica), it is known as a _____. (295)

ice sheet
icecap
continental
glacier

10. Modern glaciers are found scattered over the globe, ranging from _____ to _____ latitudes. In low latitude zones, they are found only at _____ elevations, while, at high latitudes, they may be found at _____. (296)

equatorial
polar
high
sea level

197

11. Glaciers may be subdivided into two zones on the basis of progressive movement. The upper zone or zone of _____ is where a glacier is nourished by snowfall. The lower zone or zone of _____ is where evaporation and melting marks the point of its farthest movement. If accumulation exceeds wastage, the glacier will _____. When accumulation and wastage are equivalent, the glacier will _____. If the wastage exceeds the accumulation, the glacier will _____. (296)

accumulation
wastage
advance
stagnate
retreat

12. Most of the world's glaciers are currently in the process of _____ (advance, retreat). (296)

retreat

13. The term _____ refers to the wastage of a glacier by the process of _____ and melting. Glaciers at sea level waste by a process known as _____ and produce large blocks of glacial ice called _____. (296, 297)

ablation
calving
icebergs

14. There are several direct and indirect methods and lines of evidence used to record the movement of glaciers. By placing markers on the surface of a valley glacier, observations indicate that the movement is greatest _____ (at the center, at the margins) and least _____ (at the center, at the margins). (297)

at the center
at the margins

15. The mechanics of movement are not clearly understood, but two distinct zones exist within the glacier. In the upper zone (30-60 m thick), the ice reacts like a _____ substance. This zone is called the zone of _____. Below this zone, the ice behaves like a _____ material and defines the zone of _____. The rate of movement is variable in the lower zone. As a result of this, the solid ice in the upper zone cannot easily adjust. This differential movement causes a series of fractures called _____ to develop in the upper, more rigid zone. (298)

brittle
fracture
plastic
flow
crevasses

16. The greatest velocity of a valley glacier is attained near its center at the surface and within because of the _____ encountered by the moving ice at the valley walls and valley bottom. Interior directional flow measurements show that the ice moves at low angles _____ (upward, downward) in the zone of accumulation and _____ (upward, downward) in the zone of wastage. While movement is taking place internally, the whole glacier literally slips along its base at the valley bottom. This overall movement of the glacier is called _____. A sudden rapid movement is known as a _____. (298, 299)

friction
downward
upward
basal slip
surge

17. Glaciers are often referred to as a function of
their temperature. In very cold climates, there
is virtually no surface melting, while, in a more
moderate one, there can be a significant amount
of melting. The former type is referred to as
a _____ glacier, and the latter as a _____
glacier. Because glacial ice is a poor conductor,
the heat from the sun can penetrate only a few
meters below the surface. Any melting at depth
is largely the result of the percolation of _____
into the glacier's interior. (300)

cold
warm
meltwater

18. Like streams, glaciers are very effective agents
of _____, _____, and _____. (300)

erosion
transportation
deposition

19. Valley glaciers acquire debris largely by the
mechanical weathering process of _____ and may
receive large quantities by the mass slope
movements resulting from _____ and _____.
(300)

frost action
  (frost
  wedging)
landslides
avalanches

20. The bedrock of the valley floor may contribute
large blocks of rock to the base of a valley
glacier by the process called _____ or _____.
This is especially significant if the bedrock
is highly _____ or _____. (300)

plucking
quarrying
fractured
jointed

21. If a valley glacier is traced up-valley, it will
terminate in a large, bowl-shaped depression
called a _____. The glacier tends to pull away
from the steep back wall of this feature, forming
a large, deep crevasse known as a _____. The
crevasse receives considerable quantities of rock
debris, which act as grinding agents that cut
into the back wall. As a result, the basin is
enlarged by the erosive process called _____
erosion. (300)

cirque
bergschrund
headward

22. Glaciers are very effective in the process of
abrasion. Vast amounts of rock debris may be
ground to an extremely fine powder called _____.
This powder commonly acts like a natural jeweler's
rouge to _____ bedrock surfaces. Coarser
material like sands and gravels commonly make
distinctive scratches on the bedrock called
_____. Even larger debris may cut deep gouges
called _____ into the bedrock. (300, 301)

rock flour
polish
striations
grooves

23. Valley glaciers produce very distinctive erosional   nivitation
    features on the mountains in which they develop.   meltwater
    The cirque begins as a small irregularity in the
    mountainside and is initially enlarged by erosion
    beneath and around the edges of a snowbank in a
    process called _____. As previously mentioned,
    some enlargement of the cirque is the result of the
    mechanical weathering of the head wall. However,
    since the bergschrund is open only to a depth of
    about 60 m, some students of glacial activity have
    developed the _____ hypothesis in which freeze-
    thaw conditions may enlarge the cirque by wedging
    rock fragments from the headwall beneath the
    bergschrund. Once in the glacier, they become
    part of its abrasion tool kit and serve to help
    scour and deepen the cirque. (301)

24. If a series of cirques surround a single high   headward
    mountain, they will produce by _____ erosion a   horn
    sharp spire of rock called a _____. When a   arete
    ridge is cut on both sides by a series of cirques,   col
    the ridge is eroded to a sharp and angular feature
    known as an _____. Should the cirques actually
    cut through the ridge and join, they will produce
    a gap or pass called a _____. (302)

25. Unlike a youthful stream-cut valley that is   V-shaped
    characteristically _____ in cross-valley profile,   U-shaped
    a glacially-cut valley results in a _____   truncated spurs
    cross-valley profile. As the glacier moves
    down-valley, it straightens it and cuts off any
    ridges that formerly extended into the valley
    floor. This results in a series of triangular-
    shaped cliffs with their apexes pointing upward.
    These cliffs are called _____. (302, 303)

26. When a glacier no longer occupies the cirque, it   tarn
    may fill with water and become a glacial lake   plucking
    known as a _____. Some glacial valleys contain   paternoster
    a string of small basins resulting from the _____
    of fractured bedrock. If these basins fill with
    water, they form a chain of lakes called _____
    lakes. (303)

27. A U-shaped valley cut by a tributary glacier   hanging
    and left high above the main valley floor is
    called a _____ valley. (303)

28. Assume you see an asymmetrical rock knob. One   gentle
    side has a gentle slope that is polished and   steep
    covered in places by striations. The other side
    is steeper and does not show any striae or polish.
    You may conclude that the _____ (gentle, steep)
    slope faced the advancing ice. The _____ (gentle,
    steep) slope is the result of glacial plucking. (304)

29. Any material deposited directly or indirectly by glacial activity is called _____. If deposited directly by the ice, it is known as _____ or _____. If deposited indirectly by meltwaters, it is known as _____. (304)

    drift
    unstratified
     drift
    till
    stratified drift

30. Unstratified deposits are usually a heterogeneous mixture of particle sizes. In some cases, clay-sized particles predominate, and in others, rock fragments and boulders. The former are called _____ and the latter _____. (304)

    clay tills
    boulder tills
     (stony tills)

31. Glacial deposits may also form a series of characteristic landforms composed of till. They are collectively referred to as _____. One specific type forms a distinctive ridge that marks the farthest advance of the ice in a given area. This deposit is called a _____. For this deposit to form, an equilibrium must be attained between the zone of _____ and the zone of _____. As a result, the glacier stagnates and releases debris in the latter zone, while material is still being moved internally to maintain a constant supply of debris. A series of smaller ridges may develop behind the larger ridges, marking the farthest advance of the ice. These ridges form when the glacier is in _____ and may temporarily stagnate. This deposit is called a _____. Most till deposits do not form distinctive ridges but rather form a thin veneer of till laid down at the base of a melting glacier or is dumped along valley slopes. In some cases, it may reach thick accumulations but does not result in a distinctive topographic form. These deposits are called _____. (305, 306)

    moraines
    terminal
     moraine
    nourishment
    wastage
    retreat
    recessional
     moraine
    ground moraine

32. Valley glaciers produce two distinctive ridges of till. Debris from the valley walls that is carried along the margins of the ice will produce ridges on the valley sides when the ice melts. These deposits are known as _____. If two valley glaciers meet to form a larger glacier, the latter ridges will join to form a single ridge near the center of the larger glacier. These are called _____. (306)

    lateral moraines
    medial moraines

33. In some areas, clusters of smooth, elongated hills composed of till are common. A single hill is called a _____ and the cluster a _____. The hills have a blunt nose and a longer, smoother side. The _____ (smoother side, blunt nose) faces the direction of the advancing ice. (306)

    drumlin
    drumlin field
    blunt nose

34. Suppose you are standing on a polished and scratched outcrop of granite. Sitting on the granite are several large sandstone boulders. These boulders are called _____. The boulders are found over a wide area and, when mapped, show a triangular pattern. At the apex of the triangle is the source of the boulders. All these boulders constitute a _____. If the apex of the pattern is on the northeast side of your map, you may conclude that the glacial advance came from a _____ direction. (307)

erratics
boulder train
northeast

35. Sand and gravel that are carried from a glacier by meltwaters are referred to as _____. If the deposits stretch for many kilometers beyond the ice front, they form an _____. (308)

outwash
outwash plain

36. Stagnant blocks of ice isolated from a retreating glacier and subsequently buried by till or outwash may form a pit or depression called a _____. When many are found on an outwash plain, the plain is called a _____ outwash plain. (308)

kettle
pitted

37. A long, narrow winding ridge of stratified drift deposited in an ice tunnel is called an _____. A similar but linear deposit believed to be deposited in an ice crevasse is known as a _____. (309)

esker
crevasse
  filling

38. _____ are stratified deposits of low, relatively steep-sided hills of random shape. If these deposits are formed when a wasting glacier traps them between the ice and the valley wall, it will form a continuous deposit called a _____. (309)

kames
kame terrace

39. _____ are a thin pair of sediments, one thick and one fine, that are laid down in a lake and are believed to represent the deposition of a single year. (310)

Varves

40. The theory of glaciation developed from the work of many observers carefully studying the erosional and depositional features associated with modern glaciers. The extension of these studies to regions which no longer have glaciers is a classic example of the concept of _____. (311)

uniformitar-
  ianism

41. Early workers also saw evidence of multiple
    advances and retreats of continental glaciers.
    The great Ice Age or _____ period is known to
    consist of at least _____ major advances and
    retreats. In the United States, much of the
    evidence of glacial activity was compiled by
    study of the glacial deposits of the midcontinent.
    On the basis of these studies, the Ice Age in
    North America is subdivided into four stages.
    In order of oldest to youngest, they are _____,
    _____, _____, and _____. (311, 312)

    Pleistocene
    four
    Nebraskan
    Kansan
    Illinoisan
    Wisconsin

42. Extensive glaciation seems to be associated with
    periods of _____ (high, low) continental
    elevations and continents positioned in _____
    (high, low) latitudes. It also seems probable
    that glaciers _____ (may have, did not)
    develop(ed) by a slow, long-term cooling of the
    earth since its creation. If the earth has been
    warm for most of its history, we do have evidence
    for a period of long-term cooling at the beginning
    of _____ time that culminates with the short-term
    fluctuations of the _____ period. We also know
    that the advances and retreats _____ (were, were
    not) simultaneous throughout the world. (314)

    high
    high
    did not
    Tertiary
    Pleistocene
    were

43. Current thought on the causes of glaciation
    suggests that glacial episodes are the result
    of a combination of _____ and _____ periods
    of _____. (315)

    long-term
    short-term
    cooling

44. The long-term climatic changes are believed to
    be the result of _____ (decreasing, increasing)
    continentality and _____ which slowly placed the
    large landmasses in the proximity of the _____
    latitudes. (315)

    increasing
    drift
    polar

45. The short-term climate changes which were
    responsible for the multiple glaciations of
    the _____ are most probably the result of the
    changing geometry of the _____ and is known
    as the _____ or _____ hypothesis. This
    hypothesis accounts for the periodic variations
    in the amount of _____ received by the earth
    at different places at any one time. (316)

    Pleistocene
    earth's orbit
    orbital
    Milankovitch
    heat

46. The factors which affect the earth's position
    relative to the sun are: the _____ of its
    orbit; the _____ of the _____ which determines
    the angle the earth's _____ makes with its
    orbit around the sun; and the periodic wobble
    of the earth's axis from the gravitational
    effects of the sun, moon, and planets, known
    as the _____ of the _____. (316)

    eccentricity
    obliquity
    ecliptic
    axis
    precession
    equinoxes

47. We are presently living in an interglacial epoch   Pleistocene
    of the _____ period. Some scientists believe   greenhouse
    that the continued alteration of the atmosphere   superinter-
    resulting from man-made pollution will create a   glacial
    global _____ effect and introduce a _____ period   warmer
    of _____ (colder, warmer) climate. However,   glaciation
    based on the orbital hypothesis, we must eventually
    experience another episode of _____. (316)

SELF-TESTS

Part A: True-False Statements

Each of the following statements is either true or false. Encircle either
T or F for each item.

1. A snowfield develops when the amount of winter snowfall   T   F
    exceeds the amount of summer melting.

2. The snow line is most likely to be found at sea level in   T   F
    high latitudes.

3. The initial process in the formation of firn is sublimation.   T   F

4. Firn is composed of interlocking crystals of ice.   T   F

5. Two or more coalescing valley glaciers form an ice sheet.   T   F

6. Alpine glaciers are confined to valleys.   T   F

7. The process of ablation is most active in the zone of   T   F
    accumulation.

8. Glaciers move most rapidly in the upper portions of the   T   F
    zone of flow.

9. The ice at the snout of a glacier moves upward toward the   T   F
    surface at a low angle.

10. Recrystallization of ice commonly takes place along shear   T   F
    planes.

11. Crevasses often extend deep into the zone of flow.   T   F

12. A very rapid motion of a glacier (over 100 m/day) is known   T   F
    as basal slip.

13. The large crevasse at the head of a valley glacier defines   T   F
    a cirque.

14. The abrasive action of coarse sand and gravel carried by   T   F
    a glacier will often polish bedrock surfaces.

15. The meltwater hypothesis may explain erosion of a cirque   T   F
headwall below the base of a bergschrund.

16. Any sediment deposited as a result of direct or indirect   T   F
glacial activity is referred to as drift.

17. Terminal and recessional moraines are deposited as   T   F
glaciers advance.

18. A boulder train is composed of glacial erratics.   T   F

19. In varved sediments, the coarser and thicker layer   T   F
represents the deposition during the summer season.

20. The concept of uniformitarianism formed the basis for   T   F
the development of the glacial theory.

Part B: Multiple Choice Items

Each of the following can be completed or answered correctly by choosing
only one word or phrase. Encircle the letter a, b, c, or d, designating
your choice.

1. Which set of conditions is most favorable for the formation of a
snowfield?

    a. cold, dry winters and short, cool summers
    b. cold, moist winters and long, hot summers
    c. cold, dry winters and long, hot summers
    d. cold, moist winters and short, cool summers

2. As you change your position from high to low latitude and altitude,
the snow line should

    a. increase.   c. remain the same.
    b. decrease.   d. vary in an irregular fashion.

3. Pressure on ice causes it to

    a. decrease in volume.
    b. melt at lower temperatures.
    c. develop from firn to glacial ice.
    d. all of the above.

4. Glacial ice may be considered a metamorphic rock because

    a. it flows plastically.
    b. it recrystallizes in the solid state.
    c. it has a crystalline texture.
    d. all of the above.

5. Piedmont glaciers most closely resemble the form of

    a. coalescing alluvial fans   c. levees.
    b. deltas.   d. stream terraces.

6. For a glacier to advance,

    a. ablation must exceed nourishment.
    b. nourishment must exceed ablation.
    c. ablation must equal nourishment.
    d. ablation must exceed wastage.

7. Crevasses develop because

    a. the ice in the zone of fracture moves faster than in the zone of flow.
    b. plastic deformation in the zone of fracture is at its maximum.
    c. differential movement between the zone of flow and fracture sets up stresses in the ice.
    d. the bands of shearing indicate extensive recrystallization in the zone of fracture.

8. Glacial ice most closely resembles

    a. shale.   c. marble.
    b. granite.   d. clean quartz sandstone.

9. Headward erosion of a group of cirques around a mountain may produce a(n)

    a. tarn.   c. bergschrund.
    b. arete.   d. horn.

10. Each of the following features may be used to indicate direction of ice movement except

    a. kettles.   c. rock knobs.
    b. drumlins.   d. erratics.

11. If you were to walk down-valley along an arete, you would most likely end at the apex of a

    a. col.   c. truncated spur.
    b. horn.   d. hanging valley.

12. A long, narrow and winding deposit of stratified drift describes

    a. a drumlin.   c. a kame.
    b. an esker.   d. an outwash plain.

13. Kettle lakes are found

    a. on moraines.
    b. on outwash plains.
    c. on both moraines and outwash plains.
    d. on kames.

14. Which of the following statements is not true?

    a. Glaciation is associated with high standing continents.
    b. There has been a cooling of the earth's climate from the late Cretaceous to the Pliocene.
    c. Glacial advances and retreats are associated with short-term climatic fluctuations.
    d. Continental drift may be a direct cause of glaciation.

15. During the Pleistocene glacial advances, the southwestern part of the United States

    a. was much drier than it is today.
    b. contained many large lakes.
    c. was covered by a vast ice sheet.
    d. was at a lower elevation than it is today.

SUGGESTED ESSAY QUESTIONS

The items below represent the type of discussion question to which you might be expected to respond. Try writing a response to these, and then discuss your work with another student.

1. Discuss the climatic factors that favor the development of a snowfield.

2. Why is glacial ice considered to be a metamorphic rock?

3. Contrast the events occurring in the zones of nourishment and wastage in relation to the advancement, retreat, and stagnation of a glacier.

4. Contrast the movement of ice in the zone of fracture and zone of flow.

5. Distinguish between a warm and cold glacier.

6. Contrast stream cut and glacially cut valleys.

7. What are kettles and how do they form?

8. How do terminal and recessional moraines form?

9. What features may be used to determine the direction of movement of a continental glacier, and how is each determined?

10. Trace the development of the theory of glaciation and the evidence advanced for multiple glaciations during the Pleistocene.

ANSWERS TO SELF-TESTS

Part A:				Part B:		
1. T	6. T	11. F	16. T	1. d	6. a	11. c
2. T	7. F	12. F	17. F	2. a	7. c	12. b
3. T	8. T	13. F	18. T	3. d	8. c	13. c
4. F	9. T	14. F	19. T	4. d	9. d	14. d
5. F	10. T	15. T	20. T	5. a	10. a	15. b

CHAPTER 16

THE OCEANS

OVERVIEW

The oceans of the world represent one of the last frontiers on our planet.
Prior to World War II, very little was known about the oceans, especially
in the realm of its geologic features and processes.

This chapter introduces you to the chemistry and origin of ocean water and
the physical aspects of currents and waves as they pertain to the geologic
process. The geologic features of the ocean basins and continental margins
are described in some detail, along with the sediments that blanket these
areas.

A concluding section concentrates on shoreline features and processes that
are readily observable to the interested student of geology.

LEARNING OBJECTIVES

After studying this chapter, you should be able to:

1. Describe the hypotheses presented for the origin of ocean water.

2. Understand the concept of salinity and why it varies from place to
    place in the oceans.

3. Describe how ocean currents are generated.

4. Distinguish between tidal currents, density currents, and major
    surface currents.

5. Trace the movement of major surface currents north and south of the equator.

6. Distinguish between the ocean basin and the continental margin.

7. Describe the following continental margin features:

   a. continental shelf   c. continental rise
   b. continental slope   d. submarine canyons

8. Describe the following ocean basin features:

   a. abyssal plains   d. seamounts
   b. abyssal hills   e. guyots
   c. oceanic ridges   f. trenches
      1) spreading-center
      2) aseismic type

9. Contrast the sediments and sedimentation of the ocean basins and the continental margins.

10. Discuss the formation of wind-formed waves, and trace their behavior as they approach a shoreline.

11. Sketch and label a composite profile of a shoreline from a point above high tide to seaward below low tide.

12. Distinguish between shoreline features of erosion and deposition.

13. Discuss the origin of:

   a. wave-cut cliffs   f. barrier islands
   b. wave-built terraces   g. bay barriers
   c. sea caves   h. tidal inlets
   d. sea arches   i. longshore currents
   e. stacks

14. Explain why sea level is not constant and what evidence we have for these fluctuations.

KEY TERMS AND CONCEPTS

seawater
land hemisphere
theory of continuous degassing
salinity
parts per thousand
currents
tidal currents
density currents
turbidity currents
turbidites
oceanic surface currents
gyres

Coriolis effect
ocean basins
continental margins
oceanic ridges (spreading ridge)
midocean ridges
aseismic ridges
seamounts
guyots
trenches
abyssal plains
abyssal hills
continental shelf

continental slope   water particles in a wave
continental rise   wave refraction
leading continental margin   coastal currents
trailing continental margin   longshore drift
drowned valleys   headlands
submarine canyons   wave convergence
glacial marine sediments   wave divergence
continental margin deposits   offshore
ocean basin deposits   nearshore
brown clay   shore (beach)
oozes   coast
siliceous oozes   backshore
calcareous oozes   foreshore
radiolarian oozes   sea cliff
diatomaceous oozes   berm
foraminiferal oozes   wave-cut terrace
radiolaria   wave-built terrace
diatoms   wave-cut cliff
Foraminifera   sea cave
manganese nodules   sea arch
waves   stacks
wavelength   hook
wave height   bay barrier
crest   barrier island
trough   tidal inlet
sea   sea level fluctuations
swells   glacial changes in sea level
circular orbit   tectonic changes of coastal areas
elliptical orbit

NOTES

Sec. 16.1: Seawater

Be able to discuss the theories for the possible origin of ocean water, as
well as the drawbacks of each.

You should be familiar with the major components of seawater (Table 16.1)
and what factors cause the salinity of seawater to vary. Note that,
although the total salinity may vary, the proportion of sodium to chlorine
and all the other components remain constant, no matter what the saline
content.

Tidal currents are basically surface currents and are most significant
close to shore. Density currents are a function of temperature, salinity,
and clarity of the water. These currents usually operate at great depths
and are responsible for the deep circulation and exchange of seawater
throughout the oceans. Note that the activity of turbidity currents is
recognizable by the graded bedding (Chap. 6) found in deep sea cores. They
may also be responsible for the cutting of submarine canyons on the outer
edges of the continental shelf and continental slope.

Be aware that major surface currents are generated by numerous factors, but
in their paths they are greatly influenced by the Coriolis effect and the

obstructions generated by the continental masses. You should be able to trace the paths of the major currents (Fig. 16.7), and you may be required to know their names.

Sec. 16.2: The Ocean Basins

The origin and history of the ocean basins is closely associated with sea floor spreading and plate tectonics. You may want to refer back to Chapters 1 and 11 and to Chapter 4 for the section on aseismic ridges and the origin of the Hawaiian Islands.

You may visualize the relationship of the ocean basins to the continental margins if you make an analogy with a soup dish. You can imagine the narrow, sloping edge of the dish as the continental shelf; the abrupt drop towards the bottom of the disk as the continental slope; and the deep bottom of the dish as the ocean basin.

Be aware that the ocean basins differ from the continental margins not only in their topographic features and sediments, but also in the type of bedrock that underlies each (basaltic and granitic, respectively). You should be able to describe and discuss the origin of every major geologic feature (there are not that many) presented in the text for the basins and margins.

Sec. 16.3: Sediments of the Oceans

With reference to deposition on the continental shelves, the point is clearly emphasized that particle size does not generally follow the neat model of coarse to fine with distance from shore. There are too many factors operating to allow for such a model. Know what factors cause a deviation from the general model.

Note that most of the sediments received on the margins are terrigenous (land derived) in origin and the rate of sedimentation is much greater than it is in the ocean basins.

The sediments of the ocean basins contain terrigenous material, but they also house vast quantities of authigenic (formed within the ocean basins) sediments composed of the tests (shells) of planktonic organisms. Most of these are microscopic and are referred to as zooplankton (animal) and phytoplankton (plant). The brown clays are the must abundant of the ocean basin sediments and contain land-derived materials as well as such odd objects as the remains of whale ear bones. Don't overlook the chemically formed and potentially economically valuable manganese nodules that may account for almost 20 percent of the ocean basin sediments.

A final point may need some clarification. While it is true that the ocean basins are receiving modern sediments and house the sediments deposited back to the Jurassic Period, the vast majority of the sedimentary rocks found on the continents are not typical of those presently forming in the ocean basins of today. Most of the rocks found on the continents were deposited in shallow waters when the seas flooded the continents numerous times in the geologic past. The only deep water marine sediments found on the land are associated with eugeosynclinal rocks in the world's major mountain belts. Even these deep water sediments are unlike those forming in the ocean deeps today.

Sec. 16.4: Shorelines

Note the distinction made between the movement of the wave form and the individual water particles of the wave. The particles move in a circular path by moving forward on the crest and then sinking and moving backwards under the trough, and finally rising with the advance of the next crest. However, the net horizontal displacement of the particle is zero (forward movement exactly equals backward movement). Any alteration of the circular motion will result in a change in the shape of the wave form. This is clearly explained in the description of surf. Note also that the waves can affect the bottom sediments to a depth of one-half the wavelength. Thus, a wave of 30 m wavelength would disturb bottom sediments to a depth of 15 m.

You should also be familiar with the geometry of a water wave. That is, know how to define wavelength, crest, trough, and wave height.

Know the meaning of refraction, why waves refract when they approach the shore at an angle (would a wave refract if it approached the shore head on?), and how the wave energy is dissipated in relation to headlands and bays.

You have probably experienced longshore currents if you swim at ocean beaches. Remember how you marked your position by the placement of your beach umbrella, but found yourself far to the right or left of your original position when you came out of the water? You were nothing more than a sedimentary particle being transported by the longshore current.

Shoreline features are best digested by text descriptions in conjunction with illustrations (text and others) and topographic maps at your disposal. Use them.

Sec. 16.5: Changing Sea Level

Know the evidence for changes in sea level. Do not confuse local changes of the relative position of land and sea arising from tectonic activity with the changes occurring on a worldwide basis. Note that these latter changes are closely associated with glacial episodes.

PROGRAMMED REVIEW

1. The oceans cover the least amount of earth's   Northern
    surface in the _____ Hemisphere. This region   land
    of the earth is often referred to as the _____
    hemisphere. (320)

2. The average depth of the oceans is _____ (greater   greater than
    than, less than) that of the continents. (320)

212

3. The theory that volcanic activity from deep within the earth has been continuously adding water and other elements to the earth's atmosphere and surface is called the process of _____. (320)

continuous
degassing

4. The salinity of ocean water is expressed in parts _____. The average amount of dissolved solids or inorganic salts in seawater is about _____. Approximately 86 percent of the total is composed of _____ and _____, with _____ being present in the greater amount. (321)

thousand
35 o/oo
sodium
chlorine
chlorine

5. The salinity in the wet belts of the equatorial regions is _____ (higher, lower) than the average, while it is _____ (higher, lower) in the dry subtropical belts because of the high rate of _____ (322)

lower
higher
evaporation

6. The relative proportions of the major components _____ (vary, remain constant) with changes in the salinity of seawater. (322)

remain constant

7. Ocean water is in constant motion and spatially moves horizontally as well as up and down. These movements are called _____ and are caused by the _____, differences in the _____ of seawater, and the planetary _____ systems. (322)

currents
tides
density
wind

8. Tidal currents result from the gravitational forces acting between the _____, _____, and _____. Their rate of movement is greatest _____ (in open ocean, near shore). (322)

earth
sun
moon
near shore

9. The density of seawater is a function of _____, _____, and the amount of particulate solids held in _____. (323)

salinity
temperature
suspension

10. Water with a salinity of 38 o/oo has a _____ (higher, lower) density than water of 35 o/oo if their _____ is the same. Seawater of _____ (higher, lower) density would sink below seawater of _____ (higher, lower) density. (323)

higher
temperature
higher
lower

11. Cold water has a _____ (higher, lower) density than warm water, and clear water has a _____ (higher, lower) density than muddy water. (323)

higher
lower

12. A _____ current is a density current composed of muddy water of _____ (high, low) density. These currents are responsible for the transport of _____ grained sediments to the ocean basins. Deep sea core samples of sediments deposited by these currents show _____ bedding and are called _____. (323)

turbidity
high
coarse
graded
turbidites

13. The major surface currents are driven by the   friction
    _____ of the wind moving over the water and   gyres
    follow large, looping paths or cells called _____.   clockwise
    Their direction of rotation may be _____ or   counter-
    _____, depending upon their latitude with   clockwise
    reference to the equator. (325)

14. The planetary wind systems that drive the surface   unequal
    currents are set up by the _____ heating of the   pressure
    atmosphere, creating regions of high and low   rotation
    _____. The planetary winds do not follow paths   Coriolis effect
    due north or south because of the earth's _____.   right
    The deflection of the winds that results is called   left
    the _____. Because of this phenomenon, any object
    in the Northern Hemisphere will veer to the _____
    and to the _____ in the Southern Hemisphere. (325)

15. A raft set adrift in the North Equatorial current   westerly
    would drift in a _____ direction. If the raft   westerly
    were in the South Equatorial current, it would   northerly
    drift in a _____ direction. As the rafts   right
    approach the North and South American continents,   Gulf Stream
    the northern raft may drift in a _____ direction   southerly
    and therefore to the _____ (right, left) and   left
    eventually ride along a major ocean current known   Brazil
    as the _____. The southern raft may drift in a
    _____ direction or to the _____ (right, left)
    and pick up a major ocean current known as the
    _____ Current. (326)

16. Most of the earth's ocean water is contained in   ocean basins
    the _____ with smaller amounts lapping up over   continental
    the _____. (327)   margins

17. The zone of transition between the continents and   continental
    the ocean basins is usually composed of a gentle   shelf
    slope called the _____, which steepens at its   continental
    outer edge to form the _____, which in places   slope
    grades into wedges of sediment which comprise the   continental
    _____ at the edges of the ocean basins. (328)   rise

18. In its initial phases, such as exhibited at the   Africa
    Red Sea and its adjacent borders with _____ and   Arabia
    _____, a _____ continental margin results in a   diverging
    central _____ zone that is bordered by _____   rift
    (lowlands, highlands). Given enough time, the   highlands
    typical _____, _____, and _____ sequence will   shelf
    develop. This sequence is shown along the eastern   slope
    margins of the _____ continent, which split from   rise
    the supercontinent of _____ about 200 million   North American
    years ago along what is now the _____ ridge.   Gondwanaland
    This type of margin is also called a _____   Mid-Atlantic
    continental margin, because it forms on the back   trailing
    side of a continent as it moves away from a
    spreading center. (328)

19. Along transform boundaries, the topographic texture
    of the margins is generally _____ (parallel to,
    at right angles to) the plate boundary. Margins
    of this type are also cut by a series of _____
    and _____ faults that are attendant upon the
    strike slip motion. This results in a topography
    of _____, _____, and _____ both on and off-
    shore. Margins of this type are found along the
    _____ coast of the United States. (332)

    parallel to
    normal
    thrust
    highlands
    valleys
    basins
    west

20. Stream cut valleys found on the present continental
    shelves resulted from erosion during the _____
    period, when sea level was about 100 m _____
    (higher, lower) than present. They are commonly
    referred to as _____ valleys. (332)

    Pleistocene
    lower
    drowned

21. The steep V-shaped canyons cut into some
    continental _____ are believed to be the result
    of the erosive action of _____ currents. (332)

    slopes
    turbidity

22. The ocean basins are directly linked to _____
    plate boundaries. At its boundary with the
    continental rise lie the broad, deep areas called
    the _____ that represent some of the flattest
    regions of the earth. Any topographic highs found
    in this region are the result of volcanic activity
    and fracturing and form what are called the _____.
    The regional slope of the ocean basin floor is
    _____ (toward, away from) the spreading ridge and
    _____ (toward, away from) the continental margins.
    (333)

    diverging
    abyssal plains
    abyssal hills
    away from
    toward

23. The ridges of the ocean basins fall into two major
    categories, namely, the _____ center ridges and
    the _____ ridges. The former make up a _____
    (continuous, discontinuous) system of which the
    _____ is the most representative. The latter type
    lacks _____ activity, and the thermal effects of
    volcanism are found only at the _____ (center, end)
    of the ridge which is also its _____ (highest,
    lowest) point. The _____ Islands of the Pacific
    are most characteristic of this type of system. (333)

    spreading
    aseismic
    continuous
    Mid-Atlantic
    earthquake
    end
    highest
    Hawaiian

24. Other features of the ocean basins are the
    thousands of distinctive conical-shaped hills
    produced by volcanic activity called _____. If
    these hills are truncated, they are called _____.
    These flat-topped features resulted from _____
    erosion of volcanic islands that were slowly
    sinking and subsequently sank to their present
    random depths in the ocean basins. The long,
    linear features that lie marginal to some continents
    and mark the deepest parts of the oceans are called
    _____. They are most common along the margins of
    the _____ Ocean. (334)

    seamounts
    guyots
    wave
    trenches
    Pacific

25. With relation to the distance from a shoreline, the coarsest sedimentary particles should be deposited and the finest ones _____. While this pattern may hold true in many areas, in some places it is not uncommon to see a wide variety in depositional patterns. Along a rock-bound coast swept by strong currents, the only sediments are likely to be _____ size and larger due to the _____ action of the currents. In protected bays and lagoons, the bottom sediments would be dominated by _____ grained sediments in the _____ size range. On glaciated continental shelves, it is very common to find _____ sized material mixed with sands and gravels. (334)

nearshore
offshore
gravel
winnowing
fine
clay
boulder

26. The deposits of the ocean basins are much _____ grained than those of the continental margin, and the rate of sedimentation is much _____. The sediments in the ocean basins that have been derived from the continental landmasses and slowly drifted as silts and clays to cover vast areas of the basins are collectively referred to as _____. The basin sediments that contain a mixture of mud and the siliceous and calcareous skeletal remains of pelagic plants and animals are called _____ if they are dominated by the pelagic marine protozoa called _____, and _____ when composed largely of the planktonic one-celled marine algae known as _____. The calcareous deposits are called _____ and are dominated by the pelagic unicellular group of organisms known as the _____. These deposits will not be found in depths as great as the siliceous oozes because of the solubility of the calcite shell in deep, cold waters. The depth at which solution occurs is called the _____ depth. In certain parts of the polar seas, some deep ocean sediments contain very coarse fragments that were deposited from _____. Deposits of this type are called _____ marine deposits. _____ currents from the continental slope are another contributor of coarse sediments to the ocean basins. (335)

finer
slower
oozes
radiolarian
  oozes
radiolaria
diatomaceous
  oozes
diatoms
foraminiferal
  oozes
foraminifera
carbonate
  compensation
icebergs
glacial
Turbidity

27. Valuable mineral deposits known as _____ are known to cover about 20 percent of the _____ ocean basin. They are composed largely of oxides of _____ and _____, but also contain _____ and such rare elements as _____, _____, and _____. (335, 336)

manganese
  nodules
Pacific
manganese
iron
copper
cobalt
titanium
zirconium

28. Shorelines are shaped largely by the action of _____ and _____. (336)

waves
currents

29. Most waves are formed by the action of _____   wind
    on the ocean surface. The distance between two   wavelength
    successive waves defines the _____, while the   crest
    high and low points of a wave are called the   trough
    _____ and _____, respectively. The vertical   height
    distance between the high point and low point is   sea
    a measure of the wave's _____. Waves that form   swells
    while the wind is blowing are referred to as
    _____. If the waves continue after the wind
    ceases, they are known as _____. (336)

30. The particles that comprise a wave move in _____   circular
    paths when the wave is in deep water. When the   elliptical
    water depth is about one-half wavelength, the   wave base
    particles experience interference with the bottom   lower
    and their motion follows a more _____ path. This   decrease
    depth is called _____. As the water depth   break
    continues to shallow, the _____ (lower, upper)   surf
    portion of the wave slows, causing the wavelength   currents
    and velocity to _____ (increase, decrease). When
    the wave front becomes steep enough, it will _____
    producing what is called _____. The energy from
    this activity is used to erode the shoreline and
    transport eroded materials by the _____ produced.
    (337)

31. The bending of a wave as it approaches a shoreline   refraction
    is called _____. As a result, waves that approach   head-on
    a shore at an oblique angle usually strike the   currents
    shore nearly _____. This bending of waves as they   parallel to
    approach a shore develops _____, which travel
    _____ (parallel to, at steep angles to) the
    shoreline. (337)

32. The refraction of waves causes them to _____   concentrate
    (concentrate, diverge) at headlands and _____   diverge
    (concentrate, diverge) at bays. This occurs   shallower
    because the water depth is _____ (deeper,   deeper
    shallower) at the headlands and _____ (deeper,   headlands
    shallower) in the bays. The concentration of wave   bays
    energy is greatest at _____ (headlands, bays) and
    least at _____ (headlands, bays). (337, 338)

33. A cross-section of a composite or typical shoreline   offshore
    would consist of an _____ section that extends   shore
    seaward from the low tide zone and a _____ or   beach
    _____ that extends landward from the low tide zone   sea cliff
    and may terminate at a topographic high called a   backshore
    _____. This landward section is divided into a   berms
    rear or _____ section, composed of a series of low   foreshore
    sand ridges called _____ that are built by storm
    waves, and a seaward section that extends to the
    low tide zone and is called the _____. Wave
    action may erode a broad seaward sloping platform

on bedrock called a _____ terrace. Unconsolidated debris may build up in the offshore section to form a _____ terrace. (338)

wave-cut
wave-built

34. Rocky coasts commonly exhibit _____ cliffs that result from waves breaking directly on the rocky shoreline. These cliffs are steadily cut back as the _____ terrace is expanded. The rate of erosion _____ (increases, decreases) as the terrace width increases. Differential erosion may produce such features as hollowed out cavities called _____ or isolated blocks of rock left standing offshore called _____ and natural bridges cut through a headland known as _____. (338)

wave-cut
wave-cut
decreases
sea caves
stacks
sea arches

35. Shorelines characterized by deposition are characteristic of the east coast of the United States south of New England. Wave-eroded sediments are augmented by streams bringing sediments from the land and storm waves carrying offshore sediments. These sediments are transported by _____ along the coastline and develop extensive, sandy beaches. A _____ is formed when beach sands extend out in an armlike extension that curves inward toward a bay. _____ are beaches that extend across the mouths of bays and cut them off from open ocean. Connections from bays and lagoons through the barriers to open ocean are called _____ inlets and usually result from the activity of severe storms. Long linear beaches that form offshore and have no connection with the mainland are called _____. (340)

currents
hook
barrier bays
tidal
barrier islands

36. For the last several thousand years, sea level has been _____ (falling, rising). During periods of extensive glaciation, sea level _____ (falls, rises). (341, 342)

rising
falls

SELF-TESTS

Part A: True-False Statements

Each of the following statements is either true or false. Encircle either T or F for each item.

1. More than 70 percent of the earth lies beneath the oceans.   T   F

2. Between 45 and 70 degrees N latitude, the oceans occupy 38 percent of the earth's surface.   T   F

3. The weathering of crustal rocks is the most probably origin of the ocean's waters.   T   F

4. The salinity of ocean water is a constant value of 35   T   F
   parts per thousand.

5. Ocean currents may move horizontally, downward, or upward.   T   F

6. Velocities of up to 20 km/hr may be reached by equatorial   T   F
   currents.

7. A turbidity current forms when water of high salinity   T   F
   sinks below water of low salinity.

8. The Coriolis effect causes major surface currents in the   T   F
   northern hemisphere to be deflected to the left.

9. The major oceanic ridges are composed of folded rocks   T   F
   similar to continental mountain belts.

10. The continental rise forms the transition between the   T   F
    continental slope and ocean basin in the Atlantic Ocean.

11. Drowned valleys occur on the continental slopes.   T   F

12. The abyssal plains lie between the oceanic ridges and the   T   F
    continental margin except in those areas where the
    continental slope terminates in an oceanic trench.

13. Midocean ridges exhibit little or no seismic activity.   T   F

14. Guyots are former volcanic islands truncated by wave   T   F
    action before sinking below the ocean surface.

15. The most extensive oceanic trench system is found along   T   F
    the margins of the Pacific.

16. The rates of sedimentation are considerably greater in   T   F
    the ocean basins than in the continental margins.

17. Most pelagic oozes have a terrigenous source.   T   F

18. The water particles in a moving wave follow circular   T   F
    orbits in deep water.

19. Waves diverge on headlands and converge in bays.   T   F

20. A moving wave will disturb bottom sediments up to a depth   T   F
    of approximately one wavelength.

Part B: Multiple Choice Items

Each of the following can be completed or answered correctly by choosing
only one of the selections. Encircle the letter a, b, c, or d, designating
your choice.

1. A composite profile of a shoreline shows that the backshore is characterized by one or more

   a. beaches.
   b. wave-built terraces.
   c. berms.
   d. wave-cut terraces.

2. The rate at which a wave-cut terrace develops _____ as it widens.

   a. increases
   b. decreases
   c. remains the same
   d. varies

3. Which of the following shoreline features does not belong in association with the others?

   a. stack
   b. sea caves
   c. spit
   d. sea arch

4. Which of the following features is least likely to develop along a rocky headland?

   a. sandy beaches
   b. stacks
   c. sea caves
   d. wave-built terrace

5. A wave approaches a north-south trending beach from the southeast. A sand grain along the shoreline will tend to move

   a. north.
   b. east.
   c. south.
   d. west.

6. As waves approach a shoreline,

   a. the water particles follow a more elliptical path.
   b. the waves usually refract.
   c. their velocity decreases.
   d. all of the above.

7. The term swell refers to

   a. waves breaking along a shoreline.
   b. waves traveling after the wind ceases to blow.
   c. the change from circular to elliptical orbits of the water particles in a wave.
   d. the change from elliptical to circular orbits of the water particles in a wave.

8. The most geologically recent changes in the relative position of land and sea is the result of

   a. the formation of continental glaciers.
   b. the melting of continental glaciers.
   c. local uplift due to isostatic adjustments of the crust or local tectonic activity.
   d. all of the above.

9. The most common deposit found in the ocean basin is

   a. foraminiferal mud.   c. brown clay.
   b. nodular manganese.   d. turbidites.

10. The greatest concentration of radiolarian muds is found in the

   a. North Atlantic   c. polar seas.
   b. equatorial Pacific.   d. South Pacific.

11. If you were to make a study of grain size and distance from shore on the continental shelf, you would find

   a. the sediments grade from coarse to fine with distance from shore.
   b. the sediments grade from fine to coarse with distance from shore.
   c. the grain size can be very variable, depending on local conditions.
   d. none of the above.

12. As you trace deep sea sediments away from the Mid-Atlantic Ridge, they should be

   a. getting thicker.   c. getting younger.
   b. getting thinner.   d. both (a) and (c).

13. Where the continental shelf is missing off a coast, it is probably the result of

   a. subduction of an oceanic plate.
   b. a transform boundary between ocean and continent.
   c. presence of a ridge system.
   d. a thick wedge of continental rise sediments overriding the continental slope.

14. The cold surface water from the Antarctic region is

   a. driven in an easterly direction by prevailing west winds.
   b. carried northward by winds to the equatorial region.
   c. carried northward by winds but then deflected by the Australian continent and the South African coast.
   d. not affected by the Coriolis effect.

15. In the polar seas you would expect the

   a. surface waters to be more saline than the deep water.
   b. surface water to be more dense than the deep water.
   c. surface water to be less dense than the deep water.
   d. none of the above.

SUGGESTED ESSAY QUESTIONS

The items below represent the type of discussion questions to which you might be expected to respond. Try writing a response to these, and then discuss your work with another student.

1. How do density currents develop?

2. What is the Coriolis effect, and how does it influence the path of surface currents?

3. How is the total salinity of seawater related to its constituent parts?

4. Contrast the topographic features of the continental margin and ocean basin.

5. Contrast the sediments of the ocean basin and continental margin.

6. Describe the motion of water particles as a wave travels from deep to shallow water.

7. What is the relationship between wave refraction and coastal currents?

8. Describe the behavior of a wave as it approaches a headland and adjacent bay.

9. Why has glaciation been a direct cause of the changes between the relative position of the land and sea?

ANSWERS TO SELF-TESTS

Part A: 1. T 6. F 11. F 16. F   Part B: 1. c 6. d 11. c
        2. T 7. F 12. T 17. F   2. b 7. b 12. a
        3. F 8. F 13. F 18. T   3. c 8. d 13. a
        4. F 9. F 14. T 19. F   4. a 9. c 14. a
        5. T 10. T 15. T 20. F   5. a 10. b 15. c

CHAPTER 17

WIND AND DESERTS

OVERVIEW

Wind, as a geological force, operates most obviously in certain regions of the world which are referred to as deserts. Although deserts exist at all latitudes, only the extensive non-polar deserts are discussed in this chapter. The major effects of wind include movement, erosion, and deposition of desert material. Each of these processes involves phenomena which are unique to desert environments. In addition, the intensity of weathering in a desert environment is also unique, as is the role played by water.

LEARNING OBJECTIVES

After studying this chapter, you should be able to:

1. State the basic characteristics of a desert.

2. Locate on a world map the major deserts.

3. Describe how a topographic desert is created.

4. Describe how a subtropical desert is created.

5. Describe how material is moved by the wind.

6. State how dust storms and sand storms differ.

7. State the relationship between the wind speeds and heights above the surface, as described in Figure 17.2.

8. Describe the process of saltation.

9. Describe how sand grains are moved by the wind.

10. Describe how dust particles are moved by the wind.

11. Define: abrasion, deflation, ventifacts, blowouts, desert pavement, desert varnish, loess.

12. Describe the formation of desert pavements.

13. State the reasons for believing loess is a wind-deposited material.

14. Describe the geometry of a typical sand dune and how a dune forms.

15. Define: slip face, surface of discontinuity, wind shadow, topset beds, foreset beds, backset beds.

16. Describe, with a sketch, the existence of a wind shadow.

17. Explaian why mechanical weathering seems to predominate in desert regions.

18. Describe the role of water as a desert process.

19. State a theory for the existence of pluvial periods.

20. Define: playa, playa lake.

KEY TERMS AND CONCEPTS

desert
topographic desert
subtropical desert
subtropical high pressure zone
prevailing westerlies
northeast trade winds
southeast trade winds
zone of no movement
dust storm
sandstorm
sand
dust
terminal velocity of a grain
saltation
abrasion
deflation
ventifacts
blowouts
desert pavement

loess
sand dunes
wind shadow
surface of discontinuity
windward slope
leeward slope
slip face
foredunes
transverse dunes
barchans
parabolic dunes
seif dunes
statification in dunes
foreset beds
backset beds
topset beds
desert varnish
playas
playa lakes

flash floods   pluvial lakes
pluvial periods

NOTES

Sec. 17.1: Distribution of Deserts

Deserts may exist in any part of the world, including the polar regions.
Note that emphasis here is on the extensive subtropical deserts--those
occurring near the equatorial regions. Such deserts are more or less
determined by climatic patterns. This implies that a change in the
circulation of the atmosphere could change the distribution of deserts.

Sec. 17.2: Work of the Wind

The wind is always a factor in shaping the earth, but in desert regions it
becomes most significant. Notice that the wind just doesn't pick up
particles and move them. Other factors, such as saltation, are involved,
and, surprisingly, even dust particles need more than wind in order to
move. The effects of abrasion are particularly noticeable in deserts,
because other destructive factors are either absent or minimized. Notice
that blowouts work on unconsolidated deposits and that such deposits may be
formed by the action of water (dissolving). Loess is derived from any
source which contains very fine mineral fragments. The deposits in the
mid-U.S. are most certainly of glacial origin. Note the evidence for this
and the fact that loess was deposited during the height of glaciation. The
deposition of sand depends on the decreasing of the speed of the wind.
This occurs in a wind shadow and results in the formation of dunes. Notice
that each dune has a set of characteristics and requirements for its
formation, but all require the initial existence of a wind shadow.

Sec. 17.3: Other Desert Processes

Although mechanical weathering predominates in desert regions, chemical
weathering is not entirely absent. Notice the type of soil that is formed
in deserts. Be aware that the role of streams is not an insignificant one
in desert processes, although the existence of such streams is usually
temporary. Notice also the apparent influence of continental glaciation on
the climate in desert regions.

PROGRAMMED REVIEW

1. A desert is characterized by a lack of _____.   moisture
    (346)

2. Deserts are classified as _____ deserts if they   topographic
    are located toward the centers of continents or   high mountains
    cut off from moisture-bearing winds by _____.   subtropical
    The most extensive deserts are the _____ ones   high
    that owe their origin to zones of _____ (high,
    low) pressure that result from atmospheric
    circulation. (346)

3. As air settles, it _____ (warms, cools) and
    _____ (can, cannot) retain its moisture. At the
    surface of the earth, the descending air moves
    _____ (toward, away from) zones of _____ (low,
    high) pressure. In the polar regions, the winds
    created form the _____ westerlies and, in the
    tropics, the _____ winds blow toward the equator
    where they are heated. As they _____ (warm even
    more, cool), they give up their moisture. These
    winds are then diverted to the subtropical _____
    (high, low) pressure zones north and south of the
    equator where they begin a new cycle. (346)

    warms
    can
    away from
    high
    prevailing
    trade
    cool
    high

4. The absence of _____ in deserts to anchor the
    soil makes the wind an effective agent of
    erosion. (347)

    vegetation

5. The velocity of the wind _____ (increases,
    decreases) with height above the ground, and the
    air moves in _____ (laminar, turbulent) flow. (347)

    increases
    turbulent

6. The general movement of wind across the ground
    is forward, but there is a vertical (up and down)
    set of components as well as lateral movement.
    In a zone about 1 m above the ground, the _____
    (upward, downward) movement is about one-fifth the
    average of its _____ (lateral, forward) velocity.
    Very close to the surface, there is a zone of
    _____ whose thickness is a function of the average
    size of the loose grains at the surface. (347)

    upward
    forward
    no movement

7. Particles blown by the wind are classified by
    size into _____ and _____. The particles in
    a _____ storm move as a blanket whose upper zone
    seldom exceeds 1 m above the ground, with most of
    the particles concentrated a few centimeters above
    the surface. _____ storm particles may be blown
    hundreds of meters above the ground forming great,
    dense clouds. (347)

    sand
    dust
    sand
    dust

8. The _____ velocity of a particle is reached when
    the acceleration due to _____ is balanced by the
    resistance of the _____ through which it is
    falling. (348)

    terminal
    gravity
    medium (air,
      fluid)

9. Sand grains have a terminal velocity that is
    _____ (greater, smaller) than the velocity of
    upward moving air. Because of this, sand grains
    are transported by the process known as _____.
    Unlike sand grains in a stream, which are
    transported by a similar process, the sand grains
    are kept in motion by _____ with other grains
    rather than the velocity of the wind. If the
    grains are very coarse, they will _____ or
    _____ rather than jump into the air. (349)

    greater
    saltation
    impact
    slide
    roll

10. Dust particles are transported in _____. The
    initial lifting of the particle _____ (can,
    cannot) be accomplished by wind velocity. This
    results from the shape of the grains and their
    position in the zone of _____ at the ground
    surface. (350)

    suspension
    cannot
    no movement

11. Erosion by wind in deserts is accomplished by
    the processes of _____ and _____. (350)

    abrasion
    deflation

12. Sand grains accomplish their abrasive action
    most effectively between _____ (0 to .5 m,
    .5 to 1 m) above the ground. The most common
    products of this type of erosion are the faceted
    pebbles and cobbles called _____. These abraded
    products have a relatively high gloss, but, on
    close inspection, the surfaces show a distinct
    _____. (350)

    0 to .5 m
    ventifacts
    pitting

13. Deflation produces a series of scooped out
    basins in unconsolidated deposits called _____.
    After deflation has removed sand and dust, a
    residue of pebbles and cobbles referred to as
    _____ is left behind. (350, 352)

    blowouts
    desert pavement

14. Deposition of wind-borne particles takes place
    as the wind loses its velocity. A characteristic
    deposit called _____ may form deposits of small,
    angular mineral grains, reaching a thickness of
    over 100 m in some places. Many of these deposits
    seem to be intimately associated with _____
    deposits. (353, 354)

    loess
    glacial

15. Sands are usually deposited in a variety of
    characteristic forms collectively referred to
    as _____. Any obstruction in the path of
    moving sand grains will create a _____ on its
    (windward, leeward) side. Within this zone
    the velocity of the wind is _____ (less than,
    greater than) that of the wind moving around
    the obstacle. The boundary between these zones
    is called the surface of _____. (354, 355)

    dunes
    wind shadow
    leeward
    less than
    discontinuity

16. As the sand dune increases in size, it develops
    a _____ (gentle, steep) windward side and a
    _____ (gentle, steep) leeward side. The
    leeward size of the dune is called the _____
    face because of the slides of sand that occur
    here. As this face increases in size, the
    effectiveness of the wind shadow _____
    (increases, decreases). (355, 356)

    gentle
    steep
    slip
    increases

17. Dunes may be found in any environment that
    contains a sufficient supply of sand. Along an
    ocean shoreline or that of a large lake, ridges
    of sand called _____ may develop. These dunes
    are fashioned by strong _____ (onshore,
    offshore) winds. They may migrate inland but
    are usually held in check by _____ that is
    common along most coasts and lake shores. These
    dunes form narrow belts that run _____ (parallel
    to, at steep angles to) the shore. They are
    commonly pockmarked by _____ that are the
    result of the process of _____. (356, 357)

    foredunes
    onshore
    vegetation
    parallel to
    blowouts
    deflation

18. In areas where vegetation is scarce, sand may move
    inland to form _____ dunes. These dunes form
    a series of ridges _____ (parallel to, at right
    angles to) the wind. Dunes of this type are
    most common in _____ climates and may reach
    lengths of many kilometers. (357)

    transverse
    right angles
    arid

19. Crescent-shaped dunes are known as _____. These
    These dunes develop distinctive horns that point
    _____ (upwind, downwind) and require _____
    (large, small) amounts of sand to develop. (357)

    barchans
    downwind
    small

20. A _____ dune looks similar to a barchan, but
    its horns point _____ (upwind, downwind). (358)

    parabolic
    upwind

21. _____ dunes are long ridges of sand running in
    the general direction of the wind. In North
    Africa and the Arabian deserts, they reach very
    large sizes and are called _____ dunes. (358)

    longitudinal
    seif

22. A cross-section through a dune would show that
    the sand layers are usually _____. The steeper
    layers are found on the _____ face and are
    called _____ beds. The greatest volume of
    sand is found on the gentle windward slope
    called the _____ beds. Any layers that form
    over the aforementioned beds will have a _____
    orientation and are known as _____ beds. (358)

    inclined
    slip
    foreset
    backset
    horizontal
    topset

23. The rate of weathering in desert climates is
    very slow because of the lack of _____. Any
    weathering that does takes place is dominated
    by _____ weathering. The slow rate of
    weathering is reflected in the lack of _____
    development. A thin reddish-brown to black
    coating of iron and manganese oxides develops
    on some gravels. This feature is known as
    _____ and may have a counterpart on the surface
    of the planet _____. (359)

    moisture
    mechanical
    soil
    desert varnish
    Mars

24. _____ are active agents of erosion in deserts as well as the wind. In some regions, such as the American southwest, the mountains slope down to broad, flat basins or _____. When runoff is high enough, it commonly collects in these basins to form _____ lakes. The greatest danger to travelers in the desert is a _____ flood, which can turn dry streambeds into raging torrents. (359)

streams
playas
playa
flash

25. During the Pleistocene, the climate of the arid and semi-arid southwest was much damper. The glaciations produced what was called _____ periods in areas beyond the ice margins. As a result, there was greater vegetation and much less evaporation. Because of this, the large basins were dotted by _____ lakes. The Great Salt Lake is a remnant of one of these lakes. (359)

pluvial
pluvial

SELF-TESTS

Part A: True-False Statements

Each of the following statements is either true or false. Encircle either T or F for each item.

1. Topographic deserts are deserts occurring in a flat region.   T   F

2. Most subtropical deserts owe their existence to high pressure zones occurring at about 30° on either side of the equator.   T   F

3. Wind moves much of the desert material by lifting it and then pushing it through the air.   T   F

4. Immediately above the surface, the air is moving very little or not at all.   T   F

5. The desert material blown by the wind is usually .30 mm and smaller.   T   F

6. Dust storms may occur at altitudes of thousands of meters.   T   F

7. Most sand particles in the desert are moved by the process of abrasion.   T   F

8. A significant portion of the sand being moved in a sandstorm is rolled along by the wind.   T   F

9. Wind erosion occurs by abrasion and inflation.   T   F

10. Blowouts are wind depositional features.   T   F

11. Desert pavements are formed by the wind moving large-size particles into basins.   T   F

12. The existence of extensive loess deposits in the Mississippi River region indicates that a large desert must have existed there at one time.   T   F

13. Loess deposits are unstratified deposits.   T   F

14. Sand is deposited in front of and behind an obstacle because the wind speed decreases.   T   F

15. Foredunes are ridges of wind-blown sand occurring in desert and non-desert regions.   T   F

16. Transverse dunes may vary in length from a few tens of meters to tens of kilometers.   T   F

17. Longitudinal dunes are long ridges of sand oriented perpendicular to the prevailing wind direction.   T   F

18. Sand dunes are not stratified because of the constant motion of the wind.   T   F

19. Because of the extreme temperature differences in desert regions, most weathering is chemical.   T   F

20. Water is a minor factor in shaping the desert landscape.   T   F

Part B: Multiple Choice Items

Each of the following can be completed correctly by choosing only one word or phrase. Encircle the letter a, b, c, or d, designating your choice.

1. Which of the following do not pertain to subtropical deserts?

     a. range from 5° to 30° latitude
     b. located far from oceans
     c. Sahara Desert
     d. due to general atmospheric circulation

2. The wind is a major factor operating in desert regions because

     a. it is always blowing.
     b. of the lack of protective vegetation.
     c. the ground is covered with sand.
     d. the land is flat.

3. The terminal velocity of a particle varies with the size of the particle when

     a. density is a constant.
     b. shape is a constant.
     c. density increases and shape is a constant.
     d. shape and density are constant.

4. Dust is classified as particles smaller in diameter than

    a. 0.6 mm.   c. .02 mm.
    b. 0.6 cm.   d. .20 mm.

5. Very small dust particles could be lifted into the air by

    a. the horizontal motion of air. c. downdrafts.
    b. the upward motion of air.   d. flotation.

6. Which of the following does <u>not</u> pertain to desert pavements?

    a. formed by deflation
    b. formed by abrasion
    c. consists of pebbles and cobbles
    d. no deflation occurring

7. Which of the following does not pertain to loess?

    a. forms unstratified deposits
    b. consists of angular mineral fragments
    c. occurs near deserts only
    d. some of glacial origin

8. In a wind shadow, most of the sand is deposited

    a. in front of the obstacle.
    b. directly behind the obstacle.
    c. on either side of the obstacle.
    d. far behind the obstacle.

9. The slip face of a dune is so named because

    a. it faces the wind.
    b. it is very steep.
    c. it is on the leeward side.
    d. of the sand slides occurring there.

10. Which dune will form with a limited supply of sand?

    a. barchans   c. transverse
    b. seifs   d. foredunes

11. Dunes which are shaped like a crescent, with the horns pointing downward, are called

    a. longitudinal dunes.   c. barchan dunes.
    b. seif dunes.   d. parabolic dunes.

12. The stratification in a dune

    a. is limited to the top layer.
    b. occurs throughout the dune.
    c. occurs only on the foreset beds.
    d. is non-existent.

13. What type of weathering predominates in desert regions?

    a. wind
    b. sunlight
    c. chemical
    d. mechanical

14. Water in desert region

    a. is an important agent of erosion.
    b. is not significant in erosive processes.
    c. serves only as a transportation agent.
    d. acts only to deposit material.

15. Pluvial periods occurring in the deserts of the western U.S. coincided with

    a. the development of deserts.
    b. a rise in sea level.
    c. glaciation.
    d. dry climates.

SUGGESTED ESSAY QUESTIONS

The items below represent the type of discussion questions to which you might be expected to respond. Try writing a response to these, and then discuss your work with another student.

1. Describe in detail how the atmospheric circulation contributes to the existence of the major deserts of the earth.

2. Describe the formation of desert pavements.

3. Explain the lack of a weathering zone on till deposits which are overlain by loess.

4. Use sketches to describe how a wind shadow results in the formation of a sand deposit.

5. List the various dune forms and briefly describe each one, being sure to note their major characteristics.

6. Explain how a playa might become a playa lake.

7. Explain how extensive glaciation of the U.S. might affect the climate of a desert region.

ANSWERS TO SELF-TESTS

Part A: 1. F   6. T   11. F   16. T   Part B: 1. b   6. b   11. c
         2. T   7. F   12. F   17. F   2. b   7. c   12. b
         3. F   8. T   13. T   18. F   3. d   8. b   13. d
         4. T   9. F   14. T   19. F   4. a   9. d   14. a
         5. T   10. F   15. T   20. F   5. c   10. a   15. c

CHAPTER 18

ENERGY

OVERVIEW

Your knowledge of geology should now serve you well in understanding the
problems of resource depletion and requirements, especially with respect to
our energy resources. The authors, therefore, discuss the types of energy
resources and, where appropriate, the extent of such resources. A
distinction is made between renewable and nonrenewable resources. The
fossil fuels (oil, gas, coal) are discussed extensively, with emphasis on
how they are formed and how oil and natural gas may be recovered. The
unconventional sources of petroleum (oil shales and tar sands) are also
discussed, with comments on the problems involved.

Brief mention is made of the use of water power. Nuclear power, both
fission and fusion, is then discussed, including a brief note on how
plutonium-239 may be produced to supplement the scarce uranium-235 isotope.
The technique used in the production of electricity from geothermal energy
is explained. Finally, solar energy, wind, tide, ocean thermal gradients
and biomass are noted as useful energy sources.

LEARNING OBJECTIVES

After studying this chapter, you should be able to:

1. Define and contrast renewable and nonrenewable resources.

2. Describe how coal is formed.

3. List the types of coal and describe how they differ from one another.

4. Sketch the graph which shows the relationship between the energy content of coal and its carbon content.

5. Describe how acid rain is formed.

6. Indicate on a U.S. map the location of the major coal fields.

7. Describe how hydrocarbon-rich layers are formed so that oil and natural gas are recoverable.

8. Sketch and label the six major types of oil traps.

9. Sketch a graph which shows the relationship between oil production in the U.S. and time (1880-2050).

10. Describe how oil and gas can be obtained from oil shale.

11. Indicate on a U.S. map the locations of the major organic-rich shales (oil shales).

12. Describe how tar sands are formed.

13. Describe how uranium-235 can be obtained from a sample of uranium.

14. Describe how plutonium-239 can be made from uranium-238, and explain why it is desirable to do so.

15. Describe how geothermal energy may result in the flow of hot water onto or near the earth's surface.

16. Describe two ways in which geothermal energy can be used to produce electric power.

17. Describe two ways in which solar energy can be used to generate electricity.

18. Describe how each of the following may be used to produce useable energy: wind, tides, biomass (organic waste and plants).

19. Define the following terms: kerogen, source rock, capping bed, reservoir rock, trap, oil shale, tar sand, fission, fusion, breeder reactors, deuterium, tritium.

20. List the various sources (renewable and unrenewable) of energy.

KEY TERMS AND CONCEPTS

natural resources
renewable resources
nonrenewable resources
concentration of resources
distribution of resources
finite resources
infinite resources

coal
oxidizing environment
nonoxidizing environment
coal rank
high rank
low rank
lignite

234

bituminous (soft)
anthracite (hard)
seams
liquefication of coal
gasification of coal
acid rain
acid mine drainage
oil
natural gas
hydrocarbons
marine origin
basins
oxygen-depleted waters
organic-rich sediments
sulfate-utilizing bacteria
kerogen
petroleum and gas accumulation
source rock
capping bed
reservoir rock
trap
known reserves
crude-oil production
oil shale
tar sand
tar
asphalt
bitumin
Green River shale

water storage
hydroelectric power
nuclear power
fission
fusion
radioactive isotopes
neutron bombardment
critical mass
binding energy
breeding
breeder reactor
deuterium
tritium
geothermal power
geysers
hot springs
high heat flow
hydrofraction
solar-thermal systems
photosensitive system
solar energy
wind
wind farms
tidal energy
decaying organic matter
methane gas
plant fermentation
alcohol
oceanic geothermal gradient

NOTES

Sec. 18.1: Natural Resources

Resources may be classified as renewable or nonrenewable. It is not always clear how to classify a specific resource or what criteria to use for the basis of classification. Oil is an obvious nonrenewable resource. Water may or may not be depending upon time and location. New technologies, shifts to substitute resources, and changing consumer practices could influence the classification of a resource.

No one really knows how long a given resource will last. There are too many factors involved.

Sec. 18.2: Coal

Keep in mind that coal is a rock. Know how it is formed, and be able to distinguish the different types of coal. They vary according to the carbon content per kilogram. Be aware of the relationship between carbon content and the energy content. The phenomenon of acid rain is still an active issue as far as what or who is responsible; although it is known that sulfur in fossil fuels, especially coal, can result in the formation of sulfuric acid within the atmosphere.

Sec. 18.3: Oil and Natural Gas

These resources are of marine origin. Know how these hydrocarbons are formed and the very special conditions needed for their formation. Note that the environment must be deficient in both oxygen and sulfate. Note also that the organic content of the sedimentary beds does not have to be great. Be aware that the bulk of the hydrocarbons are not present initially and that the substance kerogen forms first.

Know how these are related: source rock, capping bed, reservoir rock, and trap. Notice that the source rock is usually not the reservoir rock. Be sure you know why this is so. Be able to make labeled sketches of the various oil traps. Familiarity with Figures 18.8 and 18.9 is desirable. You should be able to read and interpret both figures, especially the event known as "Hubbert's pimple". Be clear on how oil shales and tar sands are formed and how oil and gas can be derived from them. The oil shale deposits in the U.S. are extensive, and you should know the location of them. The two major problems involved in oil shales processing are significant: shale disposal and water requirements. Be able to describe the reason for these problems.

Sec. 18.4: Water Power

This is commonly referred to as hydroelectric power. Note that, although it is a clean energy source, its total contribution to the world's supply is limited. Also the associated dam construction for storage of the water has built-in environmental problems.

Sec. 18.5: Nuclear Power

Know the distinction between fission and fusion. Notice that fusion involves light elements and fission heavy elements. Fission is easier to create because of the lower temperature required. The major factor in fission involves neutron capture by a nucleus and the splitting of the nucleus into small fragments, with a release of energy. The uranium-235 isotope does this nicely. Uranium-238, the most abundant isotope, does not fission. Note that the uranium-235 isotope myst be physically, not chemically, separated from the uranium-238 isotope. Uranium is a nonrenewable resource and uranium-235 is especially scarce, but a fissionable atom, plutonium-239, can be created from the more abundant uranium-238. Be aware of how this is done. This technique is called breeding, and the reactors are breeder reactors. Plutonium is extremely hazardous and is also used in nuclear bombs. Thus, the social and political problems involved are complex.

Fusion, on a large scale, has not yet occurred in a reactor. The major problem involves the very high temperature required. Notice that a radioactive substance (tritium) is created, and this does present disposal problems.

Sec. 18.6: Geothermal Power

This energy source has been exploited for a number of years but not on a large scale. Know how and why hot water appears on the earth's surface, and be able to describe the method now used to generate electricity from this hot water. Note that this is not a renewable source of energy.

Sec. 18.7: Solar Energy

Be able to describe the two methods for creating electricity from solar energy. Notice the major distinction between the two: one involves heating a fluid and the other the effect of light energy on photosensitive surfaces.

Sec. 18.8: Other Sources of Energy

Wind and biomass (alcohol and methane gas) production are relatively inexpensive energy sources, but their production on a global scale is limited. The tides and differences in ocean water temperatures are potentially massive stores of usable cheap energy.

PROGRAMMED REVIEW

1. The world's natural resources are found in relatively _____ (large, small) areas and are _____ (uniformly, unevenly) distributed throughout the crust. Most of the natural resources exploited by man for energy and mineral use are, unlike crop production, _____. (365)

    small
    unevenly
    nonrenewable

2. The geologic processes of weathering, erosion, igneous activity, and metamorphism are responsible for the _____ of exploitable natural resources. (365)

    concentration

3. Coal is a _____ formed sedimentary rock formed from _____. Preservation of the remains was favored if they accumulated in a(n) _____ (oxidizing, nonoxidizing) environment. (366)

    biochemically
    plants
    nonoxidizing

4. Coals are classified into ranks based on their _____ content. From lowest to highest rank, they are _____, _____, and _____ coals. These deposits occur in varying thicknesses of beds referred to as _____. (366)

    carbon
    lignite
    bituminous
     (soft)
    anthracite
     (hard)
    seams

5. The United States contains a _____ (high, low) percentage of the world's known coal reserves. (366)

    high

6. _____ gas is produced from coal by a process known as _____. It is also possible to liquefy coal and produce _____. (366)

    Methane
    gasification
    oil

7. A major problem in the exploitation and use of coal is pollution. High sulfur content coals release _____ gas into the atmosphere when burned. This gas combines with atmospheric moisture to form _____ acid. In certain regions downwind from the coal-burning plants, this has produced the phenomenon known as _____ that has had deleterious effects on forests and lakes. Another pollution problem stems from the mining of the coal. In coal-mining regions, it is not uncommon to find acidified streams. This is the result of _____ from the mines, and it makes many streams unsuitable for fish and other aquatic life. (368)

sulfur dioxide
sulfuric acid
acid rain
acid mine
    drainage

8. By comparison to coal, _____ and _____ are relatively clean fossil fuels. (368)

oil
natural gas

9. Petroleum and natural gas are almost always associated with _____ rocks of _____ origin. They were derived from _____ and are mixtures of _____ compounds. (368)

sedimentary
marine
organic remains
hydrocarbons

10. The accumulation and preservation of organic remains is favored in basins that have _____ (good, poor) bottom circulation that allows the bottoms to become depleted of _____. It is also important for the basin to have an absence of bacteria that utilize the _____ from seawater to break down the organic matter. (368)

poor
oxygen
sulfates

11. The formation of the hydrocarbons is a two-stage process. In the first stage, the organic matter is converted to _____. The second stage in the production of hydrocarbons depends upon _____. Oil is produced by the _____ end of this stage, and natural gas at the _____ end. (368)

kerogen
temperature
lower
upper

12. Any sedimentary rock that has naturally generated a great enough accumulation of hydrocarbons to form a commercial deposit of oil and natural gas is referred to as the _____. However, these rocks are usually not very permeable, and the petroleum must migrate into more permeable material. This is accomplished by the _____ of overlying rock, the production of _____ during the breakdown of the hydrocarbons which generate considerable _____, and the _____ (high, low) density of the oil, which allows it to migrate through any _____ saturated and permeable rock. (370)

source rock
weight
gas
pressure
low
water

13. If oil and gas encounter no barriers, they will
    eventually migrate to the surface. To keep them
    underground requires the presence of a _____
    bed. The oil and gas is then trapped below in
    what is known as the _____ rock. These two
    rock units form what is called a _____. (370)

    capping
    reservoir
    trap

14. The greatest oil and gas production comes from
    rocks of _____ age, followed by rocks of _____
    and _____ age. There is no production from
    rocks of _____ age. The most likely explanation
    for this distribution is the fact that the _____
    the trap, the more likely it will be destroyed by
    natural geologic processes. (370)

    Cenozoic
    Mesozoic
    Paleozoic
    Precambrian
    older

15. The major oil and gas traps of North America have
    already been discovered. Most of the new
    production from North America will come from the
    _____ of Canada and Alaska and from the _____.
    (372)

    arctic
    continental
      margins

16. A potential, though difficult to extract
    economically, source of fossil fuel are the
    _____ and _____. (374, 375)

    oil shales
    tar sands

17. The greatest concentration of oil shales in the
    United States is found in a freshwater lake
    deposit of _____ age from Colorado, Wyoming,
    and Utah known as the _____ shale. (375)

    Eocene
    Green River

18. Besides the economic considerations involved,
    there are several technical problems that must
    be overcome before commercial production becomes
    feasible. The production process requires vast
    quantities of _____ from a region in which it
    is deficient. An environmental problem stems
    from the process itself. The _____ of the shale
    increases during extraction, leaving an excess of
    spent material to be disposed. (375)

    water
    volume

19. The tar sands contain hydrocarbons that have been
    brought close to or to the surface where they
    may remain for a considerable (geologic) period
    of time. These deposits have a _____ (high,
    low) volatility and _____ (high, low) viscosity.
    These deposits are also known as _____, _____,
    or _____. In North America, the greatest
    concentration is found in _____. (375)

    low
    high
    tar
    asphalt
    bitumin
    Canada

20. Because fossil fuels are nonrenewable resources,
    the production of usable energy from alternative
    sources is of the utmost importance. At the
    present time, the most practical power sources
    seem to be _____, _____, _____, and _____.
    (376)

    water
    nuclear
    geothermal
    solar

239

21. Water power is advantageous, because it is a renewable source. However, there are drawbacks to its use. Dams are required for _____ of water, and they have a limited lifetime because of _____ that takes place in the lakes they form. The damming of rivers also destroys scenic areas, geologically and historically significant regions, takes productive land out of production, and alters the ecological equilibrium of an area by _____ its valleys. (376)

storage
sedimentation
drowning

22. The power of the atom is contained in the _____ energy of its _____. This energy may be liberated by breaking the nucleus into lighter-weight elements by the process of _____ or by the combining of nuclei to form heavier elements by the process of _____. (376)

binding
nucleus
fission
fusion

23. The fuel used to power nuclear reactors is derived from the heavy element _____. However, it is not the common isotope of this element, _____, that is the power source, but the _____ (lighter, heavier) isotope _____. This requires expensive processing to concentrate the necessary isotope. (376)

uranium
U-238
lighter
U-235

24. In the fission process, a slow-moving _____ smashes into the _____ of a _____ atom. This results in the formation of two new atomic nuclei of _____ (less, more) mass and the conversion of mass to _____. Also produced are several new _____. For the reaction to be spontaneous, there must be a sufficient number of nuclei present so the bombarding neutrons will always hit a target. The quantity of fissionable material required for this reaction is known as the _____. (376)

neutron
nucleus
U-235
less
energy
neutrons
critical mass

25. Because uranium must be mined, it is technically a _____ resource. However, there are methods available to artificially produce fissionable atoms by a process called _____. Reactors that use this process are known as _____ reactors. (376)

nonrenewable
breeding
breeder

26. The fusion process is the same process used by the sun to produce energy. That is, it requires the fusion of _____ and _____ nuclei to produce energy. Controlled fusion would rely on the isotope of hydrogen known as _____ for a fuel. The source of this fuel would be unlimited, as it would come from the _____. (376, 377)

hydrogen
helium
deuterium
ocean

27. The sources of geothermal energy are found in
    _____, _____, and _____ found in many places
    at the earth's surface. Because the heat flow
    within the earth is diffused, it is necessary to
    find areas where it is concentrated. These
    places are found along _____ boundaries and
    _____ away from the boundaries. (377)

volcanoes
geysers
hot springs
plate
hot spots

28. The bulk of the commercial production from
    geothermal sources rely on geothermal _____ as
    the energy source. (377)

steam

29. Besides the relatively restricted areas from
    which geothermal energy can be produced, a major
    problem is the vast quantity of _____ associated
    with the geothermal fluids. These can lead to
    high costs for equipment maintenance due to
    _____ of the elements. (378)

mineral matter
precipitation

30. The ultimate renewable source of power may be
    derived from _____ energy. There are two
    possible techniques that may be used to collect
    and use the sun's energy directly. The _____
    system(s) employ lenses and mirrors to focus
    sunlight onto a receiver, which is then used to
    heat a _____ to drive the turbines needed to
    generate electricity. A second system requires
    the use of a _____ material that can convert
    the sun's energy directly into electricity. (378)

solar
solar-thermal
fluid
photosensitive

31. An energy source that has been used for centuries
    on a local scale to supply the energy of
    individual homes and farms is the _____. In
    certain areas, it is possible to use a network
    of windmills to create _____ farms, which are
    capable of supplying a considerable quantity of
    electricity on a local and, in certain cases, a
    more regional basis. (378)

wind
wind

32. A major source of power to generate vast quantities
    of electricity in certain coastal areas like the
    Bay of Fundy is the _____. (378)

tide

33. _____ is easily generated from organic wastes
    (pig manure is excellent) and is a possible
    replacement for natural gas. Another fuel
    source is the production of _____ from the
    fermentation of plant material. (378)

methane gas
alcohol

34. Another large-scale energy source makes or could
    make use of the difference in temperature between
    the _____ bottom and _____ surface waters of
    the ocean. This temperature change is referred
    to as the _____ of the ocean.

cold
warm
geothermal
  gradient

SELF-TESTS

Part A: True-False Statements

Each of the following statements is either true or false. Encircle either T or F for each item.

1. Anthracite is a coal which has the highest carbon content. T F

2. The energy content of a particular coal depends directly on the amount of carbon present in the coal. T F

3. Acid rain is formed when atmospheric water combines with the sulfur in coal dust. T F

4. Oil and natural gas most likely are formed from animal remains. T F

5. In order to form petroleum, the basin in which the organic remains accumulate must be oxygen- and sulfate-deficient. T F

6. Sediments which will eventually provide petroleum are usually muds and sands. T F

7. Kerogen is formed by the chemical, biological, and physical alteration of organic matter after burial of the organic-rich sediments. T F

8. Hydrocarbons are formed from kerogen by the heat generated due to deep burial. T F

9. A "source rock" is a layer of fine-grained sedimentary rock which contains an abundance of organic material. T F

10. A "reservoir rock" is a layer to which the hydrocarbons have moved and which is overlain by an impermeable layer called a "capping bed." T F

11. Oil shales are shales which once contained enough organic matter to produce kerogen. T F

12. By heating oil shale, the kerogen can be converted to hydrocarbon, thus producing oil and gas. T F

13. The Green River formation consists of oil shales, which occur in portions of Colorado, Utah, and Wyoming. T F

14. The water power capacity of the U.S. is about 90% developed. T F

15. Uranium-235 is used in fission energy production, instead of uranium-238, because the isotope 235 is more plentiful. T F

16. Plutonium-239 is a nonfissionable element because it is derived from uranium-238. T F

17. In any sample of uranium, only about 1 atom in 140 atoms   T   F
    is uranium-235.

18. Plutonium-239 can be created by a uranium-238 nucleus   T   F
    absorbing a neutron.

19. Tritium, which is produced in the fusion of hydrogen   T   F
    isotopes, is the only nonradioactive substance produced
    in the fusion reaction.

20. One source of geothermal energy is the hot, igneous rocks   T   F
    which heat underground water.

Part B: Multiple Choice Items

Each of the following can be completed correctly by choosing only one word
or phrase. Encircle the letter a, b, c, or d, designating your choice.

1. Natural resources can be classified as renewable or nonrenewable. A
   nonrenewable energy resource is one which

   a. consists of materials which required at least 30 to 50 years to
      form.
   b. consists of materials which are being formed within three or four
      human generations.
   c. which require thousands, if not millions, of years to form.
   d. must be of extraterrestrial origin.

2. Coal is a nonrenewable resource which

   a. is a mineral and metamorphic rock.
   b. is a mineral that contains much carbon.
   c. is an organic material containing petrified organic remains.
   d. occurs in great abundance only on the American continents.

3. Coal can be classified according to the percentage of carbon it
   contains. In order of increasing carbon content, these types are

   a. anthracite, bituminous, lignite.
   b. lignite, bituminous, anthracite.
   c. bituminous, lignite, anthracite.
   d. anthracite, lignite, bituminous.

4. The amount of recoverable coal existing in the U.S. is on the order of

   a. 10^6 tons.   c. 10^{12} tons.
   b. 10^9 tons.   d. 10^{15} tons.

5. Methane can be produced from coal by

   a. combining coal with natural gas.
   b. compressing coal to drive out the methane.
   c. heating coal in a process known as gasification.
   d. melting the coal, thus converting it to a liquid.

6. Most potential oil-rich rocks begin as sediments which are

   a. muds and silts, eventually forming shales and siltstones.
   b. porous sands, eventually forming porous sandstones.
   c. rich in calcium carbonate, eventually forming limestone.
   d. rich in peat and eventually convert to oil.

7. Hydrocarbons, the chief component of natural gas and petroleum, are formed

   a. by conversion of kerogen at minimum temperatures of 50° to $60^{\circ}C$.
   b. only after kerogen is pressed out of the rock due to burial.
   c. only at depths of 10 kilometers or more.
   d. only from kerogen-rich animal remains.

8. The source for petroleum is

   a. the rock layer containing the oil being obtained.
   b. the rock layer from which the petroleum and gas were formed originally.
   c. the oceanic sediment in which the organic material lived.
   d. the oldest rock from which the secrets of oil formation were deciphered.

9. Oil traps could be formed by which of the following?

   a. barrier beaches, levees, craters
   b. synclines, faults, salt domes
   c. sinkholes, reefs, sand lenses
   d. anticlines, unconformities, salt domes

10. Kerogen occurs in oil shales because

    a. the shale was rich in organic matter and was buried deep enough.
    b. hydrocarbons were forced out of the rock.
    c. the organic matter present was not in great enough quantities.
    d. the rocks beneath the oil shale are a source of oil.

11. If all the world's water power capacity were fully exploited, how much would water power contribute to the total world energy needs (1980)?

    a. 10%   c. 75%
    b. 30%   d. 50%

12. Nuclear fusion is an energy-producing process which occurs when

    a. a light nucleus splits to form even lighter nuclei.
    b. a heavier nucleus splits to form lighter nuclei.
    c. two light nuclei combine to form a heavier nucleus.
    d. light nuclei are compressed to release the energy.

13. Fusion, as an energy source, is more desirable than fission because

    a. it is easier to make electricity from fusion than from fission.
    b. no radioactivity is involved.
    c. the sun still has billions of years left before exhausting its
       fusion fuel.
    d. much less radioactivity is involved.

14. Power produced from geothermal processes is

    a. pollution-free.   c. dependent on the use of water.
    b. infinite.   d. noiseless and odorless

SUGGESTED ESSAY QUESTIONS

The items below represent the type of discussion questions to which you
might be expected to respond. Try writing a response to these, and then
discuss your work with another student.

1. Discuss the concepts of renewable and nonrenewable resources. Be sure
   to indicate the criteria for classifying a resource as one or the
   other.

2. Explain how the various types of coal are formed, and comment on the
   relative energy content of each type.

3. What is the relationship among these phenomena: source rock, capping
   bed, reservoir rock, trap.

4. Describe the process which may be used to tap geothermal energy, even
   though no residual water supply is associated with the source of
   geothermal energy.

5. What are two techniques which may be used to produce electric power
   directly from solar energy?

ANSWERS TO SELF-TESTS

Part A: 1. T   6. F   11. T   16. F   Part B: 1. c   6. a   11. b
         2. T   7. T   12. T   17. T   2. a   7. a   12. c
         3. F   8. T   13. T   18. T   3. b   8. b   13. d
         4. F   9. F   14. F   19. F   4. c   9. d   14. c
         5. T   10. T   15. F   20. T   5. c   10. a

CHAPTER 19

USEFUL MATERIALS

OVERVIEW

All societies today require certain resources in order to function.
Industrialized societies in particular are the greatest consumers of the
planet's materials. All of these useful materials have been formed by
geological processes with which by now you are probably familiar. The
materials useful to society are the mineral deposits throughout the earth.
These deposits are obtained by a number of mining techniques. The various
mineral deposits can be classified as metal or nonmetal, with the metals
further classified according to their abundance. A number of resources,
both metals and nonmetals, are described throughout this chapter, along
with comments regarding their longevity.

LEARNING OBJECTIVES

After studying this chapter, you should be able to:

1. List and describe the types of mining operations.

2. Describe the geological processes which are responsible for the
    creation of mineral deposits.

3. Define the following: hydrothermal activity, metallic deposit, ore,
    placer, gem, magmatic segregation, nonmetallic deposit, strategic
    mineral.

4. Relate minerals to temperature and their process of formation.

5. List the common metallic and nonmetallic ores.

6. Describe the various ways in which iron ore is formed.

7. Relate metallic mineral deposits to plate tectonics.

8. List the common uses for metallic and nonmetallic ores.

9. List the elements which are important for fertilizer production.

10. Describe the sources and origins of the elements from which fertilizer is produced.

11. List the common building materials.

12. Describe the sources for building stones.

13. Describe how cement is made.

14. List the various uses for each of the building materials.

15. Describe how plaster is made.

16. Distinguish between precious and semiprecious gems.

17. Describe how diamond is formed, and state one theory for the origin of the kimberlite pipes.

18. List some key strategic elements, and describe how their demand can be met in times of scarcity.

KEY TERMS AND CONCEPTS

metallic mineral deposits
nonmetallic mineral deposits
open-pit (strip) mining
quarrying
placer mining
underground mining
ore
magma
magmatic segregation
fractionation
hydrothermal solutions
banded iron ores (taconite)
oolitic iron ores
marine evaporites
weathering and ores
groundwater and ores
placer formation ores
rock formation ores
porphyry copper deposits
fertilizers

nitrogen fixation
superphosphate
ammonium sulfate
roasting of ores
building stone
aggregate
concrete
cement
plaster
asbestos
glass
clay
gems
precious gems
semiprecious gems
kimberlite pipes
optical properties
durability of gems
strategic minerals

NOTES

Sec. 19.1: Mineral Deposits

Keep in mind that, for the most part, all the mineral deposits have been formed by the familiar geological processes, including weathering.

Sec. 19.2: Metallic Deposits

Pay careful attention to Fig. 19.7, and note the similarity between metallic mineral formation and the rock cycle. Look over Table 19.1, and make associations between the ore minerals and their contained metal, the mineral groups that contain the most common ores, the geologic process of formation, and the global distribution of the important ores. Note also the relationship between the formation of metallic ore deposits and plate boundaries.

Sec. 19.3: Nonmetallic Deposits

Notice that these minerals are heavily used in agriculture for the production of fertilizers, the chemical industry, and especially as pure rock formation in the building and construction industry. Note that the term clay could mean the mineral group or the size of the particles.

Sec. 19.4: Earth Materials and Society

This brief comment notes that any removal of a resource most likely will involve problems and questions related to economics, politics, health, environmental disruption and degradation, and the general well-being of a society. You should know what and where the key strategic minerals are and how they may be obtained in times of scarcity.

PROGRAMMED REVIEW

1. Any earth material extracted from the ground for its economic value constitutes a _____. It may be _____ or _____. (382)

    mineral deposit
    metallic
    nonmetallic

2. Material may be extracted by using surface processes. Examples of this type of extraction are _____, _____, and _____ mining. (382)

    open-pit (strip)
    quarrying
    placer

3. Building material and rock aggregate (crushed stone) is usually obtained by _____ methods. Coal and low-grade copper ores are commonly extracted by _____ mining. Gold, tin, and diamonds are most economically extracted when obtained by _____ mining. (382)

    quarrying
    open-pit (strip)
    placer

4. Any earth material that cannot be obtained by surface methods falls into the realm of _____ mining. (382)

    underground

5. If the extractable material can be removed profitably, it is referred to as an _____. (382)

ore

6. Valuable mineral deposits are formed by geologic processes. Igneous activity is a major former of ore bodies because of the concentration of elements found in the molten mixture or melt called _____. During crystallization, the early formed minerals are _____ (more, less) dense than the later ones. One of the earliest minerals to crystallize is a nonsilicate mineral known as _____. Accumulations of high-grade ore of this mineral accumulate in the process of _____, also known as _____. (384, 385)

magma
more
magnetite
fractionation
magmatic
  segregation

7. In the final stages of magmatic crystallization, the end stage fluids may give rise to a _____ (fine, coarse) textured rock known as _____. This rock is composed chiefly of _____ and _____, but in some cases contains many valuable minerals.

coarse
pegmatite
quartz
orthoclase
  (feldspar)

8. Igneous activity also gives rise to heated fluids that circulate well beyond the immediate vicinity of the activity and work their way into country rock. These fluids are called _____, and they carry metallic _____, which may crystallize into a valuable deposit under proper conditions. This type of activity is even known in the marine environment, where it is found along oceanic _____. These types of mineralizations (terrestrial and marine) result in the minerals forming _____ in the surrounding country rock. (385)

hydrothermal
  solutions
ions
ridges
veins

9. Many of the ore deposits that result from hydrothermal solutions are found in highly reactive _____ rocks. The most common group of hydrothermal minerals is the _____. Typical of this group are the ores of lead and zinc known as _____ and _____, respectively. (385)

carbonate
sulfides
galena
sphalerite

10. Some mineral deposits are formed directly by the process of sedimentation. Among these are the low grade iron ores of the Lake Superior district known as _____ iron ores or _____. These ores were believed to have formed in seas of _____ age, and they contain a high percentage of silica in the form of _____. (385)

banded
taconite
Precambrian
chert

11. Another type of sedimentary iron ore is also of marine origin but is found as individual sphere-like grains called _____. They are usually found with sandstones and shales that are often _____. (385)

oolites
calcareous

12. Important nonmetallic mineral deposits called
_____ are formed by the direct precipitation of
mineral matter from seawater. Some calcium
carbonate is formed this way, but _____ and
_____ are two useful products, used in the
building and chemical industries, that are formed
by this method. When the seawater reaches about
4 percent of its original volume, it will contain
a complex mixture of _____ and _____ salts
that, when precipitated, are valuable products
for the fertilizer industry. (385, 386)

    evaporites
    gypsum
    halite
    potassium
    magnesium

13. Uranium ores are commonly associated with buried
stream deposits and are believed to have been
deposited by _____, carrying the ore material
and subsequently depositing it in buried trees
by replacement of the organic remains. The
canary yellow uranium ore called _____ is an
example of this type of deposit. (386)

    groundwater
    carnotite

14. Many mineral deposits are created and more often
enriched by the surface process of _____. The
mineral _____, which is the principal ore of
_____, is characteristic of this type of mineral
formation. (386, 387)

    weathering
    bauxite
    aluminium

15. Minerals that are liberated by the weathering
process and are chemically stable, dense, and
abrasion-resistant are commonly transported to
other localities by _____, where they may become
concentrated enough to form a mineral deposit.
This type of formation is called a _____. (387)

    streams
    placer

16. Most metallic ores that are mined in large
quantities are usually _____ or _____. Gold,
platinum, and sometimes silver are found as
_____ elements. Tin, iron, titanium, uranium,
and chromium are usually extracted from ores as
_____. Zinc, lead, mercury, molybdenum,
and nickel most commonly occur as _____.
(387, 388)

    oxides
    sulfides
    native
    oxides
    sulfides

17. Many mineral deposits are closely associated with
igneous activity and plate tectonics. This
should not be surprising, because igneous and
hydrothermal activity is concentrated along
_____ and _____ plate boundaries. (390)

    converging
    diverging

18. Modern sediments in the Red Sea are presently
undergoing extensive mineralization by invading
_____ solutions from circulating seawater that
enters the oceanic crust below. These deposits
and the more ancient ones on Cyprus are associated
with a _____ plate boundary. (390)

    hydrothermal
    diverging

19. The low-grade copper deposits of the American southwest, Alaska, and Chile seem to be formed by _____ solutions associated with a _____ plate boundary. The copper is extracted from _____ ores by the _____ method. (390)

hydrothermal
converging
sulfide
open-pit

20. Nonmetallic mineral deposits are most commonly needed for use in agriculture to process for use as _____. They also find important uses in the _____ industry, as well as _____ and _____. (390, 391)

fertilizers
chemical
building
construction

21. Nitrogen used to be extracted from naturally occurring deposits of a mineral group known as _____. However, these deposits have been mined out, and now nitrogen for fertilizer use must be produced artifically. It cannot be extracted directly from the atmosphere, because plants cannot use it directly. It must, therefore, be _____ or combined with other elements before it can be used by vegetation. (390, 391)

nitrates
fixed

22. Although potassium is a common element found in rocks, it is only commercially valuable when found in the sedimentary rocks known as _____. The two most important mineral surces of potassium are the minerals _____ and _____, which were deposited in _____ (deep, shallow) and _____ (open, restricted) marine basins of the past. (391)

evaporites
sylvite
carnalite
shallow
restricted

23. The primary source of phosphorus is the mineral _____, which is found in _____ (nonmarine, marine) sedimentary rocks. (391)

spatite
marine

24. Sulfur is heavily used in the fertilizer industry to produce _____ and _____. Some is derived from native sulfur, but most is produced from the mineral _____ found in association with salt domes. It is also recovered as a by-product in the refining of sulfide ores by a burning process called _____. (391)

superphosphate
ammonium sulfate
gypsum
roasting

25. If a mineral deposit uses the entire rock rather than extracting a segment of it for use, it is referred to as a _____ formation. The best example of this type of deposit is _____. (392)

rock
building stone

26. Crushed rock is referred to as _____, when used to make concrete. It is also used directly as a base for _____. (392)

aggregate
roads

27. Much sand and gravel is taken from glacial _____ deposits, as well as old stream _____ deposits and beaches. (392)

outwash
terrace

28. Cement is made from a mixture of _____ and clay or shale. When mixed with an aggregate of crushed rock, sand, or gravel, it is the binding agent in the product called _____. (392, 393)

limestone
concrete

29. _____ is a very important product in the manufacture of brick, porcelain, tiles, and ceramic pipe. This material comes from the _____ of minerals in rock and is most abundant in the sedimentary rock called _____. (393)

Clay
weathering
shale

30. The raw material for the making of glass is the mineral _____. It is extracted from pure _____ and _____ deposits. (393)

quartz
sandstones
unconsolidated

31. An important material used for its thermal qualities, corrosion resistance, and fire-retardation properties is called _____. The commercial source of this material is the mineral _____ associated with the igneous rock _____. A very serious problem with this material is its direct link to certain types of _____. (393)

asbestos
chrysotile
peridotite
lung cancer

32. Minerals that are extracted for their aesthetic beauty, durability, and rarity are called _____. The physical qualities of this group of minerals is dependent upon such optical properties as _____, _____, and _____. Its durability is a function of its _____ and lack of _____ and _____. (393)

gems
color
luster
fire
hardness
cleavage
fracture

33. Gems are classified into _____ and _____ stones. The most valuable of the precious stones are the _____, which are composed of _____ formed under extremely high temperatures and pressures. They are often associated with conduits or pipes known as _____, which is a variety of the rock peridotite. Even though the diamonds are associated with this rock, most of the world supply comes from _____ deposits, where the diamonds are concentrated after being released from the rock by _____. (394)

precious
semiprecious
diamonds
carbon
kimberlites
placer
weathering

34. The sapphire and the ruby are varieties of the mineral _____. The most abundant supplies of these gems are found in southeast _____. The emerald is a variety of the mineral _____ and is found in _____ rocks. (394)

corundum
Asia
beryl
pegmatite

35. Any mineral that is very important to the security   strategic
    of a nation and is in short supply within its own   substitutes
    boundaries is called a _____ mineral. The supply   exploration
    of these minerals can sometimes be met by the   stockpiling
    development of _____, extensive _____ within
    the country, and the _____ of materials.
    Unfortunately, the demand is sometimes met by
    colonization or conquest. (394)

SELF-TESTS

Part A: True-False Statements

Each of the following statements is either true or false. Encircle either
T or F for each item.

1. Placer mining is a surface or near-surface mining technique   T   F
   usually involving the separating of economically valuable
   materials from unconsolidated sand and gravel.

2. Mineral deposits which are economically attractive are   T   F
   formed by a set of unusual and unique geological processes.

3. Because of the high density of iron ores, they are commonly   T   F
   mined as placer deposits.

4. Some soils can be mined for their iron content because   T   F
   weathering may create lateritic soils rich in iron oxides.

5. Low-grade copper ores are extensively mined by underground   T   F
   methods.

6. Bauxite is the aluminum ore formed by the weathering of   T   F
   silicate minerals.

7. Titanium can be obtained from seawater.   T   F

8. Tin, tungsten, and chromium are scarce strategic metals.   T   F

9. Copper can be formed by sedimentary processes.   T   F

10. Nickel can be formed by magmatic segregation and by   T   F
    weathering, resulting in lateritic soils.

11. The richest deposits of chromite, the ore mineral for   T   F
    chromium, occur in South Africa.

12. Nonmetallic mineral deposits include the fertilizers and   T   F
    building materials.

13. Nitrogen, essential for healthy plant growth, can be   T   F
    obtained by plants directly from the atmosphere.

14. The dried excrement of cows is useful as a source of   T   F
    nitrates.

15. Sylvite (potassium chloride) is a marine evaporite and   T   F
    one of the first compounds to crystallize during
    evaporation.

16. Diamonds are probably formed at the base of the mantle.   T   F

17. Raw materials for clay come only from the clay minerals. T   F

18. The raw material for plaster is obtained from plasterite, T   F
    which is an evaporite.

19. Most raw materials are mined in the developed countries, T   F
    and the manufactured materials are then shipped to the
    less developed nations.

Part B: Multiple Choice Items

Each of the following can be completed correctly by choosing only one word
or phrase. Encircle the letter a, b, c, or d, designating your choice.

1. The geological processes involved directly in creating mineral
   deposits do not include

   a. hydrothermal activity.   c. weathering.
   b. glaciation.   d. rock formation.

2. The abundant metallic ores include iron, aluminum, manganese,

   a. copper, and lead.   c. molybdenum, and chromium.
   b. zinc, and nickel.   d. titanium, and magnesium.

3. Bauxite, the ore of aluminum, is formed by

   a. weathering.   c. magmatic segregation.
   b. hydrothermal activity.   d. sedimentation.

4. One use for titanium is in the production of

   a. electricity.   c. cement.
   b. aircraft.   d. steel.

5. Which one of the following does not pertain to copper ore?

   a. chalcopyrite
   b. converging plate boundaries
   c. placer deposits
   d. associated with sedimentary rocks

6. Which mineral can be formed by weathering?

   a. nickel   c. gold
   b. molybdenum   d. tungsten

7. Which of the following minerals can be formed by hydrothermal activity?

   a. nickel
   b. platinum
   c. copper
   d. chromium

8. Three chemical fertilizers are

   a. magnesium, guano, basalt.
   b. carbon, oxygen, nitrogen.
   c. nitrogen, phosphorus, potassium.
   d. krypton, xenon, comeon.

9. The usual source of potassium for use as a fertilizer is

   a. the silicate minerals.
   b. marine evaporites.
   c. lava flows.
   d. the atmosphere.

10. What do the following have in common: gypsum, halite, sylvite, carnalite?

   a. They are sources for potassium.
   b. They are freshwater evaporite minerals.
   c. They are only found in the U.S.
   d. They are salts which occur in marine evaporite deposits.

11. Which of the following pertains to diamond?

   a. associated with coal
   b. formed in volcanoes
   c. mostly quartz
   d. originates in upper mantle

12. Which building material does not involve any particular mineral?

   a. clay
   b. asbestos
   c. cement
   d. plaster

13. What two materials could be obtained from the same resource?

   a. building stones and plaster
   b. cement and glass
   c. sand and glass
   d. asbestos and sand

14. Clay is a term applied to

   a. certain minerals.
   b. the composition of bricks.
   c. the mineral gypsum.
   d. all material below a certain size.

15. Which of the following is not true about the world's resources?

   a. Most are consumed in the more developed countries.
   b. Most are mined in the less developed countries.
   c. They will eventually become very scarce for most people.
   d. They are, geographically, evenly distributed.

SUGGESTED ESSAY QUESTIONS

The items below represent the type of discussion questions to which you might be expected to respond. Try writing a response to these, and then discuss your work with another student.

1. Describe and discuss the various mining techniques.

2. Give several examples of how an ore could be formed by weathering.

3. Explain what is meant by a strategic mineral and how it may be obtained in times of scarcity.

4. Describe how diamonds, which are formed in the mantle, occur on the surface.

ANSWERS TO SELF-TESTS

Part A:
1. T	6. T	11. T	16. F
2. F	7. F	12. T	17. F
3. F	8. T	13. F	18. F
4. T	9. T	14. F	19. F
5. F	10. T	15. F	

Part B:
1. b	6. a	11. d
2. d	7. c	12. a
3. a	8. c	13. c
4. b	9. b	14. d
5. c	10. d	15. d

CHAPTER 20

PLANETS, MOONS, AND METEORITES

OVERVIEW

A fitting climax to your study of the earth and the geologic principles that shaped its natural history is to see how these experiences and observations apply to extraterrestrial bodies. In this final chapter, the authors point out the similarities, differences, and relationships between the earth, its history and dynamic processes, and those of our moon, the Sun, planets, other moons, asteroids, and meteorites that comprise our solar system, as well as those occasional visitors, the comets.

LEARNING OBJECTIVES

After studying this chapter, you should be able to:

1. List the observable apparent motions of extraterrestrial bodies as seen from Earth.

2. State briefly the geocentric ideas of Aristotle and other ancient Greek philosophers.

3. State briefly the heliocentric ideas of Aristarchus and Copernicus.

4. Give a working definition of the solar system in terms of forces.

5. Describe the sun in relation to: other stars, its composition, energy production, and origin.

6. Define the term planet.

7. Describe the revolution and rotation of the planets.

8. Give a thumbnail description of each of the planets and major satellites.

9. Contrast the terrestrial and outer planets.

10. Describe the major features of the moon and what light they shed on its origin and history.

11. Contrast the composition of moon rock and earth rock.

12. Compare the geologic processes of impact, weathering and erosion, tectonics, and volcanic activity on the earth with the terrestrial planets.

13. Describe the asteroid belt and its relationship to meteorites.

14. Contrast iron and stony meteorites.

15. Describe how meteorites are used to study the history of our solar system.

16. Describe the physical composition of a comet, and distinguish between periodic and nonperiodic types.

KEY TERMS AND CONCEPTS

earth-centered solar system
    (geocentric)
sun-centered solar system
    (heliocentric)
Aristotle
Aristarchus
Copernicus
solar system
sun's gravitational control
fusion
dust cloud
nebula
planet
ecliptic
revolution
rotation
terrestrial planets
outer planets
Galileo
The Starry Messenger
maria

highlands
primary craters
secondary craters (satellite
    craters)
impact crater
ray crater
dry ice polar caps
asteroids
Galilean moons
saturnalia
heliopause
meteors
meteorites
Amor asteroids
iron meteorites
stony meteorites
chondrites
chondrules
achondrites
carbonaceous chondrites
comets

NOTES

Sec. 20.1: Our Sun and Solar System

Don't overlook the brief historical segment on the place of the earth in
our solar system. The geocentric or earth-centered system developed by the
Levantine Greek Ptolemy described the apparent motions of the heavenly
bodies as seen from the earth. This system worked very well for centuries
to make astronomical predictions and was within itself an accurate
conceptual model. Remember, it is not at all readily apparent that the
earth rotates on its axis and revolves around the sun.

Notice the emphasis placed on gravitational form in the definition of the
solar system. Table 20.1 and Table 20.2 contain a wealth of information
and are excellent summaries of the known physical characteristics of the
solar system. Use them as a handy reference.

Sec. 20.2 - Sec. 20.3: Mercury and Venus

These are pure descriptive sections for these planets. Note the mammoth
"greenhouse" effect created by the high carbon dioxide content of the
Venusian atmosphere.

Sec. 20.4: Earth

Obviously the subject of this text. Note that, for obtaining information
about the very early history of the earth, we get very valuable information
from extraterrestrial bodies.

Sec. 20.5: Earth's Moon

This is an important section on our closest neighbor. Throughout this
section, note how terrestrial geologic principles are used to describe and
interpret the history of the moon. Also note that the moon today is an
essentially quiescent body very unlike the earth.

Sec. 20.6: Mars

Another planet with a cratered surface. Note that the surface is composed
of cratered plains of different relative ages and that the planet may be
subdivided into two hemispheres at their boundary, even though it is
steeply inclined to the Martian equator. Notice also that Mars shows
evidence of extensive vulcanism but does not show any evidence of the plate
tectonics we find on earth. Don't overlook the apparent effective work of
streams on the Martian surface. The features of stream erosion are
analogous to those on earth, although there is no evidence of present
stream erosion. The characteristic features of wind erosion (Chap. 17) are
presently being formed on the surface of Mars. Finally, note that Mars
appears to have been a relatively dynamic planet in its history.

Sec. 20.7: Overview of our Moon and the Terrestrial Planets

Study this section carefully. Rather than considering the moon and the
terrestrial planets as isolated bodies to be described, the authors
integrate the similarities, differences, and unique features of the bodies,

in comparison to the earth and earth processes.

Sec. 20.8: Asteroids

Note the placement of the asteroid belt between the outermost of
terrestrial planets (Mars) and the innermost of the outer planets
(Jupiter). This region seems to be a primary source of the meteorites that
strike the earth.

Sec. 20.9 - 20.12: Jupiter, Saturn, Uranus, and Beyond Uranus

These sections describe the outer planets from Jupiter to Uranus, and
briefly mention Neptune and Pluto. Notice that, with the exception of
Pluto, these planets have a much greater equatorial diameter than the
terrestrial planets and a greater mass. However, the density is much less
as a result of their gaseous interior composition and relatively small rock
cores. It is the satellites of these planets that show the greatest
similarity to the earth and the other terrestrial planets.

Sec. 20.13: Meteorites

Note the difference between a meteor and a meteorite. Know the difference
between the iron and stony meteorites and why the information obtained from
meteorites is important in interpreting the history of the solar system.
Finally, since meteorites represent fragments from the very early
beginnings of the solar system, it is interesting to note the presence of
the building blocks of life, hydrocarbons and amino acids, in some
meteorites. Note that these components are of inorganic origin, and it is
only suggested that under the right conditions they could possibly become
the progenitors of life.

Sec. 20.14: Comets

The term perturbed refers to the astronomical phenomenon known as
perturbation. This phenomenon is the result of a gravitational force
causing an astronomical body to deviate from its normal course. Note that
most comets do not make predictable passes through our solar system.

PROGRAMMED REVIEW

1. As we observe the motion of the stars and other   east
   heavenly bodies, we see that they rise in the   west
   _____ and set in the _____. This apparent   west
   motion is the result of the earth rotating on   east
   its axis from _____ to _____. (398)

2. The idea that the earth was not at the center   Aristarchus
   of the solar system, but was rather in orbit   Copernicus
   around the sun, was first advanced by the Greek
   natural philosopher _____ and firmly established
   (at least in "scientific" minds) by the published
   work of _____ in 1543. (398)

3. Everything within the sun's _____ control
    constitutes what we call the _____. (398)

    gravitational
    solar system

4. The bulk of the sun is composed of the elements
    _____ and _____. The conversion of one of
    these elements, _____, to the other, _____, is
    accomplished by the process of _____ with an
    attendant release of _____. (398)

    hydrogen
    helium
    hydrogen
    helium
    fusion
    energy

5. A disklike cloud of dust and gas is called a
    _____. (398)

    nebula

6. The age of the solar system is believed to be
    between _____ (4-5 billion years, 12-15 billion
    years). (398)

    4-5 billion
     years

7. The term planet is given to those celestial
    bodies that maintain an orbit around the sun
    but at times appear to _____, unlike the stars
    which maintain a _____ position in the sky. (398)

    wander
    fixed

8. All the planets revolve around the sun from _____
    to _____ and lie almost in the plane of the sun
    called the _____. (399)

    west
    east
    ecliptic

9. The first four planets with increasing distance
    from the sun are _____, _____, _____, and
    _____. They are collectively referred to as the
    _____ planets, because of their similarity to
    the _____. (399)

    Mercury
    Venus
    Earth
    Mars
    terrestrial
    Earth

10. The next group of planets with distance from
    the sun are _____, _____, _____, _____, and
    _____. They are collectively referred to as
    the _____ planets. (399)

    Jupiter
    Saturn
    Uranus
    Neptune
    Pluto
    outer

11. The space or gap in the orderly position of the
    planets with distance from the sun is filled by
    _____. (399)

    asteroids or
     asteroid belt

12. The outer planets are _____ (larger, smaller)
    in size than the inner planets and have a _____
    (higher, lower) density. (400)

    larger
    lower

13. The surface of Mercury is similar to the surface of our moon because it contains _____. The planet is believed to have a core of _____. In comparison to the core of the earth, Mercury's core makes up a _____ (greater, smaller) volume of the planet. Like the earth, Mercury seems to have differentiated into a core, _____, and _____. (400, 401)

craters
iron
greater
mantle
lithosphere

14. The planet Venus is roughly equivalent to the planet _____ in size. The Venusian atmosphere is dominated by the gas _____, whose vast abundance allows for the _____ (highest, lowest) surface temperatures of all the planets as a result of an enhanced _____ effect. The surface of the planet cannot be photographed with conventional optical cameras because the surface is covered by _____. (401, 402)

Earth
carbon dioxide
highest
greenhouse
clouds

15. The first person to describe the rough and uneven surface of the moon as revealed by a telescope was _____. He published these observations in a book entitled The _____. (403)

Galileo
Starry Messenger

16. The dark, topographically low areas of the moon are known as _____, and the lighter-toned higher areas are called _____. The cratered surface is composed of two types, namely, _____ and _____. One type is formed by the direct impact of _____, while the other produces smaller craters that result from the falling of fragments _____ from the original impact crater. (404)

maria
highlands
primary
secondary
meteorites
ejected

17. The floors of moon craters have a(n) _____ (indented, raised) central area on an otherwise level floor. The materials of the rimmed portion of the craters are zoned into three distinct areas. The intermediate and outer zones are a series of light-colored radial streaks called _____ that extend many kilometers beyond the crater. The craters just described are believed to be the result of _____. The ejected material that forms the rays has also created _____ craters. (405)

raised
rays
impact
ray

18. The dominant composition of lunar rocks is _____, although the igneous rock _____ composed of the calcium-rich plagioclase _____ is also present. It is believed that the _____ are composed of the former and the _____ regions the latter. Another type of rock called a _____ is composed of fragments of these rocks. While these rocks are very similar to those found on earth, they have a higher titanium content and a slightly lower silica, alumina, and sodium makeup. Very unlike their earth equivalents, they contain no _____. (405)

basaltic
anorthosite
anorthite
maria
highlands
breccia
water

19. The production of the lunar maria happened _____ (early, late) in the moon's history. The large impact craters were eventually filled with _____ materials. (405)

early
basaltic

20. The planet Mars can be subdivided into two hemispheres. This is done on the basis of _____ plains. Of the two plains, the older is _____ (more, less) heavily impacted than the younger and is topographically _____ (higher, lower) than the younger. (406)

cratered
more
higher

21. The planet Mars has well-defined _____ in its polar regions that appear to _____ and _____ with the change of seasons. The ice of the southern region is believed to be composed of _____, while the northern pole ice was recently shown to be derived from _____. (406)

ice caps
wax
wane
dry ice
water

22. The greatest agent of erosion today on the Martian surface is _____, although there is ample evidence for large-scale _____ erosion in the past. (407)

wind
running water

23. The Olympus Mons is a major _____ center on the Martian planet and is larger than anything of its type known on Earth. (407)

volcanic

24. The earth, moon, and the terrestrial planets all show evidence of heavy meteoric bombardment _____ (late, early) in their history, as shown by the presence (except on Earth and Venus) of _____. The absence of abundant evidence on our planet is most probably the result of active _____ at the surface of the earth. The evidence on Venus can only be hinted at, because of the dense _____ cover of the Venusian atmosphere. Present evidence indicates that the rate and size of the impacts is _____ (increasing, decreasing). (410)

early
impact craters
erosion
cloud
decreasing

25. The processes of weathering and erosion are dependent upon the existence of an _____. Of the moon and the terrestrial planets, only _____ is actively affected by these processes, and it is essentially absent from _____ and _____ and very limited on _____. (410)

atmosphere
Earth
Mercury
the moon
Mars

26. Tectonic activity is a major factor on _____, but is less evident on the other _____ planets. The tectonism of the moon and the other planets is largely confined to their _____ (early, late) history. (410)

Earth
terrestrial
early

263

27. Volcanic activity is characteristic of the moon and all the terrestrial planets. However, recent activity can be found only on _____. The volcanism on the moon and the other terrestrial planets produced extensive _____ basalts that filled the impact craters and _____ type volcanoes, particularly on the planet _____ where they are extremely large. (410)

Earth
flood
shield
Mars

28. The asteroid belt lies between the planets _____ and _____ and appears to be the source of _____. (411)

Mars
Jupiter
meteorites

29. _____ is the largest of the outer planets and has an atmosphere composed largely of _____ and _____. The four largest satellites of this planet are collectively called the _____ moons. (411, 412)

Jupiter
hydrogen
helium
Galilean

30. The Galilean moons are known as _____, _____, _____, and _____. They all appear to be a mixture of _____ and rock. The innermost of these moons, _____, is the only other body besides Earth in the solar system that still has active _____. (412)

Ganymede
Callisto
Io
Europa
ice
Io
volcanism

31. The most characteristic feature of the planet Saturn is its _____. This feature is composed of _____ particles. (414)

rings
ice

32. The planet Uranus seems to have a rocky _____ about the size of the earth and an atmosphere of _____ and _____. Like the earth, it also has a very strong _____ field that _____ (is offset from, corresponds to) the axis of rotation. Recent investigation by the Voyager 2 has increased the number of its _____. (414)

core
hydrogen
helium
magnetic
is offset from
satellites

33. The _____ marks the limit of the sun's magnetic field, and it lies beyond the planet _____. (416)

heliopause
Neptune

34. The streaks of light that often traverse the earth's atmosphere are called _____. If they strike the surface of the earth, they are known as _____. The _____ asteroids have orbits whose nearest approach to the sun places them within the orbit of the earth. (417)

meteors
meteorites
Amor

35. Meteorites are subdivided into two main groups: _____ and _____. (417)

iron
stony

36. The metallic variety of meteorite contains about 90 percent _____ and 10 percent _____. The texture of these meteorites indicates that they crystallized _____ (slowly, rapidly). (417)

iron
nickel
slowly

37. The stony meteorites are composed chiefly of
_____ minerals. Most of these meteorites have
an unusual texture, as they are composed of
spherical grains called _____. This variety
is known as a _____. If the spherical grains
are absent, they are known as _____. Most
of the spherical grains are composed of _____
and _____ set in a _____ (fine-grained,
coarse-grained) groundmass of _____ (different,
similar) composition. (418)

silicate
chondrules
chondrite
achondrite
olivine
pyroxene
fine-grained
similar

38. A small number of chondrites containing carbon,
hydrogen, and amino acids are called _____
chondrites. These components are believed to
be of _____ (inorganic, organic) origin. The
chondrules of this type of meteorite are typical
of a _____ (high, low) temperature environment
of formation, while the matrix contains material
formed at _____ (high, low) temperature. (418)

carbonaceous
inorganic
high
low

39. Comets are thought to be composed of a mixture
of _____ and _____. They are believed to be
present in very large numbers in the outer
reaches of our solar system in what is called
the _____ cloud. There are two basic types of
comets. Those that make a single pass through
the solar system are called _____ comets.
Those that make a return trip on a regular basis
are called _____ comets. The tail of the comet
develops as it _____ (moves away from, approaches)
the sun. (418)

ice
dust
Oort
nonperiodic
periodic
approaches

SELF-TESTS

Part A: True-False Statements

Each of the following statements is either true or false. Encircle either
a T or F for each item.

1. As seen from the earth, the apparent motion of celestial   T   F
   bodies is from east to west across the sky.

2. The energy of the sun is derived from the fusion of helium   T   F
   to hydrogen.

3. The orbit of the planets takes them in a west to east   T   F
   circuit around the sun and in the approximate plane of
   the ecliptic.

4. The terrestrial planets have a relatively small size and   T   F
   low density when compared to the outer planets.

5. The planets are uniformly spaced with distance from the   T   F
    sun, except for the gap between Jupiter and Saturn, which
    is filled by the asteroid belt.

6. The presence of a magnetic field is a strong indicator   T   F
    that a planet has or at one time had a liquid core.

7. Most of the craters on the planet Mercury are the result   T   F
    of volcanic activity.

8. The surface of Venus is covered by a dense bank of clouds   T   F
    composed chiefly of carbon dioxide gas.

9. The earth is the only planet that is currently experiencing   T   F
    volcanic activity.

10. The lunar highlands are believed to be composed chiefly   T   F
    of anorthosite, while the maria are composed of basaltic
    material.

11. The younger craters of the moon are most likely to be   T   F
    associated with rays.

12. Wind is the most active agent of erosion on the present   T   F
    surface of Mars.

13. The polar regions of Mars contain ice caps composed of   T   F
    solid carbon dioxide or dry ice, which fluctuate with
    the seasons.

14. The sinuous valleys and canyons on Mars are evidence of   T   F
    extensive glacial erosion in the past.

15. The terrestrial planets share similarities in the nature   T   F
    of their tectonic movements.

16. All of the terrestrial planets and the moon show evidence   T   F
    of extensive volcanic activity, but present volcanism is
    only evident on earth.

17. Most of the meteorites that strike the earth are believed   T   F
    to have their origin in the asteroid belt.

18. The satellites of the outer planets show a greater   T   F
    similarity in their geologic history to the earth and the
    terrestrial planets than the planets themselves.

19. Achondritic meteorites contain a high percentage of   T   F
    hydrocarbons.

20. Most comets are periodic in that they have predictable   T   F
    orbits and travel through the solar system on a regular
    basis.

Part B: Multiple Choice Items

Each of the following can be completed correctly by choosing only one word or phrase. Encircle the letter a, b, c, or d, designating your choice.

1. Which of the following did not believe in a heliocentric solar system?

   a. Galileo
   b. Aristotle
   c. Copernicus
   d. Aristarchus

2. The apparent path of the sun against the background of the stars is called the

   a. solar wind.
   b. albedo.
   c. ecliptic.
   d. equinox.

3. Which of the following planet groups include only the terrestrial planets?

   a. Mars, Venus, Jupiter, Mercury
   b. Mars, Mercury, Earth, Saturn
   c. Mercury, Earth, Uranus, Mars
   d. Earth, Mars, Mercury, Venus

4. A characteristic feature of the terrestrial planets is

   a. their current active erosion and volcanic activity.
   b. their relatively small size and high density.
   c. their uniform surface temperatures.
   d. their similar rotational periods.

5. Which of the following characteristics of the planet Mercury is not true?

   a. Its surface is not very heavily cratered.
   b. It does not have a magnetic field.
   c. It once had a liquid core.
   d. It has no history of volcanic activity.

6. Which of the following planets has an atmosphere composed largely of carbon dioxide?

   a. Earth
   b. Mars
   c. Jupiter
   d. Venus

7. The craters of the moon are

   a. mostly of volcanic origin, light in tone, and usually associated with rays.
   b. mostly of impact origin, dark in tone, and not usually associated with rays.
   c. mostly of volcanic origin, dark in tone, and usually associated with rays.
   d. mostly of impact origin, light in tone, and not usually associated with rays.

8. Secondary or satellite craters on the moon owe their origin to

   a. secondary volcanic activity.
   b. the deflation effects of wind erosion early in the moon's history.
   c. tensional faulting similar to caldera formation on earth.
   d. falling fragments ejected from a primary crater.

9. Evidence gathered from lunar probes and expeditions indicates that today the moon is

   a. a very quiet celestial body.
   b. undergoing periodic episodes of volcanic activity.
   c. undergoing extensive wind erosion.
   d. slowly obtaining an atmosphere which includes traces of water vapor.

10. Which of the following statements about the planet Mars is incorrect?

   a. There is evidence of extensive stream erosion during an earlier part of its history.
   b. Mars is a relatively dynamic planet in terms of its past and current geologic activity.
   c. Mars has volcanic regions that dwarf any volcanic areas known on Earth.
   d. Although the planet has ice caps that wax and wane with the seasons, they are composed of solid carbon dioxide (dry ice) rather than water.

11. The processes of weathering and erosion are greatest on the earth because

   a. it has a large gravitational effect on objects near its surface.
   b. it has an atmosphere rich in oxygen and water vapor.
   c. it is a tectonically active body.
   d. it rotates on its axis, creating night and day.

12. The origin of the asteroid belt is believed to be the result of

   a. the explosion of a planet.
   b. the collision of two planets.
   c. bits of matter that never accreted to form a planet.
   d. none of the above.

13. The outer planets are characterized by

   a. their large size and high density.
   b. their large size and low density.
   c. their lack of an atmosphere.
   d. their liquid cores.

14. Which of the Galilean moons of Jupiter currently exhibits volcanic activity?

   a. Io   c. Callisto
   b. Ganymede   d. Europa

15. Which of the following is not true about stony meteorites?

    a. They are composed chiefly of silicate minerals.
    b. Some of them contain hydrocarbons.
    c. They give relatively young radiometric dates (1-2 billion years) and could not have formed during the early history of planet formation.
    d. They have crystallized at lower temperatures than iron meteorites.

SUGGESTED ESSAY QUESTIONS

The items below represent the type of discussion questions to which you might be expected to respond. Try writing a response to these, and then discuss your work with another student.

1. Compare and contrast the similarities and differences among the terrestrial planets.

2. Why are the satellites of the outer planets geologically similar to the terrestrial planets?

3. Contrast the weathering and erosion on Mars with that on the earth.

4. Describe the origin and major characteristics of the lunar craters and highlands.

5. Compare the similarities and differences between the composition of lunar and earth rocks.

6. Why are meteorites important for the study of the early history of our earth and solar system?

ANSWERS TO SELF-TESTS

Part A:					Part B:			
1. T	6. T	11. T	16. T		1. b	6. d	11. b
2. F	7. F	12. T	17. T		2. c	7. b	12. c
3. T	8. T	13. F	18. T		3. d	8. d	13. b
4. F	9. T	14. F	19. F		4. b	9. a	14. a
5. F	10. T	15. F	20. F		5. d	10. d	15. c